ENVIRONMENTAL RESEARCH ADVANCES

ENVIRONMENTAL AND AGRICULTURAL RESEARCH SUMMARIES

VOLUME 3

ENVIRONMENTAL RESEARCH ADVANCES

Additional books in this series can be found on Nova's website
under the Series tab.

Additional e-books in this series can be found on Nova's website
under the e-book tab.

ENVIRONMENTAL AND AGRICULTURAL RESEARCH SUMMARIES

VOLUME 3

LUCILLE T. CACIOPPO
EDITOR

publishers

New York

Library of Congress Cataloging-in-Publication Data

ISBN: 978-1-63117-090-4

Published by Nova Science Publishers, Inc. † *New York*

CONTENTS

PREFACE

This new book compiles research summaries from top professionals in the fields of environmental and agricultural research with a number of different focuses in these important fields.

In: Environmental and Agricultural Research Summaries …   ISBN: 978-1-63117-090-4
Editor: Lucille T. Cacioppo   © 2014 Nova Science Publishers, Inc.

Chapter 1

APPLICATIONS OF CLAY MINERALS IN ELECTROCHEMISTRY AND WASTEWATER TREATMENT

Delia-Maria Gligor[1] and Andrada Maicaneanu[2]

[1]Department of Environmental Physics, Chemistry and Technology,
"Babes-Bolyai" University, Cluj-Napoca, Romania
[2]Department of Chemical Technology, "Babes-Bolyai" University,
Cluj-Napoca, Romania

RESEARCH SUMMARY

Natural materials such as clay minerals and zeolites offers a great potential, due to their specific structure (layered and three-dimensional, respectively), in different technical applications based on the adsorptive and ionic exchange properties. Often they are used as supports (electrocatalysis) or adsorbents and ionic exchangers (wastewater treatment). Various clay mineral samples from different Romanian deposits were considered for applications in these two areas.

The use of clays as support for mediator compounds represents an useful and promising approach to obtain modified electrodes, due to their complete range of interesting properties required at an electrochemical interface (physical and chemical stability, high ion exchange capacity in a micro-structured environment, hydrophilic character etc.). Particularly, electroanalysis is of great interest for clay modified electrodes applications. In this context, two new composite electrodes, based on carbon paste incorporating a natural mineral clay (bentonite; B), impregnated with two new organic compounds, a phenothiazine derivative, 3,7-di(m-aminophenyl)-10-ethyl phenothiazine; EPh and 3,9-bis(3'-hydroxyphenyl)-2,4,8,10-tetrathiaspiro[5.5]undecane; TTU, were developed. The physical-chemical characterization of obtained carbon paste electrodes was realized using Scanning Electron Microscopy (SEM) and Energy Dispersive X Ray Spectroscopy (EDS). From cyclic voltammetric (CV) measurements the influence of some experimental parameters (pH, and potential scan rate) on the voltammetric response of modified carbon paste electrodes was studied and the electrochemical parameters for the heterogeneous electron transfer process were determined. Both (CV) and rotating disk electrode measurements were used for evaluation of the electrocatalytic efficiency for NADH mediated oxidation and electrocatalytic rate constant $k_{obs, [NADH]=0}$ at the obtained modified electrodes.

Clay mineral samples collected from different Romanian deposits were tested in wastewater treatment processes in order to remove heavy metal ions (e.g. Zn^{2+}, Pb^{2+}, Cd^{2+}), organic compounds (phenol, pesticides) or ammonium ions. Different operational parameters such as clay quantity, batch conditions (immobile phases, magnetic stirring, 3D shaker), pollutant concentration, or pH were considered, in order to establish their influence over the process efficiency (percentage removal) and adsorption capacity. As a mathematical approach, usual adsorption isotherms, kinetic models and adsorption thermodynamics, which are useful in the interpretation of adsorption/ionic exchange processes, are reviewed.

In: Environmental and Agricultural Research Summaries ...   ISBN: 978-1-63117-090-4
Editor: Lucille T. Cacioppo   © 2014 Nova Science Publishers, Inc.

Chapter 2

CLAYS AS SUSTAINABLE CATALYSTS FOR ORGANIC TRANSFORMATIONS

B. S. Jai Prakash,[1] Y. S. Bhat[2] and C. Ravindra Reddy[3]

[1]Department of Materials Sciences, Poornaprajna Institute of Scientific Research,
Bidalur Post, Devanahalli, Bangalore, India
[2]Department of Chemistry, Bangalore Institute of Technology, Bangalore, India
[3]Present address: Department of Chemical Engineering,
University of Waterloo, Waterloo, Ontario, Canada

RESEARCH SUMMARY

Catalysis is one of the important tools for sustainability and profitability of chemical production processes. The total quantity of catalysts used all over the world in all the processes together exceeds several million tonnes per annum. Their handling during use in the chemical transformation and disposal after use is of great environment concern. Many heterogeneous catalysts used for organic transformations are either toxic or non-specific or involve cumbersome procedures for their preparation and require a specialized care for their use, recovery and disposal which make the manufacturing process more and more energy intensive. There is obviously a continuous search for green catalysts which play a critical role in industrial reactions. An ideal green catalyst is a non-hazardous substance that can bring about a reaction at a faster rate and at lower temperatures than in the homogeneous conditions, yield maximum desired product with minimum waste, and which can be easily separated and recovered to be used more than once. Conventional heterogeneous catalysts such as metals, metal oxides, solid acids, low-dimensional solids and ion exchange resins are being used extensively in organic synthesis. Although very few of these fit into the definition of an ideal green catalyst, in the recent years there has been resurgence in the study of these catalysts, with or without modifications, reporting improved product yield and selectivity and reuse of the catalyst claiming green nature of the reaction.

A recent trend in the chemical industry is to switch over to catalysts that are more benign to environment. Advantages associated with this are easy handling of the catalysts during life cycle and disposal after use. In this context one such material that is being tried in variety of reactions is the clay based material. Clays may be regarded as green catalytic materials as they are abundantly available in nature and can be used with minimum processing. They are non-corrosive solid materials, have plasticity for easy fabrication into desired shape and size for use in the reactor, could easily be separated from product stream, are disposable relatively easily after use with no threat to ambience. Among the clays, the most used catalysts in chemical transformations are the montmorillonites.

Several options for the surface modification of montmorillonite practiced by clay chemists are available. These include (i) ion exchange with multivalent inorganic cations and coordination complexes to incorporate redox species and simultaneously generating acid centres (ii) ion exchange with organic cationic species having long alkyl chains with bulky head groups and intercalation with organic compounds to swell the clay layers to variable extents (iii) treatment with inorganic hydroxyl-oligomeric species followed by thermal treatment to obtain pillared clays having Lewis acidity (iv) treatment with mineral and organic acids and surfactants to get acid clays with tunable porosities (v) dealumination of structural aluminum by mild acid treatment to generate porosity in the clay platelets as well as mixed Brønsted acids in the interlayer (vi) incorporation of polymeric hydrated species of metals along with alkylamine species In the interlayer followed by removal of the organic species by washing with organic solvents and thermal treatment to get porous clay heterostructures (vii) impregnation of metal salts followed by reduction to get supported metal and metal oxide catalysts and (vii) modification for microwave-assisted reactions as clays with their variety of bipolarity are excellent absorbers of microwaves. All these are simple methods of surface modification making use of non hazardous chemicals. Modified clays are invariably stable and do not lose their characteristics easily.

There have been a number of reviews on the modification of clays in the recent years. Hundreds of publications are appearing every year on their applications in organic synthesis. Some of the reviews which have appeared recently have presented the ability of clay catalysts to bring about organic transformations such as addition, condensation, alkylation, rearrangement, isomerization, cyclization, ring-opening and closure, oxidation, hydrogenation and dehydrogenation, protection-deprotection, hydroboration and so on. But the reviewers have disregarded the role played by the modified surface. They do not relate the changed features of the modified clay surface with the performance characteristics. The objective of this chapter is to review publications appeared on clay catalysis in the recent years with a view to present to the readers a detailed discussion on the various techniques of chemical modification with particular emphasis on their utility as green catalysts.

In: Environmental and Agricultural Research Summaries …   ISBN: 978-1-63117-090-4
Editor: Lucille T. Cacioppo   © 2014 Nova Science Publishers, Inc.

Chapter 3

ANIMAL FIBRES AND SEAWEED POLYMERS TO IMPROVE UNFIRED CLAY BLOCKS CHARACTERISTICS

Carmen Galán-Marín,[1] Carlos Rivera-Gómez[1] and Jelena Petric-Gray[2]

[1]University of Seville, (Spain). School of Architecture,
Department of Building Construction
[2]University of Strathclyde (UK). Energy Systems Research Unit (ESRU),
Department of Mechanical Engineering

RESEARCH SUMMARY

Unfired clay materials provide a sustainable and healthy alternative to conventional masonry materials, such as fired clay and concrete block, in both non-load-bearing and low rise load-bearing applications. Environmental benefits include significantly reduced embodied energy, thermal mass and regulation of humidity. Materials may be taken from sustainable resources (low grade clay and overburden) and are readily re-used, re-cycled or harmlessly disposed on end use.

There are many existing references on the interest in and the use of unfired bricks in UK and other countries. The mechanical characteristics of the unfired bricks are sometimes improved by adding stabilizers such as cement. Several scientific studies analyze various aspects of thermal behaviour of unfired clay, but all of them stress the environmental benefits associated with this type of building construction material.

Our research has been developed as collaboration amongst material scientists, engineers and architects from the Universities of Strathclyde (UK) and Seville (Spain). The feasibility study was conducted with the aim to explore the potential of our natural, composite material to be used both structurally and for surface finishes. Alginate (a natural polymer from the cell walls of brown algae) has been used as bonding in the composite. Sheep wool was used as reinforcement.

The research objective is to develop a method of stabilization of natural soils with natural polymers and fibres to produce a composite, sustainable, non-toxic and locally sourced building material. Mechanical tests have been conducted with a clayey soil supplied by a Scottish brick manufacture. Our composite is based on all natural materials and it contains alginate instead of cement, as stabilizer, and animal fibers instead of vegetal ones, as reinforcement to compensate the effects of the retraction and to improve its mechanical characteristics.

In: Environmental and Agricultural Research Summaries ...   ISBN: 978-1-63117-090-4
Editor: Lucille T. Cacioppo   © 2014 Nova Science Publishers, Inc.

Chapter 4

CLAY-ORGANOCLAY AND ORGANOCLAY/ POLYMER NANOCOMPOSITES

Ahmet Gurses,[1] Mehtap Ejder-Korucu[2] and Semra Karaca[2]

[1]Ataturk University, K. K. Education Faculty,
Department of Chemistry, Erzurum, Turkey
[2]Ataturk University, Faculty of Science,
Department of Chemistry, Erzurum, Turkey

RESEARCH SUMMARY

Since ancient times, clay minerals have been investigated because of their importance in agriculture, ceramics, building and other uses such as intercalation, quasi-two-dimensional magnetism, structural phase transition, fractal characteristics, mixed-crystal behavior and so on. In the past few decades, the natural clay minerals, such as montmorillonite (MMT), kaolinite, and palygorskite (attapulgite), are widely used in catalysis, as adsorbents, in nanocomposites, in sensors, electrode, as antibacterial materials, nuclear waste storage, pesticide carriers, and so on. Nowadays, surface modification of clay minerals has become increasingly important for improving the practical applications of clays and clay minerals. Surface modifications of clay minerals have received an intensive attention because it allows the creation of new materials and new applications. Organically modified layered silicates can be produced by replacing the cations originally present in the galleries with organic cations. Ion exchange with alkylammonium ions is well-known and the preferential method to prepare organoclays. As a result, the study of clays and organoclays are large field and shows an immense potential to be explored. The physical and chemical properties of the clay minerals determine their practical use in the process industries. Especially the development of inorganic-organic hybrid materials was widespread in the past few decades. The main focus of surface modification of clays is materials science, because organoclays are essential to develop polymer nanocomposites. Nanocomposites constitute one of the most developed areas of nanotechnology.

In: Environmental and Agricultural Research Summaries ...   ISBN: 978-1-63117-090-4
Editor: Lucille T. Cacioppo   © 2014 Nova Science Publishers, Inc.

Chapter 5

SPECIFIC SURFACE AREA OF FINE-GRAINED SOILS

Yeliz Yukselen-Aksoy[1] and Abidin Kaya[2]
[1]Celal Bayar University, Manisa, Turkey
[2]Akaya and Associates, Honolulu, Hawaii, US

RESEARCH SUMMARY

Clay has a very large specific surface area, which leads to much interaction of ions and water molecules with the soil particles. However, specific surface area of soilsvaries greatly because of differences in mineralogy, organic composition, and particle-size dimension. For example, smectite has the largest SSA among the known clay minerals. Kaolinite has strong bonding forces between layers and they have no significant internal surfaces.

There are various methods to measure specific surface area including gas adsorption in dry conditions and molecular adsorption in aqueous suspensions. SSA determination methods can be grouped into two main categories: gas adsorption and adsorption of polar liquids. Some of these techniques are: EGME, MB, p-Nitrophenol, polyvinylalcohol adsorption methods, etc. Although the physical definition of SSA is very straightforward, its accurate measurement is very difficult. This is because different SSA measuring techniques yields different SSA values depending on the limitations of each method. Furthermore, some of the SSA measuring techniques are time consuming or require special and expensive instrument.

Currently, there is no standard SSA measuring technique for fine-grained soils. Researchers and engineers use the technique that is available in their institutes. Measurement of SSA of fine-grained soils resulted reports of inconsistent SSA values in the literature. Hence, a simple and easily applicable method, which would yield reliable results, is greatly needed. To investigate such a SSA measuring technique, one needs to compare the commonly employed SSA measuring techniques. This is because some SSA measuring techniques measures only external SSA whereas other methods measure total SSA (i.e., both external and internal SSA). For example, nitrogen is non-polar and does not penetrate into the interlayers of swelling clays. Thus, the SSA values obtained by this method only refer to external crystal surface. However, the retention of polar liquids such as water, ethylene glycol monoethyl ether (EGME) and methylene blue (MB) is then used to estimate the total (external + internal) area of expanding layer silicates. These methods yield widely different estimates of SSA. Therefore, it is important to interpret the results according to the soil mineral constituents and the method used to determine the SSA.

In: Environmental and Agricultural Research Summaries …   ISBN: 978-1-63117-090-4
Editor: Lucille T. Cacioppo   © 2014 Nova Science Publishers, Inc.

Chapter 6

CLAY DEPOSITS, FROM A PROBLEM TO AN ECONOMIC RESOURCE FOR THE TERRITORY: CASE STUDY IN SOUTHERN ITALY

Vito Summa[*] *and Maria Luigia Giannossi*

Institute of Methodologies for Environmental Analysis (IMAA) – CNR,
C.da Santa Loja, I-85050 Tito scalo (Pz), Italy

RESEARCH SUMMARY

Ever since the dawning of civilization clay deposits have been basic raw materials – mainly used as geo-materials in the field of ceramics – for socio-economic development.

Their applications are tightly dependent on their structure, composition, and physical properties. Knowledge of these properties is important for understanding the technology of the production and optimization of the firing cycles.

Since the Protohistoric age diversified ceramic products as well as building materials have been made with clays from Basilicata (southern Italy).

The Basilicata clay deposits are extremely suitable thanks to their natural diversity and availability.

Since clay sediments bring about intense and widespread phenomena of land degradation in Basilicata (Southern Italy), the Pleistocene clays of the Basilicata Basin have been investigated in depths over the past ten years in order to determine the nature and the origin of the main minerals and their geotechnical behaviour.

We are trying to see if clay sediments can be a resource for industries in Basilicata or else simply a problem for this area.

Important questions arise on the interrelations between the limits of raw materials and their selection which may depend on natural diversity and availability.

The Basilicata pelitic deposits with a predominant clay component were distinguished into two age groups – the Pre-Pliocene unit (including sediments dating back to the upper

---

[*]Corresponding author: Vito Summa, Institute of Methodologies for Environmental Analysis (IMAA) - CNR, C.da Santa Loja, Tito scalo (Pz), Italy., Phone: +39.0971.427.251, e-Mail: summa@imaa.cnr.it.

Cretaceous and the middle-upper Tortonian ages) and the Plio-Pleistocene unit (including deposits dating back to the post-Tortonian and the Pleistocene ages). 350 samples were chosen representing the Pre-Pliocene and Plio-Pleistocene units.

On a regional scale Italian tile classification diagrams show that the Basilicata Pre-Pliocene clays can be utilized to produce only traditional ceramics (such as red stoneware). On the other hand the Plio-Pleistocene clays can be utilized to make both traditional ceramics (such as majolica) and modern ceramics (such as red bodies and cotto toscano).

This information can be easily obtained from the Map of the vocational use of the Basilicata clays, which is a first support for planning the supply of raw materials.

On a locale scale the most detailed study carried out on the clays around Craco (Matera, southern Italy) indicates that: i) most of the outcropping clayey deposits could be utilized to produce traditional ceramics such as majolica; ii) in some areas it is possible to find raw materials with a similar composition to some more valuable ceramics, e.g. cotto toscano; iii) the composition of Craco clayey sediments is similar to that of the blends used by manufacturers of artistic ceramic working in Basilicata, so we may suggest new resources to Basilicata industries.

In: Environmental and Agricultural Research Summaries …   ISBN: 978-1-63117-090-4
Editor: Lucille T. Cacioppo   © 2014 Nova Science Publishers, Inc.

Chapter 7

USE OF CLAYS TO MANUFACTURE HONEYCOMB MONOLITHS FOR POLLUTION CONTROL APPLICATIONS

J. M. Gatica and H. Vidal[*]
Departamento C.M., I.M. y Química Inorgánica,
Universidad de Cádiz, Puerto Real, Spain

RESEARCH SUMMARY

The growing interest for using clays in the production of structured materials with application in the technological field of environmental protection is emphasized. In particular, here we examine the design of clay-containing honeycomb monoliths that can be employed in the abatement of some of the main hazardous species in polluted emissions such as nitrogen oxides, carbon monoxide, toxic organic compounds and heavy metals. This review does not only include the well-known cordierites but also other innovative and more recent clay-based honeycombs. Distinction is made between honeycomb monoliths that are basically composed of clays and those in which the clayey fraction is used as an additive to extrude other materials. Special attention is paid to the versatility of these filters as they may operate both in gas and liquid phase, either acting as adsorbents, carriers or even active phases in catalytic processes, and for treatments having to deal with pollutants present in a very wide range of concentration. In addition, a general overview of the methods and general principles followed to prepare honeycomb monoliths from clays is also given.

---

[*]Corresponding author. Tel.: +34 956 016286; fax: +34 956 016288, E-mail address: hilario.vidal@uca.es (H. Vidal).

In: Environmental and Agricultural Research Summaries …   ISBN: 978-1-63117-090-4
Editor: Lucille T. Cacioppo   © 2014 Nova Science Publishers, Inc.

Chapter 8

POLYMER-CLAY NANOCOMPOSITE ELECTROLYTES FOR RECHARGEABLE LITHIUM BATTERIES

A. Kumar[*] and M. Deka
Materials Research Laboratory, Department of Physics,
Tezpur University, Assam, India

RESEARCH SUMMARY

Ion conducting polymers or polymer electrolytes have received considerable attention in the last three decades due to their technological implications in the development of solid polymer electrolyte batteries, super capacitors, electrochemical sensors and electro-chromic windows. The first ion conducting polymer: poly(ethylene oxide) (PEO) complexed/dissolved with alkali metal salt, was discovered in 1973 by P.V. Wright in collaboration with David Fenton and crystallographer John Parker. The initial realization that these materials could be used as electrolytes in battery applications was however proposed by Armand and his influential work inspired scientists/researchers both from academic institutions and industrial sectors to intensively pursue research in this area of materials science. Consequently, a large number of polymer electrolyte materials involving different kinds of transporting ions, namely, H^+, Li^+, Na^+, K^+, Ag^+, Mg^{2+} etc, have been reported since then. Various theoretical approaches have been adopted to understand the mechanism of ion transport in the polymer electrolyte materials as well as the physical/ chemical processes occurring at the polymer electrolyte/electrode interfaces. A number of books/ monographs/research papers have been published which deal with materials designing aspects as well as a variety of techniques usually employed during material/ structure/ thermal/ion transport characterization studies in the polymer electrolyte systems. The main reason for using polymeric electrolytes over other liquid and solid electrolytes lies in the free standing consistency, which allows easy handling and cell design, modularity and reliability combined with flexibility and conformability to the electrodes. Ionically conducting phases, free from low molecular weight solvents, based on

---

[*]Corresponding author: ask@tezu.ernet.in

the dissolution of salts in suitable ion-coordinating polymers are key components in new types of batteries for portable electronic devices and electric cars.

In batteries, being a separator polymer electrolyte must meet the requirements in terms of ionic conductivity, electrochemical performance, processibility and safety. In addition high cationic transport number, good dimensional stability, improved chemical and thermal are essential requirements of an electrolyte material to be used in batteries. The need for high ionic conductivity arises from the fact that at what rate or how fast energy from a Li-battery can be drained, which largely depends on the extent of ionic mobility in the electrolyte and hence on ionic conductivity. For battery applications, along with high ionic conductivity the electrolyte material must be dimensionally stable since the polymer electrolyte will also function as separator in the battery, which will provide electrical insulation between the cathode and the anode. This implies that it must be possible to process polymer electrolyte into free-standing film with adequate mechanical strength. Requirement of high cationic transport number rather than anionic is also important in view of the battery performance because concentration gradients caused by the mobility of both cations and anions in the electrolyte arise during discharging, which may result in premature battery failure.

In: Environmental and Agricultural Research Summaries ...   ISBN: 978-1-63117-090-4
Editor: Lucille T. Cacioppo   © 2014 Nova Science Publishers, Inc.

Chapter 9

CLAYS AND ITS MODIFIED FORMS FOR REMOVAL OF DYES FROM AQUEOUS SOLUTION

Fiona Patricia Sisnandy[1,2], Yesi[1,2], Yi-Hsu Ju[1],
Felycia Edi Soetaredjo[2], Aning Ayucitra[2], and Suryadi Ismadji[2]*

[1]Department of Chemical Engineering, National Taiwan University of Science
and Technology, Taipei, Taiwan[1]
[2]Department of Chemical Engineering, Widya Mandala Surabaya
Catholic University, Surabaya, Indonesia[2]

RESEARCH SUMMARY

The presence of dyes in water cause serious problems in aquatic systems due to its toxicity. Clays and clays materials are widely used to remove these contaminants from water and wastewater. This paper discussed recent progress on application of clays and clays materials and their modified forms for the removal of dyes from water and wastewater or aqueous systems. Different aspects of process adsorbent modification, adsorption mechanisms, adsorption equilibria, kinetics as well as thermodynamic are discussed in this paper. Also future perspective of industrial application of clays and clays materials as adsorbent for the treatment of dye-containing wastewater is also given.

*Corresponding author: email: suryadiismadji@yahoo.com, Tel. +62313891264, Fax. +62313891267.

In: Environmental and Agricultural Research Summaries …   ISBN: 978-1-63117-090-4
Editor: Lucille T. Cacioppo   © 2014 Nova Science Publishers, Inc.

Chapter 10

BEARING CAPACITY OF CLAY: INFLUENCE OF SPATIAL VARIATION OF SOIL PROPERTIES AND RELIABILITY BASED APPROACH

Amit Srivastava

Department of Civil Engineering, Jaypee University
of Engineering & Technology, Guna, MP, India

RESEARCH SUMMARY

In the conventional design, the allowable bearing pressure on a shallow footing resting on clayey deposit is estimated by dividing its ultimate bearing capacity by a *factor of safety*. The selection of appropriate value of factor of safety depends on various factors that involve social and economic considerations, type of structure and its importance, type of soil, size of footing, and type and amount of load on the footing. Based on past experiences and engineering judgments, it is established that a minimum factor of safety of 3.0 is desirable. The approach is straight forward but does not handle variability in an appropriate manner.

It should be noted that soil is a natural material and therefore geotechnical data are always random and variable in space. Different sources of uncertainties include: inherent variability, model transformation uncertainty, testing errors. In conventional procedure, it is assumed that the selection of appropriate value of factor of safety takes into consideration all the variability in the geotechnical parameters.

In the recent years, there have been considerable advances in the characterization of soil variability and its application in geotechnical designs. It is realized that the use of Reliability Based Design (RBD) is necessary to consider all sources of uncertainty in the analysis and incorporate them in geotechnical design. The approach provides mathematical basis to handle variability and gives rationality in the decision making. In the present chapter, the influence of spatially variable soil parameters on the reliability-based geotechnical deign is studied by considering the case of bearing capacity analysis of a shallow strip footing resting on a clayey soil. For numerical modeling and analysis, commercially available finite difference numerical code FLAC 5.0 is used.

In: Environmental and Agricultural Research Summaries …   ISBN: 978-1-63117-090-4
Editor: Lucille T. Cacioppo   © 2014 Nova Science Publishers, Inc.

Chapter 11

MONTMORILLONITE CLAY BASED SOLID ACID CATALYSTS FOR ORGANIC REACTIONS

Dipak Kumar Dutta[*]

Materials Science Division, North East Institute of Science
and Technology (CSIR), Jorhat, Assam, India

RESEARCH SUMMARY

Supported inorganic reagents are rapidly emerging as new and environmentally accepted materials for improving process efficiency or to replace environmentally unacceptable reagents and catalysts. Solid acid catalysts based on Montmorillonite clay having layered structures or modified acid-activated (AT) non-layered matrix leading to innovative properties like high surface area: 200 - 600 m^2/g, mesopores: 30 - 40 Å, average specific pore volume: 0.3 - 0.6 cc/g, and surface acidity about 0.41 mmol/g; have got much importance in the recent developments in designing and applications as supported catalysts for potential clean organic synthesis. Industrially important reactions like Friedel-Crafts alkylation and acylation, Esterification, Diels-Alder reaction, Isomerization etc. catalysed by such clay based catalysts have been reported. Exchange of interlayer cations of Montmorillonite by high charge density cations such as Al^{+3}, Fe^{+3}, etc. leads to acidity as high as 10 mol dm^{-3} which forms the basis of broad spectrum catalysts for organic synthesis. A newer type of metal salt-metal ion exchanged Montmorillonite (Mont), MCl_2-Mn^{2+}-Mont (M = Ni, Cu, Zn) have been prepared and evaluated as solid acid catalysts for Friedel-Crafts reactions particularly for benzylation of benzene. The commercially important aroma compound 4-(4′-hydroxyphenyl)butan-2-one (Raspberry ketone) can be prepared by the Friedel-Crafts alkylation of phenol with 4-hydroxybutan-2-one catalyzed by acid activated Montmorillonite (Mont K-10 and Mont(GMB)-AT). The Mont(GMB)-AT catalyst with mesoporosity 5.6 nm pore diameter and surface area (> 400 m^2/g) exhibited the highest selectivity (~ 80%). Esterifications of acetic acid with *n*- and *sec*-butanol catalysed by supported dodecatungstophosphoric acid $H_3PW_{12}O_{40}$ (DTP) on acid modified Montmorillonite clay

[*]Dipak Kumar Dutta: Fax: +91-3762370011; Ph. +91-376-2370081; Email: dipakkrdutta@yahoo.com.

(Mont-AT) showed high catalytic conversion in the range 80-88% and nearly 100% selectivity towards *n*- and *sec*-butyl acetate. The catalysts were characterized by powder XRD, N_2 sorption, TG-DTA and temperature programmed desorption of ammonia (ammonia-TPD). GC, NMR, IR, HPLC and elemental analyses were utilized to analyze the reaction products.

In: Environmental and Agricultural Research Summaries …   ISBN: 978-1-63117-090-4
Editor: Lucille T. Cacioppo   © 2014 Nova Science Publishers, Inc.

Chapter 12

STRUCTURAL MODIFICATION OF MONTMORILLONITE CLAY BY PILLARING PROCESS: ITS CHARACTERIZATION AND APPLICATIONS

Kanattukara Vijayan Bineesh and Dae-Won Park[*]
Division of Chemical Engineering, Pusan National University,
Busan, Republic of Korea

RESEARCH SUMMARY

Layered minerals, structures consisting of stacked sheets and abundant lamellae, can be used to design a variety of novel materials. The features of layered minerals most frequently exploited in various preparative approaches are the expandability of their structure, their ion exchange properties, and/or the flexibility of their layer composition. This chapter focuses on the structural modification of montmorillonite clay through the pillaring process, using large inorganic metal cations to produce various pillared clays (Ti-PILC, Zr-PILC and Fe-PILC). The main objective of this process is to develop pillared clays with excellent textural and structural properties. The general characteristics of such clays, in terms of their high *d*-spacing, large surface area, high thermal stability and acidity, are discussed in detail. Similarly, the most important synthesis parameters that have a clear and marked influence on the final characteristics of the materials are summarized. A discussion of the catalytic applications of these pillared clays in various liquid-phase and gas-phase reactions is also included.

[*]Corresponding author. Tel.: +82 51 510 2399; Fax: +82 51 512 8563, E-mail: dwpark@pusan.ac.kr (D.W. Park)

In: Environmental and Agricultural Research Summaries …   ISBN: 978-1-63117-090-4
Editor: Lucille T. Cacioppo   © 2014 Nova Science Publishers, Inc.

Chapter 13

THE USE OF MONTMORILLONITE CLAY TO PREPARE NANOCOMPOSITES AND POLYMERIC MEMBRANES

Amanda Melissa Damiao Leite[*1], *Edcleide Maria Araújo*[1],
Rene Anísio da Paz[1], *Vanessa da Nobrega Medeiros*[1],
Helio de Lucena Lira[1] *and Tomás Jeferson Alves de Mélo*[1]
Federal University of Campina Grande/CCT/DEMa/Bloco CL, Brazil[1]

RESEARCH SUMMARY

The combination of clays and polymers has been used in the last two decades to produce high performance composites. The natural bentonites in general are polycationics, presents hydrated ions such as Na^+, Ca^{2+} and K^+. Obviously, in this state, the silicate layers are only miscible in hydrophilic polymers. To turn these silicates miscible in others polymers matrix is need to convert the hydrophilic surface in organophilic one to make the intercalation with others polymers possible. In general, this can be done by exchange reaction of ions by surfactant cations type quaternary, tertiary, secondary and primary alkyl ammonium. Different way can be used to add in the silicate layers in the polymers, by *in situ* polymerization, solution intercalation or simple mixing of polymer melts. In all cases, nanoparticles are added in the matrix. The hybrid of silicate layers with polymers has unique properties that can be attributed to the nanometric size and high surface area of the used filler. In reality, some physical and mechanical properties are improve, such as, tensile strength and modulus, HDT and permeability with small amount of clay in polymer. The improvements of these properties are interesting to prepare membrane for separation process. In a modern world, the polymeric membranes are widely used in the industry. Some industrial applications include gas separation, microfiltration, ultrafiltration and reserse osmosis. The morphological control of the membranes is very important in the performance and configuration to specific application. Some researchers indicated that the appropriated addition of inorganic nanoparticles in a melt polymer solution can eliminate the formation and growing of macroporous, increasing the number of small porous, improving the porosity, hydrophilicity

---

[*]amandamelissa.lins@yahoo.com.br.

and permeability and improvement of the mechanical, thermal stability and anti incrustation properties. In these work, it was evaluated the properties of the nanocomposites and membranes prepared by phase inversion with the incorporation of clay into polymer. The results showed the intercalation of the salt molecules in the clay and also the preparation of nanocomposites with partially exfoliated structure, also the nanocomposites presented better mechanical properties. The membranes prepared from the nanocomposites were evaluated by XRD and it was confirmed the results of exfoliation. From MEV, it was confirmed the strong influence of the clay in the pore formation and distribution on the top surface and also in the bulk of the membrane when compared with that one obtained with pure polyamide 6.

In: Environmental and Agricultural Research Summaries …   ISBN: 978-1-63117-090-4
Editor: Lucille T. Cacioppo   © 2014 Nova Science Publishers, Inc.

Chapter 14

TRACE ELEMENT UPTAKE FROM VERMICULITE BY THE BACTERIUM PSEUDOMONAS FLUORESCENS AND ITS GENETIC DERIVATIVES TO PROTECT PLANTS AGAINST SPECIFIC DISEASES

Barbara Müller[*]

Clay Mineralogy Group, Institute for Geotechnical Engineering,
ETH Zurich, 8093 Zurich, Switzerland and Plant Pathology,
Institute of Integrative Biology, ETH Zurich, Switzerland

RESEARCH SUMMARY

Since a long time it is well known that the clay mineral vermiculite in interaction with the soil bacterium *Pseudomonas fluorescens* protects plants from particular diseases (e. g. tobacco black root rot is suppressed). Moreover, the wildtype CHA0 was once isolated from plant disease suppressive soils containing vermiculite. Trace elements like Cu and Zn play a major role in biocontrol activity of plant-associated bacteria. Laser ablation inductively coupled plasma mass spectrometry (LA ICP-MS) has been used to determine the trace elemental composition of an expanded and crushed vermiculite. The identical procedure was then used to determine the trace elemental composition of the same mineral having been affected by the aerobe bacterium *Pseudomonas fluorescens* strain CHA0 and its genetic derivatives namely CHA631, CHA77, CHA89, CHA400 and CHA661. The genetic derivatives used differ from the wildtype CHA0 through the absence, synthesis or overproduction of metabolites involved in complexing trace elements. Trace elements micronutrients like V, Mn, Fe, Co, Ni, Cu or Zn are widely found in microbial proteins. Among all analyzed trace elements, Fe, Mn and Cu are the most interesting. Fe and Mn are taken up from the clay mineral by all bacterial strains whereas Cu is only removed from vermiculite by strains CHA0, CHA77, CHA400 and CHA661. The latter mentioned strains

---

[*]Present address: EAWAG, Swiss Federal Institute of Aquatic Science and Technology, 8600 Dübendorf, Switzerland, barbara.mueller@eawag.ch.

all produce the antibiotics 2,4-diacetylphloroglucinol and monoacetylphloroglucinol which can complex Cu efficiently. Therefore, the alteration of only one gene of the bacteria is causing significant effects on the clay mineral.

In: Environmental and Agricultural Research Summaries ...   ISBN: 978-1-63117-090-4
Editor: Lucille T. Cacioppo   © 2014 Nova Science Publishers, Inc.

Chapter 15

IMPACT OF CLAY CONTENT ON INITIATION AND CHARACTERISTICS OF DEBRIS FLOWS

Chen Ningsheng[*], Zhou Wei, Hu Guisheng, Deng Mingfeng and Yang Chenglin

Key Lab of Mountain Hazards and Surface Processes,
Chinese Academy of Sciences, Chengdu, China
Institute of Mountain Hazards and Environment,
Chinese Academy of Sciences, Chengdu, China

RESEARCH SUMMARY

Clay is a kind of soil particle which is smaller than a certain value, and follows the sedimentological definition and refers to the particles < 0.005 mm in this paper. Most of the clay particles in the world are Montmorillonite, illite or kaolinite. Comparing with other soil particles, clay particles have some unique characteristics. Clay particles have large ratio of surface area to their weight, so they can have strong force to absorb the water. After absorbing the water, clay particles will lose positive ions, leading them to reject each other because of electrical force; on the other hand, clay particles will dilate. Based on clay structure, Wang pointed out the dilatant extent of kaolinite, montmorillonite, and illite were within 5%, 90-100%, and 25%, respectively.

The clay content is one of the important parameters affecting the soil mass strength and debris flow initiation. The clay content produces influence on cohesive force. After absorbing the water, clay dilates and leads to the increase of water pore pressure. Wang and others found that failure of soil mass often appeared before pore-water pressures reached the maximal value. The impact of clay under the action of rainfall leads to the decline of soil mass strength, which is beneficial for the debris flow initiation.

The clay content has close relationship with initiation, movement of debris flows , and is effective to reduce the resistance of debris flow. Pierson and Ellen and Fleming found that debris flow movement needed a sufficient clay content. In view of the impact of clay content

---

[*]Corresponding author: chennsh@imde.ac.cn.

on debris flow initiation, scientists have taken clay content as a significant factor when conducting their researches. Takahashi paid some attention to clay content when analyzing the mechanical model for initiation and movement process of debris flows through observation and experiment. M. E. Reid et al. found dilation of clay particle produces significant impact on the increase of pore water pressure during the process when landslide transfer to debris flows. Based on the model experiment for debris flow initiation from Jiuzhaigou debris flows, Cui pointed out initiation force and gradient will drop with the increase of fine particle (<1 mm).

As for debris flow characteristics, clay content produce impact on debris flow concentration. Generally, viscous debris flows with high concentration always contain clay of 5%, and non-viscous debris flows contain less clay. For example, on 15-16 December 1999 in the central coast of Venezuela, the viscous debris flows had clay contents (clay particle diameter <0.005 mm) of 3% - 5%. In southern California, USA, 30 viscous debris flows occurred after a forest fire in 1997-1998. The clay contents (with particle diameter < 0.005 mm) of those debris flows were mostly around 5%. The clay contents of the famous St. Helen volcano (USA) viscous debris flow deposits were commonly > 10% (Scott, 2000). At the same time, clay contents of viscous debris flow deposits of Jiangjiagou valley which is located in Yunnan province of China, are mostly between 8 and 10%.

Considering the importance of clay content, the author conducted debris flow initiation experiment and statistical analysis to study the impact of clay content on initiation and characteristics for debris flows.

In: Environmental and Agricultural Research Summaries ...   ISBN: 978-1-63117-090-4
Editor: Lucille T. Cacioppo   © 2014 Nova Science Publishers, Inc.

Chapter 16

PILLARED CLAYS AS GREEN CHEMISTRY CATALYSTS: APPLICATION TO WASTEWATER TREATMENT

C. B. Molina, J. A. Casas, A. H. Pizarro, and J. J. Rodriguez

Universidad Autónoma de Madrid, Madrid, Spain

RESEARCH SUMMARY

Clay minerals have received considerable attention in the last years because of their environmental compatibility, low cost, high selectivity, reusability and operational simplicity. Porosity and stability of these materials are improved by pillaring, which leads to materials known as pillared clays (PILC). These materials show increased surface area, pore volume, thermal and mechanical stability and, depending on the pillars, improved catalytic activity compared to the parent clays, making them suitable catalysts and adsorbents. The interest for pillared clays has suffered a dramatic increase in the last years in a great part due to their potential applications as catalysts. The metals incorporated in the pillared clay structure are crucial and make them suitable for a number of different applications, most of them belonging to the named "green chemistry". This chapter shows an overview of the different reactions performed using pillared clays as catalysts, focusing on those addressed to the abatement of water pollutants. In this way, pillared clays have been tested as catalysts for the treatment of wastewater containing different types of contaminants. Among them, the treatment of chlorophenols-bearing effluents has been investigated. Chlorophenols (CPs) are among the most concerning pollutants in industrial wastewater and contaminated groundwaters, being highly resistant to biodegradation. Their removal or conversion into environmentally harmless species is a current need. From a chemical point of view, they can be removed by oxidative or hydrogenation treatments. Our research group has been working within the last decade on the use of catalysts based on pillared clays for both processes, specifically catalytic wet peroxide oxidation (CWPO) and catalytic hydrodechlorination (HDC). Both CWPO and HDC have advantages and drawbacks. In this chapter we summarize the main results from our work including a comparison with those reported by other authors.

In: Environmental and Agricultural Research Summaries …   ISBN: 978-1-63117-090-4
Editor: Lucille T. Cacioppo   © 2014 Nova Science Publishers, Inc.

Chapter 17

CLIMATE AND DISTRIBUTION OF VEGETATION IN EGYPT'S DESERTS

*M. A. Zahran**

Department of Botany, Faculty of Science,
Mansoura University, Mansoura, Egypt

RESEARCH SUMMARY

Egypt occupies the northeastern corner of Africa with an area of slightly more than one million square kilometers. It extends over ten latitudes: Lat. 22° N and Lat. 32° N, i.e lies mostly within the temperate zone, less than a quarter being south of the Tropic of Cancer. It is a part of the great desert belt of North Africa.

Egypt comprises four main geomorphological regions: The River Nile with its Nile Delta, Nile Valley and Nile Fayium, The Western Desert, The Eastern Desert and The Sinai Peninsula (the Asian part of Egypt). The coastal deserts of Egypt extend along the Mediterranean Sea in the North and the Red Sea including the Gulfs of Suez and Aqaba in the east.

The climate of Egypt is, generally, dry with two climatic provinces: arid and hyperarid. The average annual rainfall over the whole country is only 10 mm. However, along the less arid northern Mediterranean coastal belt, the average annual rainfall is usually less than 200 mm. Aridity increases southwards, the average annual rainfall decreases to 60 mm in the Nile Delta, 24 mm in Cairo and less than 5 mm in Upper Egypt. The coastal mountains of the Sinai Peninsula and Red Sea in the southeastern corner of the Eastern Desert receive, relatively, greater amount of orographic rain.

The framework of the desert vegetation of Egypt is formed mainly of perennial xerophytic, halophytic and psammophytic herbs, shrubs and bushes, trees are few. Latitudinal climatic variation in the three geomorphological units of Egypt's desert is associated with seven vegetation types namely: mangrove swamps, reed swamps, salt marshes, sand dunes, rocky ridges, wadis and mountains.

* Email: zahrancabi2001@yahoo.com

The altitudinal climatic changes produced zonation of vegetation on the slopes of the mountains. The distribution of these vegetation types and their characteristic species in the two climatic provinces of Egypt's deserts (arid and hyperarid) are described.

In: Environmental and Agricultural Research Summaries …   ISBN: 978-1-63117-090-4
Editor: Lucille T. Cacioppo   © 2014 Nova Science Publishers, Inc.

Chapter 18

CLIMATE CHANGE IN THE ARCTIC REGIONS OF RUSSIA

O. A. Shilovtseva[1], N. K. Kononova[2] and F. A. Romanenko[1]
[1]Moscow State Lomonosov University, Russia
[2]Institute of Geography Russian Academy of Science, Russia

RESEARCH SUMMARY

The results of the long-term meteorological observations (surface air temperature, atmospheric precipitation and sun shine duration) are performed. The ground-based data of 19 meteorological stations along all the Arctic shore of Russia were analyzed. The stations with the most prolonged observation period were selected. All of these stations are still working at the present time. The World Data Center's (Obninsk, Russia) data bank was used. For each station, two average values of the surface air temperature (SAT) were calculated: for the whole period of observation (t_{av}) and for the period 1961-1990 (according to the recommendation of the World Meteorological Organization (t_n). It was shown that the longer period of observations is present, the less the difference between the averages is. The usage of one of these average values doesn't have an impact on the linear tendency of parameter, but the usage of t_n leads to the SAT amplitudes increase toward positive magnitudes.

Within the last century, the linear trend value of meteorological parameter can differ from one region to another and even in the same region. According to the comparison of the linear trend for the period 1933-2009, which is the only one for all selected 19 stations, the most significant warming is evident in Chukchi Peninsula. On the opposite, Taymyr Region is characterized by cooling, which is not statistically significant.

In: Environmental and Agricultural Research Summaries …   ISBN: 978-1-63117-090-4
Editor: Lucille T. Cacioppo   © 2014 Nova Science Publishers, Inc.

Chapter 19

TOWARDS ADAPTATION MEASURES IN PROTECTING MANGROVES FROM CLIMATE CHANGE

Colin Field

University of Technology Sydney, Gordon, Australia

RESEARCH SUMMARY

A brief account of the nature of mangrove ecosystems is given. This shows that mangroves are generally resilient to climate change and are aggressive colonizers if suitable land is available. An examination of the current worldwide status of mangrove ecosystems and loss of area shows that the quantification of worldwide mangrove area needs improvement. There is an analysis of the response of mangroves to changes in climate: rise in sea level, rise in atmospheric carbon dioxide, rise in air and water temperature, ocean acidification and change in precipitation and storm frequency. A significant lack of information exists on some aspects of these responses. The literature proposes a range of adaptation strategies to prevent the loss of mangrove ecosystems. In the main, these are concerned with the effects of sea level rise and involve planting mangroves, preserving space for mangrove migration or preventing erosion. An examination of these strategies shows the need for extensive local knowledge. Adaptation and mitigation strategies will be useless without an intimate understanding, both spatially and temporally, of the local physical, chemical and biological structures. Such information is often ignored or not available. The management of adaptation strategies requires knowledge of population pressure as well as the effects of climate change. In the near future, the impact of population growth and development is more likely than climate change to impinge on mangrove ecosystems.

In: Environmental and Agricultural Research Summaries ...   ISBN: 978-1-63117-090-4
Editor: Lucille T. Cacioppo   © 2014 Nova Science Publishers, Inc.

Chapter 20

REDUCING TRANSPORT'S IMPACT ON CLIMATE CHANGE

Patrick Moriarty[1] and Damon Honnery[2]
[1]Department of Design, Monash University, Australia
[2]Department of Mechanical and Aerospace Engineering,
Monash University, Australia

RESEARCH SUMMARY

In 2004, transport was responsible for 23% of global energy-related CO_2 emissions, or some 6.3 gigatonnes (Gt) CO_2. The 2007 Intergovernmental Panel on Climate Change (IPCC) Report on Mitigation projected a rise of 80% in CO_2 emissions by 2030 in the absence of specific reduction policies. The report estimated that emission reduction policies would only lower the total in 2030 from 11.34 Gt to at best 8.8 Gt. Yet elsewhere the IPCC report showed that to limit global temperature rise since the industrial revolution to 2°C, thought to represent a prudent limit for avoiding dangerous climatic change, CO_2 emissions may have to be cut by the year 2050 to as little as 15% of the year 2000 values. In this chapter we look at the emission reduction potentials for the various transport modes, both passenger and freight, that could be achieved by the year 2030. The major options for each transport mode include increases in vehicle fuel efficiency and loading, and shifts to non-carbon fuels. We show that these options, even combined, cannot deliver anywhere near the reductions needed. Instead we will need not only massive shifts to more energy-and greenhouse-efficient transport modes, especially for passenger transport, but particularly in the high-income countries, travel reductions as well.

In: Environmental and Agricultural Research Summaries ...   ISBN: 978-1-63117-090-4
Editor: Lucille T. Cacioppo   © 2014 Nova Science Publishers, Inc.

Chapter 21

MITIGATING CLIMATE CHANGE

Patrick Moriarty[1] and Damon Honnery[2]
[1]Department of Design, Monash University, Australia
[2]Department of Mechanical and Aerospace Engineering,
Monash University, Australia

RESEARCH SUMMARY

The 2007 Intergovernmental Panel on Climate Change (IPCC) report showed that to limit global temperature rise since the industrial revolution to 2° C (thought by the European Union to represent a prudent limit to avoid dangerous climatic change) CO_2 emissions may have to be cut by the year 2050 to as little as 15% of the year 2000 value, with the peak emission year in 2000-2015. Since about 77% of the climatic radiative forcing of anthropogenic greenhouse gas emissions from all sources comes from carbon dioxide, (with most of this in turn coming from fossil fuel use) this chapter mainly considers these emissions. Geoengineering is the only mitigation approach that does not require emission reductions, but carries serious risks— in attempting to solve one problem it creates others. Mitigating climate change will thus require that large emission reductions be made rapidly. The three most commonly discussed measures, carbon sequestration, use of non-carbon fuels and energy efficiency, can do little to reduce emissions in the time frame required, a point tacitly acknowledged by the IPCC and other authorities. Heavy emphasis will therefore need to be placed on a very different approach. Particularly in countries with high-energy per capita use, we argue emission cuts will also require reductions in the use of energy-using devices—including cars, airplanes and domestic appliances. Although this approach can be implemented quickly, it evidently requires profound changes in the global economy.

In: Environmental and Agricultural Research Summaries …   ISBN: 978-1-63117-090-4
Editor: Lucille T. Cacioppo   © 2014 Nova Science Publishers, Inc.

Chapter 22

SPATIAL-ENERGY FRAMEWORK AIMING AT BREAKTHROUGHS BRINGS GOALS BEYOND POLICY OBJECTIVES WITHIN REACH

Rob Roggema[1], Andy van den Dobbelsteen[2], Sven Stremke[3] and Wim Mallon[4]

[1]Delft University of Technology, Faculty of Architecture,
Climate Design and Sustainability and Wageningen University
and Research Centre, Earth Systems Science, the Netherlands
[2]Delft University of Technology, Faculty of Architecture,
Climate Design and Sustainability, the Netherlands
[3]Wageningen University and Research Centre,
Chair Landscape Architecture, the Netherlands
[4]KEMA, Groningen, the Netherlands

RESEARCH SUMMARY

The energy supply system is approaching fundamental changes. The traditional fossil-based provision of energy is not eternal. It needs to be replaced by an alternative. Current policy agreements stand in the way of fundamental changes towards a fully renewable energy supply, because they set targets based on political compromises instead of on the potential production of renewable energies. If the energy supply is approached from the local energy potential point of view more ambitious goals can be achieved. The methodology developed for the Groningen region in the Netherlands consists of three basic phases: the mapping of energy potentials, the development of a conceptual design and a realisation strategy, based on swarm planning principles. The constellation of local networks is an important feature of this approach. The results illustrate that confidence may arise about the potential renewable energy production as well as the potentials of reducing CO_2 emissions.

In: Environmental and Agricultural Research Summaries …   ISBN: 978-1-63117-090-4
Editor: Lucille T. Cacioppo   © 2014 Nova Science Publishers, Inc.

Chapter 23

ADAPTATION OPTIONS TO CLIMATE CHANGE IMPACTS IN EUROPEAN AGRICULTURE

J. Eitzinger[*,1], *G. Kubu*[1], *S. Thaler*[1], *J. Glauninger*[1],
V. A. Alexandrov[2], *A. Utset*[3], *D. T. Mihailović*[4], *B. Lalić*[4], *M. Trnka*[5],
Z. Zalud[5], *D. Semeradova*[5], *D. Ventrella*[6], *D. P. Anastasiou*[7],
M. Medany[8], *S. Altaher*[8], *J. Olejnik*[9], *J. Leśny*[9], *N. Nemeshko*[10],
M. V. Nikolaev[11], *C. Simota*[12] and *G. Cojocaru*[12]*

[1]University of Natural Resources and Applied Life Sciences, Vienna, Austria
[2]National Institute of Meteorology and Hydrology, Sofia, Bulgaria
[3]Agrarian Technological Institute of Castilla and Leon, Valladolid, Spain
[4]University of Novi Sad, Novi Sad, Serbia
[5]Mendel University of Agriculture and Forestry, Brno, Czech Republic
[6]Instituto Sperimentale Agronomico, Bari, Italy
[7]Institute of Environmental Research and Sustainable Development, Athens, Greece
[8]Central Laboratory for Agricultural Climate, Giza, Egypt
[9]August Cieszkowski Agriculture University of Poznan, Poznan, Poland
[10]State Hydrological Institute, St. Petersburg, Russia
[11]Agrophysical Research Institute, Petersburg, Russian Federation
[12]TIAMASG Foundation, Romania

RESEARCH SUMMARY

Ongoing climate change will significantly change agricultural production conditions in Europe during the next decades. An early recognition of risks and implementation of adaptation strategies is crucial as anticipatory and precautionary, adaptation is more effective and less costly than forced, last minute, emergency adaptation or retrofitting. Results of climate change impact and adaptation studies often show considerable different results,

* Corresponding author: E-mail address: josef.eitzinger@boku.ac.at; Phone: +43 1 476545622, Fax: +43 1 476545610

depending on the spatial scale of regionalization. However, for a decision maker, only a high spatial resolution of related study results is useful as it can represent local conditions and its spatial variability much better. Therefore the ADAGIO project (adagio-eu.org) was designed to focus on regional studies in order to uncover regional specific problems. In this context, a bottom-up approach is used beside the top-down approach of using scientific studies, involving regional experts and farmers in the evaluation of potential regional vulnerabilities and adaptation options. Results of the regional studies and gathered feedback from experts and farmers show in general that (increasing) drought and heat is the main factor of agricultural vulnerability not only in the Mediterranean region, but also in the Central and Eastern European regions. Another important aspect is that the increasing risk of pest and diseases may play a more important role for agricultural vulnerability than assumed before, however, till now this field is only rarely investigated in Europe. An important aspect is also that there are increasing regional differences in the crop production potential in Europe due to climate change and that positive or negative impacted agricultural systems can vary in a relatively small spatial scale, depending on the specific limiting environmental conditions such as climate or soil conditions (especially in complex terrain). Although dominating risks such as increasing drought and/or heat are similar in most regions, the vulnerabilities in the different regions are very much influenced by characteristics of the dominating agroecosystems and prevailing socio-economic conditions. Most important adaptation options in Europe concern changes in crop and soil management, pest and disease management as well as land use options at different scales. The feasibility of many adaptation options, however, is strongly influenced by regional socio-economic conditions, which can vary significantly within regions and countries in Europe.

In: Environmental and Agricultural Research Summaries …   ISBN: 978-1-63117-090-4
Editor: Lucille T. Cacioppo   © 2014 Nova Science Publishers, Inc.

Chapter 24

GLOBAL WARMING, CROP SELECTION AND ADAPTATION OPTIONS IN KENYAN AGRICULTURE

Jane Kabubo-Mariara[*]
School of Economics, University of Nairobi, Nairobi, Kenya

RESEARCH SUMMARY

Available evidence suggests that the world is getting warmer and this is expected to have adverse impact on agriculture in the future. Global circulation models predicted that global warming will lead to increased temperatures of up to $8.7^{\circ}C$ and cause variability of rainfall by up to 34% in Kenya by the year 2100. From these predictions, the two extreme climate events that may adversely impact on the agricultural sector are drought and flooding in both the arid and semi-arid lands (ASALs) and the higher potential areas. The major challenges to sustainable agricultural production in Kenya are low, poorly distributed and unreliable rainfall, climate and ecological extremes. The impacts of the extreme weather and climate events could have severe socio-economic impacts including water and energy shortages, and also shortage of other essential basic commodities and long term food insecurity. Previous studies show that the country will incur huge losses in farm revenues due to climate change. This makes it important to understand adaptive mechanisms by farmers to circumvent the potential welfare loss due to climate change in Kenya. To address this issue, this chapter examines the impact of climate change on crop selection and also assesses farmers' awareness of climate change. The chapter also examines the main adaptation measures employed by farmers to counter adverse impacts of climate change, upon perceiving climate change. The results suggest that the decision to farm a crop or a portfolio of crops responds to climate change and that the choice of most crops is more sensitive to temperature than to precipitation. Further, choice of most crops exhibit a significant hill shaped relationship with temperature and precipitation.

---

[*] E-mail address: jmariara@mail.uonbi.ac.ke. Tel: 254 20 318262, ext 28122. Fax: 254 20 245566.

In: Environmental and Agricultural Research Summaries …   ISBN: 978-1-63117-090-4
Editor: Lucille T. Cacioppo   © 2014 Nova Science Publishers, Inc.

Chapter 25

INVESTIGATING POSSIBLE CAUSATIVE MECHANISMS BEHIND THE HOUSTON CLOUD-TO-GROUND LIGHTNING ANOMALY

Michael L. Gauthier[*]

Department of Physics, The United States Air Force Academy
Colorado Springs, Colorado, US

RESEARCH SUMMARY

Previous studies have demonstrated that, in a regional context, the Houston cloud-to-ground (CG) lightning anomaly is a non-unique feature, embedded within the larger-scale enhancement of CG lightning along the Texas and Louisiana Gulf Coasts, and that inland cities like Dallas see far more CG lightning on a per-event basis. Despite the fact that the Houston area is located at the western edge of this coastal enhancement, it has been shown that this anomaly is a persistent summer-season feature with flash densities over and downwind of the Houston metropolitan area on the order of 1.5-2 times that of its immediate surroundings.

---

[*] The views expressed in this paper are those of the author and do not reflect the official policy or position of the U.S. Air Force, Department of Defense or the U.S. Government.

In: Environmental and Agricultural Research Summaries …   ISBN: 978-1-63117-090-4
Editor: Lucille T. Cacioppo   © 2014 Nova Science Publishers, Inc.

Chapter 26

CLIMATOLOGY: THE EFFECTS OF HEAT STRESS ON BEEF CATTLE PRODUCTION

Laun W. Hall, Samuel Garcia and Robert J. Collier
The University of Arizona, Tucson, Arizona, US

RESEARCH SUMMARY

Heat stress in cattle occurs when the heat load associated with ambient air temperature solar radiation and humidity exceeds the ability of the cow to dissipate excess heat from work and metabolism. This results in an elevated core body temperature, above the normal physiological range. The primary environmental factors causing the stress are temperature and humidity (measured by the THI index), solar radiation, and wind speed. Heat stress results in disruption of homeostasis, elevated basal metabolism and initiation of physiological acclimation responses. Cattle experiencing heat stress have an elevated body temperature, an increased respiration rate, and decreased feed intake. Insulin production increases and adipose tissues are unavailable for catabolic fuel. Many additional physiological pathways are compromised resulting in a loss of production (growth, reproduction, lactation). Reduced production always has an economic impact. The two major beef production entities affected by heat stress are: cow-calf operations, and feedlots. The ability of animals to adapt to the environment is known as acclimatization and is essential to long-term success of cow-calf operations. In contrast, feedlot populations have a constant turnover in cattle that are often shipped from various climates and sudden changes in environmental conditions can lead to high rates of death loss as animals are unable to quickly alter their metabolism to acclimate to the stress. The ability to acclimate is influenced by breed of cattle. Traits such as hair type, skin pigment, and ability to sweat can precondition cattle for heat resistance. Both short and long term management can reduce the magnitude of climate related stress. In feedlots, fat steers get preferential treatment and location. This group is the most susceptible to heat stress and should receive top priority in hot and humid scenarios. Nutrition is also a tool to reduce the heat load caused by metabolism (heat of fermentation). Feedlots have no natural covering for the ground or shade for the animals that many cow-calf operations benefit from. In beef cattle production, market economics are the driving force for determining degree of environmental protection. Heat stress can decrease milk production in cows resulting in lower 205 day weaning weights, and decrease feed intake and efficiency in a feedlot. Any loss in performance results in a reduced profit. This loss in value provides an estimate of the size of capital expenditure that can be justified to be put towards improvements in facilities to reduce heat stress in future beef cattle production.

In: Environmental and Agricultural Research Summaries ...   ISBN: 978-1-63117-090-4
Editor: Lucille T. Cacioppo   © 2014 Nova Science Publishers, Inc.

Chapter 27

CLIMATOLOGY AND COSMIC RAYS IN NEW DEVELOPMENT

Neïla Zarrouk[*] and Raouf Bennaceur

Laboratoire de Physique de la Matière Condensée,
Faculté des Sciences de Tunis, Tunisia

RESEARCH SUMMARY

Seventeen years of monthly averaged low cloud cover data from the International Satellite Cloud Climatology Project (ISCCP) are examined towards amplitude antipodal index and sunspot number. Indeed although much evidence implying correlations between low cloud cover variations and solar activity, the physical phenomenon explaining this is still poorly pronounced.

We have used in our previous study Morlet wavelets to examine the processes and structures behind the variability of solar activity indicators and galactic cosmic rays variations. Morlet wavelets analysis continues to prove its power in this study field. Thus we invest in the present work Morlet wavelets tool to examine closely the possible links between solar activity and climate. The purpose of this work is to examine once for all the geomagnetic aa-index and sunspot number variations towards low cloud cover amounts variations. One of the procedures to analyse nonstationary series, to discern whether there is a linear relation or not between low cloud amounts variations on a side and the geomagnetic aa-index and the solar activity on the other side is by means of wavelet method. Thus we have analysed variations in time, we arose hidden periods and structures being able to highlight a physical causal link between solar, geomagnetic activity and low cloud cover.

Besides of well known 11 years cycle which was found common to all parameters, low cloud amounts, geomagnetic aa-index and sunspot number, three structures of 5-7 months, 12-13 months and 60-70 months (5-5.8 years) were found common to low cloud amounts variation and geomagnetic aa-index variations. Thus the iterative method used particularly in this study for extrapolation revealed more closely common hidden structures.

---

[*] Email adress: neila.zarrouk@yahoo.fr

If relatively long periods such as 11 years cycles highlight globally the GCR-cloud connection, the community of structures and short periods highlighted through this Morlet analysis zoom prove closely the link between these parameters and low cloud amount as a measure of climate.

The Morlet wavelet analysis and our new iterative procedure for extrapolation prove with a good agreement that it is a suitable tool to reveal really hidden common structures and cycles. This analysis should be an answer to GCR-climate link around which several questions were discussed.

In: Environmental and Agricultural Research Summaries …   ISBN: 978-1-63117-090-4
Editor: Lucille T. Cacioppo   © 2014 Nova Science Publishers, Inc.

Chapter 28

DETECTION OF FIVE-DAY TO ONE-MONTH SURFACE AIR TEMPERATURE PREDICTABILITY USING INFORMATION THEORY

Gustavo Naumann[*] *and Walter M. Vargas*
National Scientific and Technological Research Council (CONICET)
Department of Atmospheric and Oceanic Sciences. Faculty of Sciences,
University of Buenos Aires, Argentina

RESEARCH SUMMARY

This paper investigates the detection of particular conditions in which the surface air temperature shows evidence an increased predictability for periods greater than five days. Analysis was performed on the maximum and minimum pentad temperature anomalies at San Miguel de Tucumán (1891-2007). To investigate the conditions, conditional-entropy and mutual-information metrics coupled with a cluster-analysis algorithm are proposed. Using these methodologies, it is possible to detect defined trajectories where the entropy of certain transitions decreases significantly. These decreases imply an increase in the predictability under these defined trajectories. Few weather patterns associated with enhanced predictability exist. It is mostly the warm and humid events that have these characteristics. Additionally, particular periods during which physical processes tend to vary more slowly and produce greater predictability structures can be found through local analysis of mutual information. For these periods, the predictability can be two times greater than the average. Additionally, these events tend to show a seasonal behavior, appearing mainly during the winter and spring.

[*] Corresponding Author: Gustavo Naumann; F.C.E. y N. Universidad de Buenos Aires; Intendente Güiraldes 2160 - Pab II, 2° floor; Buenos Aires, Argentina C1428EGA; E-mail:gnaumann@at.fcen.uba.ar

In: Environmental and Agricultural Research Summaries …   ISBN: 978-1-63117-090-4
Editor: Lucille T. Cacioppo   © 2014 Nova Science Publishers, Inc.

Chapter 29

TROPICAL CYCLONE-OCEAN INTERACTION: CLIMATOLOGY

Akiyoshi Wada[†]

Meteorological Research Institute, Tsukuba Ibaraki, Japan

RESEARCH SUMMARY

The ocean is an energy source for developing tropical cyclones (TCs) that originate over the tropical oceans. Warm water and winds are crucial factors for determining heat and moisture fluxes from the ocean to the atmosphere. These fluxes are closely associated with cumulus convection and large-scale condensation due to latent heat release in the upper troposphere. Both physical processes are essential for increasing the upper tropospheric warm-core temperature around a TC. Therefore, warm water over the tropical oceans is required to generate and intensify TCs. Recently, tropical cyclone heat potential (TCHP), a measure of the oceanic heat content from the surface to the 26°C-isotherm depth, is frequently used for monitoring TC activity in global oceans, particularly in the Atlantic and western North Pacific. Recent studies have reported that TC intensity was correlated with accumulated TCHP (ATCHP), calculated as a summation of TCHP every six hours from TC genesis upon first reaching categories 4 and 5 of the Saffir-Simpson scale, as well as sea-surface temperature (SST) and TC duration. This implies that both SST and upper ocean stratification such as temperature, salinity, and mixed-layer and seasonal-thermocline depths play crucial roles in determining TC intensity and intensification. Conversely, TCHP can be varied by mixed-layer deepening and Ekman pumping induced by TC passage through TC-induced sea-surface cooling (SSC). The SSC is evidence that the ocean energy is consumed for developing and sustaining TCs. In that sense, a climatological map of TCHP distribution is valuable for acquiring the potential of TC activity. A 44-year mean climatological TCHP distribution in the North Pacific indicates that TCHP is locally high in the Southern Hemisphere Central Pacific (SCP) and Western North Pacific (WNP). TCHP varies on

---

[†] E-mail address: awada@mri-jma.go.jp. TEL: +81-29-852-9154 FAX: +81-29-853-8735. Meteorological Research Institute, 1-1 Nagamine Tsukuba Ibaraki, 305-0052 Japan. (Corresponding author)

interannual and decadal time scales and is related to TC activity. The relatively low TCHP in the WNP is associated with an increase in the total number of TCs. This may indicate that low TCHP is caused by the frequent TC-induced SSC. When an El Niño event enters the mature phase, it leads to an increase in the number of super typhoons corresponding to categories 4 and 5. The increase in the number of super typhoons is related to an increase in ATCHP due to the trend of long-duration TCs. This chapter addresses the benefits of TCHP as a useful ocean-energy parameter for monitoring interannual and decadal variability of TC activity in the global ocean.

In: Environmental and Agricultural Research Summaries …   ISBN: 978-1-63117-090-4
Editor: Lucille T. Cacioppo   © 2014 Nova Science Publishers, Inc.

Chapter 30

PECULIARITIES OF PHOTOSYNTHESIS OF WHEAT GENOTYPES CONTRAST IN GRAIN YIELD AND THEIR USE IN BREEDING PROGRAMS

Jalal A. Aliyev[1,2,*]

[1]Department of Plant Physiology and Biotechnology,
Research Institute of Crop Husbandry,
Ministry of Agriculture of Azerbaijan Republic, Baku, Azerbaijan
[2]Department of Fundamental Problems of Biological Productivity,
Institute of Botany, Azerbaijan National Academy of Sciences,
Baku, Azerbaijan

RESEARCH SUMMARY

Sixty years of comprehensive research on photosynthesis and productivity of various wheat genotypes in natural conditions of cultivation, characteristics and parameters of photosynthetic activity of these genotypes in crop fields have finally established the high grain yield of an "ideal type" of wheat variety. For this purpose, the rich genefund, comprising several thousand wheat genotypes, selected from both the ancient and aboriginal varieties of national selection and introduced from the world genefund, particularly from *CIMMYT, ICARDA* and other International Centers, with contrasting grain yield, photosynthetic traits (stem height, area and architectonics of the leaf surface, etc.), duration of the vegetation, and other morphophysilogical traits, as well as drought resistance, was created. These genotypes, with two or three times less leaf areas than those with broad leaves, produce similar or even greater grain yield. Analysis of various wheat genotypes with different values of photosynthetic traits and productivity in conjunction with a range of environmental factors, including mineral nutrition, water, light, etc. showed the wide range of CO_2 assimilation variability in ontogenesis, depending on the morphophysiological peculiarities of genotypes and their sink-source relations.

* Email: aliyev-j@botany-az.org.

The diurnal changes in the photosynthetic rate of leaves of all layers and genotypes with contrast architectonics are characterized by a double-peaked pattern indicating a drastic increase in the photosynthetic rate in the morning and a decrease in the evening. Not all genotypes with small leaves are highly productive and not all genotypes with broad leaves are considered high or low productive.

Genotypes with broad leaves and high yield require sufficient water supply. Genotypes with vertically oriented short and narrow leaves and a high tolerance to water stress yield up to 10 t ha^{-1}. The rate of biosynthesis of the main transport form of carbon, sucrose, and products of glycolate metabolism as well as the rate of CO_2 release in the light due to photorespiration were higher in highly productive genotypes. The lower leaves of highly productive genotypes export more assimilates to the ear than lower leaves of low productive ones.

Favorable architectonics that provides optimal assimilating surface and sufficient attractive force of genotypes in sowings with high photosynthetic activity of the ear create the basis for a high grain yield. Throughout the entire period of flag leaf development, highly productive intensive genotypes in comparison with extensive ones were distinguished by higher activities of RuBP carboxylase and carbonic anhydrase that play a significant role for the maintenance of CO_2 assimilation on the high level.

The activities of the RuBP oxygenase were higher in the highly productive wheat genotypes than in the lower ones. The activity of RuBP carboxylase in different ear elements varies deeply depending on the development and genotypical features of the plants. The ear glume and awns of the intensive genotype had a higher activity of RuBP carboxylase than those of the extensive genotype. Thus, the high level of metabolism, high activity of the key enzymes and the primary photochemical processes, in conjunction with favorable phenotypic traits, optimum leaf index and architectonics are crucial to the high productivity of wheat genotypes.

In: Environmental and Agricultural Research Summaries ...   ISBN: 978-1-63117-090-4
Editor: Lucille T. Cacioppo   © 2014 Nova Science Publishers, Inc.

Chapter 31

OPTIONS FOR OPTIMISED USE OF WATER RESOURCES FOR SECURING FUTURE AGRICULTURAL PRODUCTION

Christian Richardt Jensen*, Sven-Erik Jacobsen,
Søren T. Jørgensen and Fulai Liu
Department of Plant and Environmental Sciences, Faculty of Sciences,
University of Copenhagen, Taastrup, Denmark

RESEARCH SUMMARY

Agriculture is the main user of fresh water resources in the World. However, irrigation water has become less available in many areas due to an increased competition for water among industries, households and the environment and due to global climate change. Thus, there is a growing interest of using irrigation water resources in a more efficient manner. Here a viewpoint is made by looking on the efforts and knowledge already existing about optimising the use of irrigation water resources. Main tools for optimising the use of water resources in agriculture can be obtained by: selection of water efficient irrigation methods like drip and micro irrigation, use of low quality waters such as treated wastewater, use of salt tolerant crops, optimising irrigation scheduling by using plant and soil sensors, remote sensing, irrigation models, using the 'virtual water' principles so that water rich regions secure food supply to dry regions. In dry regions small areas with high value crops should be irrigated securing net income and livelihood. In general water can be saved by reducing the overall waste of food throughout the food chain from post-harvest to the end-consumer. Recent findings on these options are discussed and evaluated.

* E-mail crj@life.ku.dk (C.R. Jensen); Phone: 0045 35 33 33 92; FAX: 0045 35 33 34 78.

In: Environmental and Agricultural Research Summaries ...   ISBN: 978-1-63117-090-4
Editor: Lucille T. Cacioppo   © 2014 Nova Science Publishers, Inc.

Chapter 32

CLIMATE CHANGE AND WHEAT CROP YIELDS IN AUSTRALIA: A REVIEW

Qunying Luo[*]

University of Technology, Sydney, NSW, Australia

RESEARCH SUMMARY

The potential impact of climate change on wheat production is a key concern to Australia due to its importance to the nation's economy and to global food security as wheat is a key player in the world grain market. This work extensively reviewed the relationship between wheat crop production including yield and future climatic change based on both experimental and modelling studies conducted in Australia over the last four decades. Experiment studies evolved from adopting glasshouse, gradient tunnel facility to free air CO_2 enrichment facility, evolved from studying enhanced CO_2 effect alone to the combined effects of increased atmospheric CO_2 concentration along with other environmental factors such as light, temperature, soil water and nutrient, and with various soil types, and evolved from wheat monoculture to wheat-pulse rotation system. Modelling approaches evolved from sensitivity analysis, to scenario analysis and to Bayesian analysis. The advantage and disadvantage of each research method were discussed where appropriate. Future research directions were identified to better address future climate change, food security and sustainability issues.

---

[*] Corresponding author Email address: luo.qunying122@gmail.com.

In: Environmental and Agricultural Research Summaries …   ISBN: 978-1-63117-090-4
Editor: Lucille T. Cacioppo   © 2014 Nova Science Publishers, Inc.

Chapter 33

IMPROVEMENT OF COTTON PRODUCTION IN ARID SALINE SOILS BY BENEFICIAL MICROBES

Egamberdieva Dilfuza and Jabborova Dilfuza
Faculty of Biology and Soil Sciences, National University of Uzbekistan,
Vuzgorodok, Tashkent, Uzbekistan

RESEARCH SUMMARY

Crop cultivation in saline soils is one of the major agricultural challenges world-wide. Cotton production in Uzbekistan is limited by soil salinization and disease caused by soil borne pathogens. The use of plant growth promoting rhizobacteria (PGPR) to control plant diseases and stimulation of plant growth has been considered a viable alternative and environmentally friendly method. The strain *P. putida* BIST and *B. subtilis* SUBTIN significantly ($p<0.05$) increased the total N, P, and K contents of shoot and root (13-27%), plant height (15%), and yield (16%) of cotton in small plot experiments. They were able to produce phytohormone indole-acetic-acid (IAA) under saline conditions and were positive for ACC deaminase activity. On the basis of results, it may be concluded that plant growth promoting rhizobacteria are potential option for improvement of cotton growth and development in salinated arid soil.

In: Environmental and Agricultural Research Summaries …   ISBN: 978-1-63117-090-4
Editor: Lucille T. Cacioppo   © 2014 Nova Science Publishers, Inc.

Chapter 34

THE ROLE OF HYDROGEN CYANIDE IN THE ORIGIN OF LIFE

Alicia Negrón-Mendoza[1], Alejandro Heredia[1],
Maria Colín-García[2] and Sergio Ramos Bernal[1]
[1]Instituto de Ciencias Nucleares,
Universidad Nacional Autónoma de México
[2]Instituto de Geología, Universidad Nacional Autónoma
de México, México, Mexico

RESEARCH SUMMARY

Chemical evolution encompasses physical and chemical processes that took place on Earth before the appearance of life. To simulate the chemical process that may have occurred, a heterogeneous medium is geologically more likely to succeed than a homogeneous phase. The main interest of this research is to stress the relevance of radiation chemistry as a tool to elucidate the importance of ionizing radiation to study the formation of biologically-relevant compounds from HCN and its derivatives and to remark on the importance of the chemical reactions that may occur at hydrosphere/lithosphere interfaces. To this end, we study the adsorption capacity of HCN in different surface minerals that may have been present in the primordial epoch and study the chemical reactions that occur when the system HCN-mineral surface is exposed to a high-energy source. These studies show that HCN can be adsorbed readily from the surfaces studied. This adsorption is influenced by pH and type of adsorbent. Irradiation of HCN solutions produced simple organic compounds and an oligomeric material that, upon hydrolysis, yields compounds of biological importance such as amino acids, carboxylic acids, and purines. These products are formed even at low temperatures and low radiation doses. This work strongly reinforces the hypothesis of the central role of HCN as a parent molecule in the process of chemical evolution on early Earth, comets, and other extraterrestrial environments and the use of ionizing radiation as an energy source to induce chemical changes in these systems.

In: Environmental and Agricultural Research Summaries ...   ISBN: 978-1-63117-090-4
Editor: Lucille T. Cacioppo   © 2014 Nova Science Publishers, Inc.

Chapter 35

CYANIDE POISONING IN ANIMALS AND HUMANS

Antônio Carlos Lopes Câmara[a] *and Benito Soto-Blanco*[b]

[a]Veterinary Hospital, Universidade Federal Rural do Semi-árido (UFERSA),
Mossoró, RN, Brazil
[b]Department of Veterinary Clinics and Surgery, Universidade Federal
de Minas Gerais (UFMG), Belo Horizonte, MG, Brazil

RESEARCH SUMMARY

Cyanide is a ubiquitous substance in the environment. It can be released from cyanogenic plants, industrial processes (such as metal processing, electroplating, and acrylic and chemical synthesis), and medicinal drugs (such as nitroprusside). Cyanide inhibits several cellular enzymes, including cytochrome oxidase, which is a key enzyme in the cellular respiratory chain. Most of the cyanide absorbed by an organism is detoxified by enzymatic combination with sulfur, and acute poisoning occurs when detoxification systems are overwhelmed. Acute cyanide poisoning is potentially fatal and is a result of cellular hypoxia and cytotoxic anoxia. Long-term exposure to cyanide is responsible for various toxic effects, including reduced weight gain, damage to the liver, impaired thyroid function, and neuropathies. Furthermore, various experimental studies and field cases in several animal species have verified that exposure to cyanide or to cyanogenic plants results in reproductive disturbances.

In: Environmental and Agricultural Research Summaries … ISBN: 978-1-63117-090-4
Editor: Lucille T. Cacioppo © 2014 Nova Science Publishers, Inc.

Chapter 36

ESTIMATING THE HYDROGEN CYANIDE GENERATION: THERMODYNAMICS AND MASS TRANSFER

Humberto Estay[*]

Arcadis Chile, Santiago, Chile
Laboratory of Membrane Separation Processes (LabProSeM),
Department of Chemical Engineering,
University of Santiago de Chile (USACH), Santiago, Chile

RESEARCH SUMMARY

The industries related to the production or use of cyanide must ensure high safety standards in order to minimize the risk to personnel exposed to hydrogen cyanide (HCN). This can be reached by accomplishing a global search of all parameters involved in the process, taking also into account the local regulations for HCN emanations. In this scenario, there is a high interest in developing methods capable of quantifying the HCN generation in different processes or equipment and in that way the implementation of remediation actions in the process operations or in the design of future projects can be taken. Nowadays, the most used method to estimate HCN generation is based on the dissociation curve of free cyanide and the Henry's law constant. However, this method consistently overestimates the volatilized HCN in exit gases due to there is no inclusion of the chemical interactions of cyanide with others species (e.g., zinc, copper, and nickel), and also does not consider the mass transfer of HCN, the most influential factor on HCN volatilization. The mass transfer of HCN in the liquid phase represents the main resistance of HCN transport into the gas phase, which is dependent on system characteristics such as geometry, hydrodynamics and state conditions. With this background in mind, a phenomenological method to estimate HCN generation in any system is proposed in the current chapter. This theoretical method is mainly based on the thermodynamic equilibrium of the different cyanide complexes species present

* Corresponding author: Tel +56(2) 2386 20 54, Fax +56(2) 2381 6001, E-mail: humberto.estay@arcadis.cl, humberto.estay@gmail.com.

in a solution, the phase equilibrium behaviour based on the Henry's law equilibrium, and the mass transfer of HCN into the air based on a resistances-in-series model to determine the HCN content in the liquid and gas phases. In addition, the proposed method also evaluates the effect of system conditions (temperature, pressure, and pH) and the operation characteristics or equipment used. Thus, this phenomenological method can be a powerful and valuable tool for quantifying HCN generation in realistic simulations, along with providing rapid identification of risk conditions in the process and more criteria for investment project decision-making.

In: Environmental and Agricultural Research Summaries ...   ISBN: 978-1-63117-090-4
Editor: Lucille T. Cacioppo   © 2014 Nova Science Publishers, Inc.

Chapter 37

APPLICATION OF CYANIDE-BRIDGED COORDINATION POLYMERS FOR ELECTRODE MATERIALS OF RECHARGEABLE BATTERIES

Masashi Okubo

National Institute of Advanced Industrial Science
and Technology, Japan

RESEARCH SUMMARY

Development of novel host materials with enhanced ion storage ability is of particular importance in a wide range of applications, especially the electrode materials for batteries. A cyanide-bridged coordination polymer is one of the most attractive host materials, because both the ionic-diffusion channel and electron conduction path frequently coexist within the framework. For example, a cyanide-bridged perovskite-type framework, so-called Prussian blue analog (PBA), has been studied intensively for decades from the viewpoint of electrochromism. However, the electrochemical properties, i.e. electrochemical ion intercalation/extraction of PBAs can also be applied to the electrode materials of the batteries. In this chapter, the solid state electrochemistry of PBA is briefly explained. Then, the cyanide-bridged coordination polymer electrodes for the battery application are reviewed.

In: Environmental and Agricultural Research Summaries …   ISBN: 978-1-63117-090-4
Editor: Lucille T. Cacioppo   © 2014 Nova Science Publishers, Inc.

Chapter 38

POSSIBLE ROLES OF CYANOTOXINS IN SPECIES INTERACTIONS OF PHYTOPLANKTON ASSEMBLAGES

*István Bácsi[1], Viktória B-Béres[2] and Gábor Vasas[*3]*
[1] University of Debrecen, Department of Hydrobiology, Debrecen, Hungary
[2] Environmental Protection, Nature Conservation and Water Authority,
Trans-Tiszanian Region, Debrecen, Hungary
[3] University of Debrecen, Department of Botany, Debrecen, Hungary

RESEARCH SUMMARY

Cyanobacteria ("blue-green algae") are among the most well studied organisms; above all because of their ability to produce an extremely diverse array of biologically active metabolites, cyanotoxins among them. It is known that the biosynthesis of cyanotoxins requires a significant amount of energy and nutrient resources of the cyanobacterial cells. With this knowledge, the question that arises is '*what could be the functional role of these "expensive" metabolites in the ecology and distribution of cyanobacteria*'.

One function of the metabolites in question could be that they serve as allelochemicals. Allelopathy between phytoplankton organisms in aquatic habitats is not as well studied as between e. g. vascular plant in terrestrial systems, although it is considered as an important regulating factor of phytoplankton dynamics and community composition. The discussion of cyanotoxins as allelochemicals is a controversial issue. Some authors say that toxins have effect on several organisms, including some that may not be present in the producer immediate environment (toxicity), while allelopathic compounds play role in the interactions between the emitter organisms and their direct competitors or predators. From this point of view cyanotoxins are not specifically allelochemicals. However, a number of observations indicated allelopathic nature of cyanotoxins, so in some cases it is difficult to isolate clearly these two phenomena: toxicity and allelopathy. The issue is further complicated by the following facts: (i) A natural cyanobacterial population is a mixture of toxin producer and non-producer ecotypes in most cases; (ii) the release of cyanotoxins varies in a very wide

* E-mail address: vasas.gabor@science.unideb.hu.

range, usually they are released in the surrounding water only in small amounts by living cells. Most recently new hypotheses arise according to which cyanobacterial secondary metabolites, especially cyanotoxins can serve as signal molecules among the cells within one or different genera. Thus, despite the increscent number of studies the question about the role of cyanotoxins still remained mostly unanswered. This chapter will discuss the existing evidence for the roles of cyanobacterial secondary metabolites, mainly toxins, in the interactions of phytoplankton species; trying to highlight the functions of these compounds in dynamics of phytoplankton assemblages.

In: Environmental and Agricultural Research Summaries ...   ISBN: 978-1-63117-090-4
Editor: Lucille T. Cacioppo   © 2014 Nova Science Publishers, Inc.

Chapter 39

NEGATIVE ALLELOPATHY AMONG CYANOBACTERIA

Miroslav Švercel[*]

Institute of Evolutionary Biology and Environmental Studies,
University of Zurich, Winterthurerstrasse, Switzerland

RESEARCH SUMMARY

Cyanobacteria are well known producers of a wide variety of allelochemicals, which positively or negatively affect sympatric organisms from similar or even different taxons. In the traditional approach for studying allelopathy in water systems, cyanobacteria and photoautotrophic micro-eukaryotes were grouped together under the term of micro-algae. Because these two groups are phylogenetically and phenotypically distinct and the production of allelopathic compounds is often highly species- and even strain-dependent, it is appealing to assess the present available knowledge concerning allelopathy within and among cyanobacteria separately.

In this chapter, information is reviewed about i) cyanobacteria production of alleopathic substances, ii) the chemical nature of these allelopathic secondary metabolites, and iii) the mechanisms of the allelopathic inhibition. Furthermore, (iv) the possibility to use allelopathy to control harmful cyanobacterial blooms is discussed.

[*] E-mail address: miro.svercel@gmail.com.

In: Environmental and Agricultural Research Summaries …   ISBN: 978-1-63117-090-4
Editor: Lucille T. Cacioppo   © 2014 Nova Science Publishers, Inc.

Chapter 40

THE BLOOM-FORMING CYANOBACTERIUM *NODULARIA SPUMIGENA*: A PECULIAR NITROGEN-FIXER IN THE BALTIC SEA FOOD WEBS

Rehab El-Shehawy[1] and Elena Gorokhova[2]*
[1]IMDEA Water (Instituto Madrileño de Estudios Avanzados, IMDEA AGUA), Alcalá de Henares, Spain
[2]Applied Environmental Science, Stockholm University, Stockholm, Sweden

RESEARCH SUMMARY

A peculiar feature of the Baltic Sea is the massive summer blooms of cyanobacteria. Various environmental, economic and sanitation repercussions of these blooms have attracted considerable attention among the scientific community, water management agencies and general public. Of particular concern is the increase in frequencies and amplitude of the hepatotoxic blooms of *Nodularia spumigena*. This is a planktonic, toxic, filamentous nitrogen-fixing cyanobacterium capable of forming massive blooms when environmental conditions are suitable. The toxicity of *N. spumigena* is mainly attributed to the production of the hepatotoxin nodularin, which is also a tumor promoter. Furthermore, through its nitrogen fixation activity, *N. spumigena* contributes significantly to the total annual nitrogen load in the Baltic Sea. Here, we highlight the physiological peculiarity of *N. spumigena* related to nitrogen fixation and heterocyst formation and how this may be regulating its ability to form blooms. We also discuss some key molecular and physiological aspects of the toxin production. Furthermore, we highlight the interactions between *N. spumigena* and its grazers in the food webs and potential effects of climate-related factors on these interactions. All these aspects are important to consider if we want to predict consequences of the

---

* E-mail address: rehab@imdea.org.

eutrophication and global change for bloom proliferation and toxin production by *N. spumigena*.

In: Environmental and Agricultural Research Summaries …   ISBN: 978-1-63117-090-4
Editor: Lucille T. Cacioppo   © 2014 Nova Science Publishers, Inc.

Chapter 41

WHICH FACTORS ARE RELATED TO THE SUCCESS OF *CYLINDROSPERMOPSIS RACIBORSKII* IN BRAZILIAN AQUATIC SYSTEMS?

Andreia M. A. Gomes[1,2], Marcelo M. Marinho[2]*
and Sandra M. F. O. Azevedo[1]

[1]Laboratório de Ecofisiologia e Toxicologia de Cianobactérias, IBCCF,
Universidade Federal do Rio de Janeiro, Rio de Janeiro, Brazil
[2]Departamento de Biologia Vegetal, Laboratório de Ecofisiologia de Algas,
Universidade do Estado do Rio de Janeiro, Rua São Francisco Xavier,
PHLC, Rio de Janeiro, Brazil

RESEARCH SUMMARY

Blooms of *Cylindrospermopsis* have become more and more frequent in Brazilian aquatic systems because of its competitiveness in tropical eutrophic systems. Beyond of ecological effects of the blooms, this genus is a potential producer of toxins (cylindrospermopsin/ hepatotoxin and saxitoxin/neurotoxin), which cause problems to public health and environmental hazards. *C. raciborskii* is usually described as invasive specie and can represent up to 100% of total algal biomass under certain environmental conditions. This occurrence in tropical systems is usually associated with low light availability and its high affinity for nutrients. In order to evaluate these generalizations, we analyzed limnological data of 51 Brazilian aquatic ecosystems, where *C. raciborskii* occurs. The data base included limnological information of reservoirs and coastal lagoons, comprising a latitudinal gradient from the northeast, south, southeast and central regions of the country. Nutrient concentration showed widely range from oligotrophic to hypereutrophic conditions. In general these systems presented low water transparency (Secchi disk: 0.05 to 1.7m) and the annual average temperature is higher than 22°C. Relative contribution of *C. raciborskii* in these systems ranged from 0.01 to 99% of phytoplankton biomass. The data analysis showed that relative

* E-mail address:manzi.uerj@gmail.com.

contributions of *C. raciborskii* greater than 80% were associated with high values of temperature, pH, alkalinity and conductivity. In general, low DIN concentrations were also related to high percentage contribution. So the success of *C. raciborskii* in Brazilian aquatic ecosystems can be related to its low light requirements, high affinity for ammonium and phosphorus and its ability to tolerate high ionic concentration. Moreover, some of these systems have high ion concentrations which reflect in elevated conductivity values.

In: Environmental and Agricultural Research Summaries ...   ISBN: 978-1-63117-090-4
Editor: Lucille T. Cacioppo   © 2014 Nova Science Publishers, Inc.

Chapter 42

IS CYANOBACTERIAL DOMINANCE IN BRAZILIAN SEMI-ARID RESERVOIRS REGULATED BY ENVIRONMENTAL OR STOCHASTIC FEATURES?

José Etham de Lucena Barbosa[1*]
and Janiele França Vasconcelos[2]

[1]Departamento de Biologia. Universidade Estadual da Paraíba
Programa de Pós-graduação em Ciência e Tecnologia Ambiental (PPGCTA)
Programa de Pós-graduação em Ecologia e Conservação (PPGEC)
[2]Programa de Pós-graduação em Ecologia de Ambientes Aquáticos (PEA),
Núcleo de Pesquisas em Limnologia, Ictiologia e Aquicultura (Nupélia),
Departamento de Biologia, Universidade Estadual de Maringá

RESEARCH SUMMARY

Cyanobacterial blooms have been associated with eutrophication process in aquatic ecosystems; however, more importantly than identifying the general conditions that determine the cyanobacterial occurrence, is the understanding of the factors that regulate the occurrence of the individual species that can be related with the temporal dynamic of composition and biomass of this group. The neutral model of biodiversity describes how local communities are structured if population dynamics are statistically identical among species in a constant, possibly patchy, environment with random speciation. Our objective was to determine whether cyanobacterial communities exhibit spatial structuring, thus suggesting neutrality, or are structured by local environments features, suggesting that they are under niche-based control. We analyzed the determinants of cyanobacterial community structure across three reservoirs located in Brazilian semi-arid region. Eight components of species variation were separated and identified: pure environmental, pure temporal, pure spatial, spatially and temporally structured environmental variation, spatial-temporal, spatial-environmental, and temporal-environmental component. Our results suggest that the distribution of cyanobacteria

---
[*] E-mail: ethambarbosa@hotmail.com.

community is affect mainly by the environmental component, with an important temporal component in species distribution. The finding that temporal configuration, with dominance interchanges among *Microcystis protocystis*, *Cylindrospermopsis raciborskii,* and *Planktotrhix agardii*, was more important than spatial factors, can be related to temperature and water transparence as the main controlling factors of cyanobacterial community in semi-arid ecosystems.

In: Environmental and Agricultural Research Summaries …   ISBN: 978-1-63117-090-4
Editor: Lucille T. Cacioppo   © 2014 Nova Science Publishers, Inc.

Chapter 43

PICOPHYTOPLANKTON COMMUNITY STRUCTURE IN A HYPERSALINE COASTAL LAGOON: ROLE OF SALINITY AND LINKS WITH VIRAL AND MICROBIAL COMMUNITIES

Mathilde Schapira[1],* and Laurent Seuront[1,2,3]
[1]School of Biological Sciences, Flinders University,
Adelaide, South Australia, Australia
[2]South Australian Research and Development Institute, Aquatic Sciences,
West Beach, South Australia, Australia
[3]Centre National de la RechercheScientifique,
Laboratoired'Océanologieet de Géosciences,
Université des Sciences et Technologies de Lille,
Station Marine, Wimereux, France

RESEARCH SUMMARY

Picophytoplankton (i.e. cyanobacteria and pico-eukaryotes) are abundant and ecologically critical components of the autotrophic communities in the pelagic realm. These micro-organisms colonized a variety of extreme environments including hypersaline waters. However, the distribution of these organisms along strong salinity gradients has barely been investigated. The abundance and community structure of pico-phytoplankton, heterotrophic bacteria and virus-like particles (VLP) were investigated along a natural continuous salinity gradient (18‰ to 155‰) in a South Australian temperate coastal lagoon, using flow cytometry. A concomitant increase in viral and bacterial abundances with salinity was observed from 50‰ to 150‰, where the highest abundances were observed. Highest picophytoplankton abundances were recorded under salinity conditions ranging between 80‰ and 110‰. A viral population, exhibiting flow-cytometric characteristics of

---

* Present address: IFREMER, Laboratoire Environnement Ressources de Normandie, Avenue du Général de Gaulle, Port en Bessin, France. E-mail address: mathilde.schapira@ifremer.fr.

picophytoplankton viruses was observed from 50.3‰ to 100‰. Two populations of cyanobacteria (likely *Synechococcus* and *Prochlorococcus*) and 5 distinct populations of pico-eukaryotes were identified along the salinity gradient. The picophytoplankton cytometric-richness decreased with salinity and the most cytometrically-diverse community (4 to 7 populations) was observed in the brackish-marine part of the lagoon (i.e. salinity below 35‰). One population of pico-eukaryotes dominated the community throughout the salinity gradient and was responsible for the bloom observed between 80‰ and 110‰. Finally only this halotolerant population and *Prochlorococcus*-like cyanobacteria were identified in hypersaline waters (i.e. above 140‰). The complex patterns described here represent the first observation of cyanobacteria and pico-eukaryotes dynamics along a continuous gradient where salinity increases from 18‰ to 155‰. Although the spatial dynamics observed here are in accordance with the patterns observed previously along discontinuous salinity gradients, the high abundances of pico-phytoplankton as well as the existence of a *Prochlorococcus*-like population in hypersaline waters set this saline lagoon apart from the systems studied previously.

In: Environmental and Agricultural Research Summaries …   ISBN: 978-1-63117-090-4
Editor: Lucille T. Cacioppo   © 2014 Nova Science Publishers, Inc.

Chapter 44

ACCUMULATION AND PHYTOTOXICITY OF MICROCYSTINS IN VASCULAR PLANTS

Jian Chen, Hai Qiang Zhang and Zhi Qi Shi[*]
Institute of Food Quality and Safety,
Jiangsu Academy of Agricultural Sciences,
Nanjing, China

RESEARCH SUMMARY

Microcystins contamination resulted from cyanobacterial blooms in eutrophic water has received increasing attention worldwide. Aquatic plants have been shown to absorb microcystins from water and exposure of microcystins has adverse effects on the growth of aquatic plants.

In addition, terrestrial plants could be exposed to microcystins via the use of eutrophic water that may contain cyanobacterial blooms and microcystins from irrigation. Microcystins transporters have not been identified in plants, but microcystins has been detected in both shoots and roots of terrestrial plants, which implicates that microcystins could be absorbed and transported in terrestrial plants.

The absorption, transportation, and metabolism of microcystins in plants will be discussed in the first part of this chapter. Microcystins accumulated in plants can result in phytotoxicity by inducing growth limitation and histological alterations.

Besides of the inhibition of microcystins to phosphatases 1 and 2A, lipid peroxidation and the increase of anti-oxidative enzymes induced by microcystins suggested that oxidative damage might contribute to the phytotoxicity of microcystins in plants.

Our recent study also suggests that nitric oxide is involved in physiological process of microcystins-induced phytotoxicity. The advances in the mechanisms of microcystins-induced phytotoxicity will be reviewed in the second part of this chapter.

---

[*] E-mail address: shizhiqi@jaas.ac.cn.

In: Environmental and Agricultural Research Summaries ...   ISBN: 978-1-63117-090-4
Editor: Lucille T. Cacioppo   © 2014 Nova Science Publishers, Inc.

Chapter 45

CYANOTOXIN HEALTH HAZARD AND RISK ASSESSMENT IN FRESHWATER LAKES

*Milena Bruno**

Department of Environment and Primary Prevention,
National Institute of Health, Rome, Italy

RESEARCH SUMMARY

Cyanobacterial toxins are very toxic for animals and human beings, and are endowed with severe acute and chronic intoxications. It is therefore very important to provide people toxin-free water, or at least guarantee a toxins level below secure threshold limits. If contamination of water can't be avoided, adequate measures have to be taken to avoid intoxication episodes and exposure of humans to toxins. Such measures should be as environmental friendly as possible, but nonetheless effective and definitive. These should include actions to avoid exposure and to minimise contamination of drinking water plants. In addition, since intoxication cases can occur, the best diagnostic and medical treatments have to be addressed, for an adequate first aid intervention. Health hazard from microcystin contaminations in drinking water, food supplements, commercial fish and edible mussels has been studied in several lakes from Northern, Central and Southern Italy, in order to evaluate the human risk resulting from several routes of exposition. Many countries have adopted monitoring programs which take into consideration for the risk assessment only the abundances of cyanobacterial cells.

This view does not take sufficiently into account the relationships between cyanobacterial abundance and cyanotoxin concentrations in water. There is a strong need to homogenize the procedures for risk assessment evaluation and to define threshold limits based on cyanobacterial abundance and/or cyanotoxin concentrations, studying the implications deriving from the presence of risk cofactors like heavy metals or pesticides, too. These aspects are propaedeutic for the preparation of transnational guidelines for risk assessment and management.

---

* E-mail address: milena.bruno@iss.it.

In: Environmental and Agricultural Research Summaries ...   ISBN: 978-1-63117-090-4
Editor: Lucille T. Cacioppo   © 2014 Nova Science Publishers, Inc.

Chapter 46

CONFOCAL LASER SCANNING AND ELECTRON MICROSCOPIC TECHNIQUES AS POWERFUL TOOLS FOR DETERMINING THE *IN VIVO* EFFECT AND SEQUESTRATION CAPACITY OF LEAD IN CYANOBACTERIA

Isabel Esteve[1], Juan Maldonado[1], Álvaro Burgos,[1, 2]
Elia Diestra[1], Mireia Burnat[1] and Antonio Solé[1]
[1]Department of Genetics and Microbiology, Universitat Autònoma
de Barcelona, Edifici C – Campus de la UAB, Bellaterra
(Cerdanyola del Vallès), Barcelona, Spain
[2]Departamento de Recursos Hidrobiológicos,
Universidad de Nariño, Pasto (N), Colombia

RESEARCH SUMMARY

Microbial mats are laminated benthic ecosystems made up of microorganisms having diversely coloured layers due to the photosynthetic pigments of cyanobacteria, algae and purple anoxygenic phototrophic bacteria. For many years, our group of work has been studying the microbial mats in the Ebro Delta (Tarragona, Spain). Despite the fact that the Ebro Delta has been a protected area for years, is currently subjected to anthropogenic pollution. Heavy metal contamination in these environments is very considerable, making the microorganisms in these ecosystems a subject of great interest when analyzing their ability to sequester metals. Our group has optimized different high-resolution microscopy techniques such as Confocal Laser Scanning Microscopy (CLSM), Transmission Electron Microscopy (TEM) and Scanning Electron Microscopy (SEM), these last two techniques coupled to an Energy dispersive X-ray detector (EDX). The CLSM coupled to a spectrofluorometric detector (CLSM-$\lambda scan$) was applied in determining the in vivo effect of lead (Pb) in phototrophic microorganisms (tolerance/resistance), and the CLSM and image analysis (CLSM-IA) were used in determining changes in total and individual cyanobacteria biomass.

Additionally, the electron microscopic techniques were utilized in determining the ability of these microorganisms to capture metal both externally in extrapolymeric substances (EPS) and internally, in polyphosphate inclusions (PP). For this purpose, we used different cyanobacteria from Pasteur culture collection (*Oscillatoria* sp. PCC 7515, *Chroococcus* sp. PCC 9106 and *Spirulina* sp. PCC 6313) and *Microcoleus* sp. isolated from Ebro Delta microbial mats. Pb was selected because the Ebro River is polluted by this metal and also because it is a non-essential toxic metal. An inverse correlation between the mean fluorescence intensity (MFI) and the concentration of the metal used have been demonstrated in all phototrophic bacteria tested in CLSM-$\lambda scan$. On the other hand, the SEM-EDX and TEM-EDX analysis showed that all phototrophic microorganisms have the ability to accumulate Pb in EPS and in PP inclusions. Experiments made in unpolluted and polluted microcosms, demonstrated that cyanobacteria from the polluted microcosm accumulate Pb in PP inclusions, whilst no Pb was detected in the unpolluted microcosm by means of TEM-EDX. Finally, the TEM-EDX analyses spectra from PP inclusions of different cyanobacteria from Ebro Delta microbial mats samples, demonstrated that no type of metal pollution was detected. It can be deduced that this ecosystem was pristine during the sampling procedure. In conclusion, the combination of the techniques outlined here provides valuable information to select cyanobacteria as bioindicators of metal pollution and its potential for bioremediation.

In: Environmental and Agricultural Research Summaries …   ISBN: 978-1-63117-090-4
Editor: Lucille T. Cacioppo   © 2014 Nova Science Publishers, Inc.

Chapter 47

A NEW METHODOLOGY FOR RAPID ASSESSMENT OF SPATIAL DISTRIBUTION OF PHYTOPLANKTON BLOOMS: CASE STUDY IN PAMPULHA RESERVOIR

Ricardo M. Pinto-Coelho[1]*, Maíra O. Campos[1],
Eliane C. Elias[2], Simone P. dos Santos[2],
Denise P. Fernandes[2], Gabriela P. Fernandes[1],
Aloízio P. P. Gomes[1] and Laila O. Ribeiro[1]

[1]Departamento de Biologia Geral, ICB, UFMG. Belo Horizonte (MG), Brazil
[2]Programa de Pós-Gradução em Ecologia,
Conservação e Manejo da Vida Silvestre – PG ECMVS, ICB, UFMG.
Belo Horizonte (MG), Brazil

RESEARCH SUMMARY

Hypertrophic lakes and reservoirs frequently suffer from algal and cyanobacterial blooms. In general, this phenomenon causes a rapid decrease of water quality. Traditional monitoring programs of these systems usually cover only a limited number of sampling points. Furthermore, counting of phytoplankton or laboratory analysis of chlorophyll require time-consuming procedures. Thus, local managers have access to the required information only after the undesirable effects of a bloom have become established. Since these lakes are usually located near urban areas, algae blooms in hypertrophic lakes are prone to affect local human populations in different ways. Thus, the prompt availability of this kind of data is of great importance for managers. We present a new methodology for monitoring chlorophyll-a that makes it possible to gather a very large and fine-scale amount of spatial data concerning the subsurface concentrations of this pigment. The proposed method consists of an integrated use of a highly sensitive fluorescent limnological probe, coupled to a high-precision D-GPS that provides geographical coordinates with sub-metric precision. We developed a structure

---

* E-mail address: rmpc@icb.ufmg.br.

that can be easily mounted on every kind of small boat. A new software program was also created, to precisely synchronize the data files delivered by two different devices. The final result is the production of a detailed thematic chart that shows the spatial pattern of chlorophyll in great detail. This makes it possible for local managers to initiate measures to mitigate or even prevent the wider spread of an algae bloom soon after the first signs of this undesired phenomenon are detected.

In: Environmental and Agricultural Research Summaries ...   ISBN: 978-1-63117-090-4
Editor: Lucille T. Cacioppo   © 2014 Nova Science Publishers, Inc.

Chapter 48

ECOLOGICAL CONTROL OF CYANOBACTERIAL BLOOMS IN FRESHWATER ECOSYSTEMS

Alan E. Wilson[*] *and Michael Chislock*

Fisheries and Allied Aquacultures,
Auburn University, Alabama, US

RESEARCH SUMMARY

Cyanobacterial blooms pose one of the most serious threats to freshwater ecosystems by producing toxic secondary metabolites that can poison aquatic food-webs, pets, livestock, and humans. Consequently, water resource managers routinely employ a variety of strategies aimed at controlling blooms of cyanobacteria, including reducing nutrient inputs, using potent herbicides, disrupting stratification, and shading waterbodies with water-based stains. The role of ecology in cyanobacterial bloom management is poorly understood despite a decades-long history of studies using biomanipulation: the manipulation of higher trophic levels (adding piscivores or removing planktivores) to increase the size, abundance, and grazing pressure of herbivorous zooplankton to reduce algal abundance. Past biomanipulation efforts conducted primarily in temperate systems have provided equivocal results, and the presence of the generalist herbivore, *Daphnia*, seems to be critically important to the success of biomanipulation efforts.

While cyanobacteria are relatively poor quality food for planktonic herbivores including cladocerans, copepods, and rotifers, recent meta-analyses of zooplankton-cyanobacteria studies show that, in general, cyanobacteria can support positive zooplankton population growth and purportedly toxic cyanobacterial secondary metabolites have, if any, ambiguous effects on zooplankton. Furthermore, recent research has shown that freshwater zooplankton, including the cladoceran *Daphnia* and the calanoid copepod *Eudiaptomus*, can adapt to tolerate toxic cyanobacteria in the diet following prolonged exposure to cyanobacterial blooms. Related field experiments clearly show that *Daphnia* can control cyanobacteria when freed from fish predation. In this review, we argue that cyanobacteria may serve as a

---

[*] E-mail address: wilson@auburn.edu.

beneficial food resource for zooplankton, that ecological control of cyanobacterial blooms is practical for some systems, and that greater attention should be placed on direct biomanipulation of zooplankton communities (e.g., stocking *Daphnia*) in conjunction with the manipulation of higher trophic levels. We also highlight the need for more data documenting zooplankton-cyanobacteria interactions in tropical freshwater ecosystems, whose biological, chemical, physical, and geological characteristics vary remarkably from their temperate counterparts.

In: Environmental and Agricultural Research Summaries …   ISBN: 978-1-63117-090-4
Editor: Lucille T. Cacioppo   © 2014 Nova Science Publishers, Inc.

Chapter 49

TROPICAL CYCLOGENESIS IN WIND SHEAR: CLIMATOLOGICAL RELATIONSHIPS AND PHYSICAL PROCESSES

David S. Nolan[*] *and Michael G. McGauley*
Rosenstiel School of Marine and Atmospheric Science,
University of Miami, Miami, Florida, US

RESEARCH SUMMARY

The formation of tropical cyclones remains a topic of great interest in the field of tropical meteorology. A number of influential studies have considered the process of tropical cyclone formation (also known as TC genesis) from a pre-existing, weak tropical disturbance in a quiescent atmosphere from theoretical perspectives and using numerical simulations. However, it is shown that the large majority of TC genesis events occur under the influence of significant vertical wind shear. The effects of wind shear on TC genesis is explored from both a climatological perspective and from the statistics of wind shear in environments around individual TC genesis events. While earlier studies suggested that moderate wind shear values, in the range of 5 to 10 ms^{-1}, were the most favorable states for genesis, it is shown that small values of wind shear in the range of 1.25 to 5 ms^{-1} are the most favorable, and very little shear (less than 1.25 ms^{-1}) is not unfavorable. Statistically, easterly shear appears to be more favorable than westerly shear.

The physical process of TC genesis in wind shear is explored with high-resolution numerical simulations using a mesoscale model in an idealized framework. The transformation of a weak, mid-level vortex into a warm-cored tropical cyclone is simulated in environments with no flow, with mean flow and no wind shear, and with mean flow and wind shear. The simulations show that in terms of the formation of a closed, low-level circulation, moderate wind shear is indeed more conducive to genesis, but is also prohibitive to further development. However, in contrast to the statistical findings and some previous results, westerly shear is found to be significantly more favorable for TC genesis than easterly shear.

---

*E-mail address: dnolan@rsmas.miami.edu

The reasons for the greater favorableness of wind shear versus no wind shear, and of westerly shear versus easterly shear, are discussed within the context of the numerical simulations. Further statistical analysis suggests that the greater favorableness for easterly shear in the real atmosphere may be due to a correlation between easterly shear and more favorable thermodynamic conditions.

In: Environmental and Agricultural Research Summaries ...   ISBN: 978-1-63117-090-4
Editor: Lucille T. Cacioppo   © 2014 Nova Science Publishers, Inc.

Chapter 50

ANALYSIS OF TROPICAL CYCLONE ACTIVITY IN THE SOUTHERN HEMISPHERE USING OBSERVATION AND CGCM SIMULATION

Satoshi Iizuka[1] and Tomonori Matsuura[2]*

[1]National Research Institute for Earth Science and Disaster Prevention, Japan
[2]Graduate School of Science and Engineering, University of Toyama, Japan

RESEARCH SUMMARY

This chapter presents the relation between El Niño / Southern Oscillation (ENSO) and tropical cyclone (TC) activity over the Southern Hemisphere, using both observations and outputs of a high-resolution (T213) coupled ocean-atmosphere general circulation model. Both observations and simulations show that, in El Niño (La Niña) years, the TC genesis frequency is enhanced in the northeastern (southwestern) South Pacific Ocean. However, no remarkable change in the ratio of annual number of intense TC is found in either the observations or simulations. Therefore, changes in environmental conditions associated with ENSO contribute to TC frequency over the South Pacific, but they do not seem to affect TCs in terms of developing and sustaining their intensity.

The interannual variability of TC activity over the southern Indian Ocean and its relation with Indian Ocean Dipole (IOD) are also examined using partial regression technique. Both observations and simulations show the nearly zonal uniformly reduction (enhancement) in the annual TC frequency in El Niño (La Niña) years after taking away the effect of IOD, whereas the east-west dipole structure characterized by an increase (decrease) in the annual TC frequency in the western (eastern) part of the southern Indian Ocean during positive IOD events after excluding influences arising from ENSO. The results suggest that the interannual variability of TC activity over the southern Indian Ocean can be affected by both ENSO and IOD. Furthermore, observations show that the annual TC frequency formed over both the eastern and western parts of the southern Indian Ocean is related more closely to IOD events than ENSO. During positive (negative) IOD events, the TC frequency generated in the early

*E-mail address: iizuka@bosai.go.jp

TC season is reduced (enhanced) over the eastern part of the southern Indian Ocean. The TC genesis frequency and associated TC days in the western part of the southern Indian Ocean tend to increase (decrease) in positive (negative) IOD events. However, there are not significant relations for the ratio of the annual number of intense TCs to total TCs over both the eastern and western parts of the southern Indian Ocean.

In: Environmental and Agricultural Research Summaries …   ISBN: 978-1-63117-090-4
Editor: Lucille T. Cacioppo   © 2014 Nova Science Publishers, Inc.

Chapter 51

SYNOPTIC AND CLIMATIC ASPECTS OF TROPICAL CYCLOGENESIS IN WESTERN NORTH PACIFIC

Tim Li[*]

International Pacific Research Center and Department of Meteorology,
University of Hawaii at Manoa, Honolulu, Hawaii, US

RESEARCH SUMMARY

In this chapter, I first describe various precursor synoptic signals prior to tropical cyclone genesis in the western North Pacific. Then, I discuss the origin of summertime synoptic-scale wave trains in the western Pacific and the energy source and dispersion characteristics of Pacific easterly waves. Next, I present two cyclogenesis modeling results, focusing on the energy dispersion of a preexisting tropical cyclone and the genesis efficiency of initial mid-level versus bottom vortex. The climatologic aspect of tropical cyclogenesis is discussed, with a focus on the large-scale control of the atmospheric intraseasonal oscillation (ISO) and El Nino-Southern Oscillation (ENSO). A methodology is developed to rank key cyclogenesis parameters at different basins. Finally, I describe the robust signals of future TC projection in the North Pacific from high-resolution global model simulations.

---

[*] E-mail address: timli@hawaii.edu

In: Environmental and Agricultural Research Summaries ...   ISBN: 978-1-63117-090-4
Editor: Lucille T. Cacioppo   © 2014 Nova Science Publishers, Inc.

Chapter 52

VARIABILITY OF TYPHOON TRACKS AND GENESIS OVER THE WESTERN NORTH PACIFIC

Hisayuki Kubota[*]

Research Institute for Global Change,
Japan Agency for Marine-Earth Science and Technology
(RIGC, JAMSTEC), Yokosuka, Japan

RESEARCH SUMMARY

The variability of typhoon tracks and genesis over the Western North Pacific (WNP) is reviewed in terms of intraseasonal to interdecadal time-scales. Intraseasonal variability of typhoon activity is related to the phase of Madden-Julian Oscillation and to shorter periods of 10-30 day westward propagating disturbances. Modulations of typhoon activity associated with the El Niño Southern Oscillation are found in typhoon genesis location, landfall numbers, intensity, lifespan, and typhoon rainfall; the mechanism is mainly due to the relocation of monsoon trough with the eastward shift of the Walker circulation. Pacific-Japan pattern of the Asian summer monsoon, Indian Ocean warming, and Quasi-Biennial Oscillation also influence the interannual variability of typhoon activity. Interdecadal variability of typhoon activity is found in the WNP: however there are many discrepancies among various studies on this topic. Short period of typhoon track dataset and difference between typhoon track datasets make it difficult to draw a unified picture of typhoon variability. The recovery of historical typhoon track data, which has not been used in the typhoon studies, will be a great tool for studying long-term variability.

[*] E-mail address: Kubota@jamstec.go.jp

In: Environmental and Agricultural Research Summaries ...   ISBN: 978-1-63117-090-4
Editor: Lucille T. Cacioppo   © 2014 Nova Science Publishers, Inc.

Chapter 53

REDUCTION OF GLOBAL TROPICAL CYCLONE FREQUENCY DUE TO GLOBAL WARMING

Masato Sugi[*]

Japan Agency for Marine-Earth Science and Technology,
Yokohama, Japan

RESEARCH SUMMARY

In this chapter, we review recent medium and high resolution GCM studies on the changes in tropical cyclone (TC) frequency due to global warming, and present a coherent explanation for the mechanism of projected changes, with a main focus on the reduction of global TC frequency. The reduction of global TC frequency is explained by a weakening of tropical circulation, which is closely related to a large increase in atmospheric stability and a small increase in precipitation. An interesting point is that the overlap effect of CO_2 and water vapor absorption bands in long wave radiation is playing an important role in the small increase in precipitation.

[*] E-mail address: msugi@jamstec.go.jp

In: Environmental and Agricultural Research Summaries …   ISBN: 978-1-63117-090-4
Editor: Lucille T. Cacioppo   © 2014 Nova Science Publishers, Inc.

Chapter 54

ESTIMATION OF CHANGES IN TROPICAL CYCLONE INTENSITIES AND ASSOCIATED PRECIPITATION EXTREMES DUE TO ANTHROPOGENIC CLIMATE CHANGE

*Junichi Tsutsui**

Central Research Institute of Electric Power Industry, Japan

RESEARCH SUMMARY

On the basis of theoretical models for the maximum potential intensity of tropical cyclones and general precipitation extremes, a simple scheme has been developed to estimate climatological changes in tropical cyclone intensities and associated precipitation extremes as a function of global surface temperature anomalies caused by anthropogenic climate changes. Since intensity changes strongly depend on the upper-air warming relative to the surface, this scheme incorporates the uncertainty of the variation in the upper-air temperature anomalies obtained from multiple-climate model experiments. A case study of Typhoon Flo in 1990 right before its landfall in Japan has revealed that its intensity, measured by a central pressure drop at sea level, and peak precipitation are projected to increase by 6.5% and 9.3%, respectively, under a globally 1- # C warmed environment relative to the present. These quantities and associated wind speed changes are directly calculated with uncertainties for arbitrary warming anomalies, which enables quantitative assessment for a wide range of greenhouse-gas emissions pathways in the future.

*E-mail address: tsutsui@criepi.denken.or.jp

In: Environmental and Agricultural Research Summaries …   ISBN: 978-1-63117-090-4
Editor: Lucille T. Cacioppo   © 2014 Nova Science Publishers, Inc.

Chapter 55

SENSITIVITY OF TROPICAL CYCLONES TO LARGE-SCALE ENVIRONMENTS IN A GLOBAL NON-HYDROSTATIC MODEL WITH EXPLICIT CLOUD MICROPHYSICS

Yohei Yamada[1, 2], Kazuyoshi Oouchi[1], Masaki Satoh[1, 2],*
Akira T. Noda[1] and Hirofumi Tomita[1, 3]

[1]Japan Agency for Marine-Earth Science and Technology,
Yokohama, Japan
[2]The University of Tokyo, Kashiwa, Japan
[3]RIKEN, Kobe, Japan

RESEARCH SUMMARY

Using a global non-hydrostatic model with a horizontal 14 km mesh, we investigated intensities and spatial distributions of tropical cyclones (TCs) and their relationships to large-scale environments. We conducted three cases of boreal summer experiments (June-October) using explicit cloud microphysics schemes without cumulus parameterization. The differences among the three experiments are the implemented physics schemes (i.e., a radiation scheme, a cloud microphysics scheme, a land model, and treatment of the sea surface temperature). One of the experiments is regarded as a control case. Only the radiation scheme used in another case differs from that in the control case in terms of the number of absorption bands. The other case uses a more comprehensive cloud microphysics scheme compared to the control case. The land and ocean processes are also changed in the last case. The radiation scheme in the last case is the same as that in the second case.

We examined the sensitivity of the simulated TC frequencies, tracks, and intensities. The relationship between the maximum wind speed (MWS) and minimum sea level pressure (MSLP) is quite similar among the cases. However, TC frequencies and tracks depend on cases; in terms of the frequency, the last case best reproduces the global observed cyclogenesis number, while the second case reproduces the most realistic intensity histogram of TCs. Comparisons of the relationship between the tropical cyclogenesis and the large-scale environment using a genesis potential index (GPI) show that the spatial distribution of cyclogenesis is generally consistent with that of the GPI. Among the physical factors that contribute to the GPI, the absolute vorticity, relative humidity, and vertical wind shear are primarily relevant to the difference of the GPI. The change of these variables seems to be associated with convergence of the zonal wind at 850 hPa, and the zonal wind is affected by atmospheric circulation, such as the Walker circulation. Therefore, it is speculated that the changes in atmospheric circulation with the physical schemes play an important role for determining the spatial distribution of tropical cyclogenesis.

In: Environmental and Agricultural Research Summaries …   ISBN: 978-1-63117-090-4
Editor: Lucille T. Cacioppo   © 2014 Nova Science Publishers, Inc.

Chapter 56

VARIABILITY OF EXTRATROPICAL CYCLONIC ACTIVITY IN THE NORTHERN HEMISPHERE ASSOCIATED WITH GLOBAL PROCESSES IN THE OCEAN-ATMOSPHERE SYSTEM

Alexander Polonsky[1]*, Mikhail Bardin[2]
and Elena Voskresenskaya[1]

[1]Marine Hydrophysical Institute, Sevastopol, Ukraine
[2]Institute of Global Climate and Ecology, Moscow, Russia

RESEARCH SUMMARY

In this chapter, we describe connections between the seasonal statistics of extratropical synoptic-scale atmospheric vortices in the Northern Hemisphere, and particularly in the North Atlantic and Pacific regions, and phases of principal interannual to multi-decadal climatic signals, or leading climate modes, such as El Ninio-Southern Oscillation (ENSO), North Atlantic Oscillation (NAO), Pacific Decadal Oscillation (PDO) and Atlantic Multi-decadal Oscillation (AMO). These modes account for the essential proportion of both SST anomalies and associated atmospheric signal in the Northern Hemisphere on the interannual to multi-decadal scale. The relationships are derived from empirical data. Archives of Northern Hemisphere extratropical cyclones and cyclone tracks from 1951 to 2010 were compiled based on 6-hrs the 1000 hPa geopotential heights from NCEP/NCAR reanalysis data. The monthly characteristics of the cyclonic activity (cyclone frequency, area and intensity) for the cells of a 5-degree grid and for selected regions were used to calculate climate statistics and evaluate relationships between cyclonic activity and climate modes. Analysis of the interannual to multi-decadal variability of cyclonic characteristics associated with the NAO, ENSO, PDO and AMO showed that their joint influence accounts for significant proportion

---

* E-mail: apolonsky5@mail.ru

of total variance of winter cyclone parameters in the neighborhood of principal stormtracks and in other regions of the Northern Hemisphere.

In: Environmental and Agricultural Research Summaries …   ISBN: 978-1-63117-090-4
Editor: Lucille T. Cacioppo   © 2014 Nova Science Publishers, Inc.

Chapter 57

TROPICAL CYCLONE SIMULATION IN A HIGH-RESOLUTION ATMOSPHERE-OCEAN COUPLED GENERAL CIRCULATION MODEL

Wataru Sasaki[1], Jing-Jia Luo[1,2] and Sebastien Masson[3]

[1]Japan Agency for Marine-Earth Science and Technology, Yokohama, Japan
[2]Centre for Australian Weather and Climate Research, Melbourne, Australia
[3]Laboratoire d'Océanographie Expérimentation et Approches Numériques, Paris, France

RESEARCH SUMMARY

A global high-resolution coupled general circulation model (CGCM) consisting of a T319 atmosphere general circulation model and an eddy-permitted ocean general circulation model is examined in terms of the reproducibility of the northern hemisphere tropical cyclone (TC) activity as well as the large-scale environmental conditions. The CGCM successfully simulates the realistic TC structure, TC-induced ocean response, and TC genesis frequency. The global TC genesis frequency simulated by the high-resolution CGCM is much closer to the observed, compared that simulated by the medium-resolution (T106) CGCM. In addition, the high-resolution CGCM partially reproduces the bimodal seasonal cycle of the North Indian Ocean cyclogenesis, while the medium-resolution CGCM fails to simulate it. The high-resolution CGCM also reasonably reproduces the environmental conditions favorable for the TC genesis: warm sea surface temperature, low-level cyclonic circulation, weak vertical wind shear, and high relative humidity in the mid-troposphere. The eastward extension of monsoon-trough is well simulated by the high-resolution CGCM as observed, compared to the medium-resolution CGCM. There are, however, still some discrepancies between the modeled and observed TC activity. We discuss about the following two discrepancies from the view point of the simulated large-scale environmental conditions: the high-resolution CGCM fails to reproduce the bimodal seasonal cycle of the Arabian cyclogenesis during the pre-monsoon period, and the western North Pacific TC genesis locations are confined in the southwestern part of the western North Pacific. It is found that less Arabian cyclogenesis during the pre-monsoon period is due to the weak low-level cyclonic circulation in the Arabian Sea during this period, although the weak vertical wind shear is well simulated as observed. For the western North Pacific, less TC genesis in the southeastern part of the western North Pacific is found to be due to the failure to simulate the eastward extension of the monsoon-trough up to the international dateline. Compared to a medium-resolution CGCM, one of the advantages of the high-resolution CGCM is the reproduction of the intense TC. Surface wind speed exceeding 20~40 ms^{-1} is successfully simulated by the high-resolution CGCM, while the TC wind speed simulated by the medium-resolution CGCM is less than 20~30 ms^{-1}. The frequency distribution of TC surface wind speed simulated by the high-resolution CGCM is closer to the observed compared to the medium-resolution CGCM.

In: Environmental and Agricultural Research Summaries …	ISBN: 978-1-63117-090-4
Editor: Lucille T. Cacioppo	© 2014 Nova Science Publishers, Inc.

Chapter 58

MULTI-SCALE DYNAMICS OF TROPICAL CYCLONE FORMATIONS IN AN EQUILIBRIUM SIMULATION USING A GLOBAL CLOUD-SYSTEM RESOLVING MODEL

Wataru Yanase[1], Masaki Satoh[1,2], Shin-ichi Iga[3],
Johnny C. L. Chan[4], Hironori Fudeyasu[5],
Yuqing Wang[6] and Kazuyoshi Oouchi[2]
[1]The University of Tokyo, Kashiwa, Japan
[2]Japan Agency for Marine-Earth Science and Technology, Yokohama, Japan
[3]RIKEN, Kobe, Japan
[4]City University of Hong Kong, China
[5]Yokohama National University, Yokohama, Japan
[6]University of Hawaii at Manoa, Honolulu, Hawaii, US

RESEARCH SUMMARY

An equilibrium July simulation was attempted to examine how well a global cloud-system resolving model (GCRM) simulates the multi-scale dynamics of tropical cyclone (TC) formations. Results for the eastern North Pacific were analyzed to elucidate the capability of the model in capturing the multi-scale dynamics of TC formation in the basin where both the TCs and the large-scale environmental fields were simulated the best. The lifetimes and intensities of the simulated TCs were comparable to the best-track data, which is attributed to the model resolution marginally high enough to represent essential dynamics within a TC inner-core, such as a precipitation-free eye and eye-wall updrafts. Consistent with previous observational studies, some TCs were transformed from synoptic-scale tropical easterly waves that propagated from the North Atlantic. The model also showed meso-scale vortex dynamics related to TC genesis, such as ITCZ-breakdown, vortex merger, and Rossby-wave energy dispersion. Thus, the results of the 14-km simulation encourage us to use GCRMs for understanding the multi-scale dynamics of vortices responsible for TC formations, and provide a useful benchmark for the longer-time or higher-resolution GCRM simulations in the future.

In: Environmental and Agricultural Research Summaries …   ISBN: 978-1-63117-090-4
Editor: Lucille T. Cacioppo   © 2014 Nova Science Publishers, Inc.

Chapter 59

A Prototype Quasi Real-Time Intra-Seasonal Forecasting of Tropical Convection over the Warm Pool Region: A New Challenge of Global Cloud-System-Resolving Model for a Field Campaign

Kazuyoshi Oouchi[1]*, Hiroshi Taniguchi[2], Tomoe Nasuno[1], Masaki Satoh[1,3], Hirofumi Tomita,[1,4], Yohei Yamada[1], Mikiko Ikeda[1], Ryuichi Shirooka[5], Hiroyuki Yamada[5] and Kunio Yoneyama[5]

[1]Japan Agency for Marine-Earth Science and Technology, Yokohama, Japan
[2]International Pacific Research Center, University of Hawaii at Manoa, Honolulu, Hawaii, US
[3]The University of Tokyo, Kashiwa, Japan
[4]RIKEN, Kobe, Japan
[5]Japan Agency for Marine-Earth Science and Technology, Yokosuka, Japan

Research Summary

A new prototype of quasi real-time forecast system for tropical weather events with timescales spanning across diurnal-to-intra-seasonal ranges is developed. Its hallmark is the use of a global cloud-system resolving model (GCRM) that avoids uncertainties arising from cumulus convection schemes inherent to traditional hydrostatic models. This allows forecasting of multi-scale convective disturbances such as tropical cyclones and super cloud clusters that are particularly associated with Madden-Julian Oscillation (MJO), even more straightforwardly, with unprecedented details, and disseminate detailed forecast products to *in-situ* observation networks. The system can operate, for example, in an observation campaign in the tropical ocean, where observation network is in synchronous with modeling

* E-mail address: k-ouchi@jamstec.go.jp

components to investigate the atmospheric and atmosphere-ocean interaction processes controlling tropical disturbances such as MJO.

This chapter overviews the prototype system and reports a first pilot forecast example of tropical cyclone LAILA that happened over the Indian Ocean in the late May 2010. The forecast system with the finest mesh of 14 km over the target region projected the overall track and evolution of LAILA quite decently prior to its landfall with up to about five days lead time. LAILA featured north-westward movement after its genesis in association with a propagation of the predicted MJO. The MJO traversed the Indian Ocean up about 5-7 days before the genesis of LAILA, according to an MJO index analysis from observation. A key ingredient of the encouraging forecast is inferred to be the GCRM's capability of representing a mechanistic link between LAILA and MJO. Additionally, the forecast system captured a northward migration of precipitation embedded in a synoptic-scale low-level westerly intrusion over the Indian Ocean region, which signals the onset of southwesterly monsoon for this particular year.

These findings, albeit from only one specific forecast experiment, lend some reliability to the GCRM-based research forecast of MJO-associated convection events to assist on-site observation planning. Moreover, this suggests a potential pathway of future GCRM-based forecast system development towards extended seamless intra-seasonal forecast of MJO-associated weather events that would threaten the tropical warm-pool and neighborhood regions.

In: Environmental and Agricultural Research Summaries …   ISBN: 978-1-63117-090-4
Editor: Lucille T. Cacioppo   © 2014 Nova Science Publishers, Inc.

Chapter 60

PROJECTION OF FUTURE TROPICAL CYCLONE CHARACTERISTICS BASED ON STATISTICAL MODEL

Nobuhito Mori[*]
Kyoto University, Uji, Kyoto, Japan

RESEARCH SUMMARY

As a consequence of global warming, several climate models suggest that the frequency and intensity of tropical cyclones will change by the end of the 21st century. A brief review of future tropical cyclone characteristics and stochastic tropical cyclone models is summarized in the first half of this chapter. Future tropical cyclone projections are based on stochastic tropical cyclone models with global climate change effects incorporated, and the analysis of the averaged and extreme conditions of tropical cyclones is discussed in the second half of this chapter. The future projection of TC tracks and intensities were computed by stochastic tropical cyclone models as discussed in the second half of this chapter. Based on the analysis of general circulation models and stochastic tropical cyclone models, both a decrease in cyclogenesis frequency and changes in track have regional impacts to annual tropical cyclone frequency. Using mean statistical characteristics from a general circulation model to run a stochastic tropical cyclone model, it is possible to estimate the uncertainty associated with these future tropical cyclone changes.

---

[*] E-mail address: mori@oceanwave.jp

In: Environmental and Agricultural Research Summaries …   ISBN: 978-1-63117-090-4
Editor: Lucille T. Cacioppo   © 2014 Nova Science Publishers, Inc.

Chapter 61

A NOVEL, ILLUSTRATED CLASSIFICATION SYSTEM TO DEFINE THE CAUSES OF BOVINE PERINATAL MORTALITY INTERNATIONALLY

John F. Mee[*]

Animal and Bioscience Research Department, Teagasc,
Moorepark Research Centre, Fermoy, Co. Cork, Ireland

RESEARCH SUMMARY

Currently there is no published classification system for the causes of death in cases of bovine perinatal mortality internationally. In addition, the criteria used to define these causes of death are also not standardised, nor published. This results in inconsistent reporting of many different causes of death and often a high proportion of cases being unexplained.

A system is required for codifying bovine perinatal mortality for epidemiological surveillance and perinatal audit, as in human perinatology where the World Health Organisation's International Classification of Diseases Manual is used internationally. Hence, the objective of this study was to develop a novel classification system for both the criteria and the causes of death in cases of bovine perinatal mortality internationally in order to improve our understanding of the main causes of such reproductive loss. A foeto-maternal, clinico-pathological classification system was developed over a period of three years using three primary sources of information. A systematic literature-based review, the findings of an international Delphi survey and epidemiological and pathological data from an active surveillance, whole-herd necropsy study were used to design the system. Ten major causal categories of death were assigned with sub-classification as required; alphabetically – combination of contributory factors (more than one cause of death), congenital defect (economically lethal and lethal), dystocia (bradytocia, traumotocia, bradytocia and traumotocia, dystocia anamnesis, dystoxia and fetal maldisposition), eutoxia, haemorrhage and anaemia (external omphalorrhagia, internal omphalorrhagia, idiopathic hemoperitoneum,

---

[*] E-mail: john.mee@teagasc.ie.

anaemia), infection, iodine imbalance, premature placental expulsion, prematurity and other specific disorders (e.g. accidental death, hypothermia, intra-uterine growth retardation, etc..). Each cause of death was assigned a degree of confidence of diagnosis from certain through probable to possible.

These causes of death were assigned using the written anamnesis from the farmer or veterinary practitioner, gross necropsy observations (including photo-documentation) and the associated laboratory tests, i.e. an algorithmic, summary diagnosis. The cause of death indicated the pathological condition of the fetus or calf which made the greatest contribution towards the death. Only proximate (immediate) factors were listed in the cause of death, e.g. a genetic mutation may be the ultimate cause of a lethal congenital defect but the defect was the proximate cause of death. Some causes of death, e.g. dystocia, were disaggregated in order to differentiate separate components (where a portmanteau is used, e.g. dystoxia) which can be re-aggregated as necessary for different reporting formats.

Differential diagnoses were reached through both processes of inclusion and of exclusion. This ten-level classification system can be used to calculate cause-specific mortality rates (CSMR) and the attributable fraction (AF) of perinatal mortality due to each cause of death.

In: Environmental and Agricultural Research Summaries …   ISBN: 978-1-63117-090-4
Editor: Lucille T. Cacioppo   © 2014 Nova Science Publishers, Inc.

Chapter 62

RESETTING PRIORITIES FOR SUSTAINABLE DAIRY FARMING UNDER GLOBAL CHANGING

I. Blanco-Penedo[1,] J. Perea[2], J. O. L. Cerqueira[3] and R. Payan-Carreira[4]*

[1]Animal Welfare Subprogram, IRTA, Finca Campsi Armet,
(Girona), Spain
[2]Departamento de Producción Animal, Facultad de Veterinaria,
Universidad de Córdoba, Campus de Rabanales, Córdoba, Spain
[3]Escola Superior Agrária do Instituto Politécnico
de Viana do Castelo, Portugal
[4]Animal and Veterinary Research Center (CECAV),
University of Trás-os-Montes and Alto Douro, Vila Real, Portugal

RESEARCH SUMMARY

Global change increasingly affected agricultural production and global community has begun to refocus in a change in livestock production, defending the use of sustainable strategies. Considerations with respect to changing environments should also address the dairy farm systems and new goals have to be designed. Good farming practices should regard their need for on-going adaptation to an ever-changing environment that should offer solutions for buffering against climatic extremes, disease epidemics, changing nutrient availability, seasonal availability of forage and other stresses that will add to an already heterogeneous environmental condition. Sustainable dairy systems should be adjusted to these new expectations, and be indeed adapted to the new agricultural policies and the increasing demands of the consumers for products free of drug residues (safety) and be more ecofriendly produced. The key to success is to maximise farm efficiency finding the right balance between the production system and the management techniques to maximise the output for food production, involving a suitable dairy cow biotype, which may trigger new strategies for feeding, breeding and health control whilst minimising impact on the environment and

---

* Corresponding author e-mail: isabel.blanco@irta.cat.

ensuring animal welfare and profitability for their business. This chapter book pretends to present a holistic capture of main issues regarding management, feeding regimes, breeding, reproductive efficiency with examples of current sustainable production systems.

In: Environmental and Agricultural Research Summaries ...   ISBN: 978-1-63117-090-4
Editor: Lucille T. Cacioppo   © 2014 Nova Science Publishers, Inc.

Chapter 63

SOMATIC CELL COUNT AS THE FACTOR CONDITIONING PRODUCTIVITY OF VARIOUS BREEDS OF COWS AND TECHNOLOGICAL SUITABILITY OF MILK

Joanna Barłowska[1], Zygmunt Litwińczuk[2],
Aneta Brodziak[2] and Jolanta Król[1]
[1]Department of Commodity Science and Processing
of Animal Raw Materials, Poland
[2]Department of Breeding and Protection of Genetic Resources of Cattle
University of Life Sciences in Lublin, Faculty of Biology
and Animal Breeding, Poland

RESEARCH SUMMARY

Early detection of mastitis with subclinical symptoms is possible by determining somatic cell count (SCC). SCC is the most widely accepted indicator of the mammary gland health as well as milk quality and its technological suitability. The authors' research has revealed that an increase of SCC (independently of a breed of cows) mainly causes a rise in a total crude protein content and a distinct reduction in lactose level ($P \leq 0.01$). Moreover, SCC also lengthens the time of milk enzymatic coagulation ($P \leq 0.01$) but it does not influence its thermal stability. Distinct negative relationship between casein content and SCC is confirmed by relatively high value of correlation coefficient ($r=-0.59$). In the authors' studies the significant interactions (breed of cows x SCC) for the daily yield of cows, content of protein, casein and lactose, protein to fat ratio and rennet-induced milk coagulation time also have been stated, which indicates a differentiated response of various breeds of cows to udder inflammations. Holstein-Friesian cows are more sensitive to decline of daily yield, which is reflected in higher negative value of correlation coefficient between SCC and milk yield (-0.245). In Simmental and Jersey cows the correlations were negative as well but their values were substantially lower ($r=-0.123$ and $r=-0.148$) and statistically insignificant. With the age of cows increase in SCC was noted and in the cows of local breeds (Polish Red, Polish Black and White, Whitebacked) and Jersey that rise was much smaller in comparison to Polish Holstein-Friesian cows. Significant interaction (P≤0.05) for SCC between breed of cows and subsequent lactation was indicated. However, the significant changes in milk constituents were recorded only when the SCC exceeded 500 thous. ml^{-1}, that is in milk that does not meet the current regulatory quality standards.

Somatic cell count also affects the changes in whey protein content. Rise of SCC decreased the content of major albumins, i.e. alpha-LA and beta-LG, by small degree, and that was confirmed by very low statistically insignificant correlation coefficients (r=-0.07 i r=-0.05). Negative value of both correlations, though, indicates a direction of changes and may imply that in more advanced stages of udder diseases the decrease of milk proteins is likely to be higher. However, with rise of SCC, content of immunoactive proteins (lactoferrin and lysozyme) as well as bovine albumin serum (BSA) significantly increased. The significant impact of SCC on content of these proteins in milk is confirmed by relatively high positive values of computed correlation coefficients (lactoferrin r=0.65, lysozyme r=0.63 and BSA r=0.59). In the case of BSA that correlations were clearly differentiated in particular breeds of cows, i.e. r=0.711 for Holstein-Friesian, r=0.577 for Simmental and r=0.472 for Jersey. Thus, it can be assumed that there is a differentiated degree of permeability of mammary gland cell membranes in cows of various breeds.

In: Environmental and Agricultural Research Summaries ...   ISBN: 978-1-63117-090-4
Editor: Lucille T. Cacioppo   © 2014 Nova Science Publishers, Inc.

Chapter 64

STRATEGIES TO IMPROVE THE REPRODUCTIVE EFFICIENCY OF DAIRY CATTLE

L. S. R. Marinho, F. Z. Machado and M. M. Seneda [*]
Laboratório de Reprodução Animal, DCV-CCA-UEL, Londrina PR, Brazil

RESEARCH SUMMARY

The reproductive performance of a lactating herd is a major component of the profitability of a dairy farm. Factors such as negative energy balance, heat stress and failures in heat detection can severely compromise reproductive parameters. To overcome these problems, a variety of strategies can be used. For example, failures in estrus detection can be solved with the use of fixed-time artificial insemination (FTAI). Progesterone implants combined with estradiol administration are very effective in promoting the onset of a new follicular wave. With the use of a luteolytic agent and an inducer of ovulation, AI can be performed at the appropriate time without the need for estrus observation. In countries where the use of such drugs is not allowed, protocols based on GnRH and PGF2α may also offer optimal synchronization of ovulation. In locations where pregnancy rates are compromised by high temperatures, a viable alternative to FTAI may be the fixed-time embryo transfer (FTET). Embryos at the morula and blastocyst stage are more resistant to heat stress than gametes and embryos in early stages of development. Thus, embryo transfer (ET) on day 7 of development can ensure satisfactory pregnancy rates throughout the year, even in months and/or regions with higher average temperatures. ET has also been effective in preventing early embryonic mortality and increasing pregnancy rates in repeat breeders. Another strategy that can enhance the reproductive efficiency of dairy herds is the cryopreservation of embryos; embryos are stored and can be used at strategic times, such as in the warmer months of the year. This chapter will discuss technological strategies that can lead to higher breeding efficiency, improved reproductive efficiency and increased profitability of livestock on dairy farms.

---

[*] Corresponding author: Marcelo Marcondes Seneda, Laboratório de Reprodução Animal, DCV, CCA, Rodovia Celso Garcia Cid, Pr 445, Km 380, State University of Londrina (UEL), Londrina, PR, Brazil, 86051-990, Phone: +55 43 3371-4064, Fax: +55 43 3371-4063, Email: mseneda@uel.br.

In: Environmental and Agricultural Research Summaries ...   ISBN: 978-1-63117-090-4
Editor: Lucille T. Cacioppo   © 2014 Nova Science Publishers, Inc.

Chapter 65

GLOBALIZATION AND DEFORESTATION: AN EXAMINATION OF THE ENVIRONMENTAL EFFECTS OF DIRECT INVESTMENT IN THE FOREST SECTOR IN CAMEROON

Richard S. Mbatu[*]

Department of Environmental Science, Policy and Geography
University of South Florida St. Petersburg, St. Petersburg, Florida, US

RESEARCH SUMMARY

The process of globalization has become a central issue in contemporary environmentalism in recent decades after the process assumed a capital and product market orientation after World War II, intensifying the desire for resource access, control, ownership, extraction and transformation. In this chapter we argue that the current wave of globalization that began in the late 1950s, driven by petrochemical industrialization and the global expansion of capital and product market is in many ways responsible for the environmental degradation experienced at local and global scale. We employ an analytical approach that mediate the global wood industry's complex process-cause activities and capture their environmental outcome-effect at the micro level in the forest sector in Cameroon.

The focus here is on the ecological economics and the political ecology of Cameroon; looking at how capital and product market mechanisms in the country's forest sector is linked to environmental outcomes.

---

[*] Address: Department of Environmental Science, Policy and Geography, University of South Florida St. Petersburg, Dav 100, St. Petersburg, FL 33701, US.

In: Environmental and Agricultural Research Summaries …   ISBN: 978-1-63117-090-4
Editor: Lucille T. Cacioppo   © 2014 Nova Science Publishers, Inc.

Chapter 66

THE ENVIRONMENTAL IMPACTS OF RESETTLEMENTS AND REFUGEES ON THE FOREST RESOURCES OF SOUTHWESTERN ETHIOPIA

Mekuria Argaw[1] and Tamrat Kassa[2]
[1]Addis Ababa University, Center for Environmental Science,
Addis Ababa, Ethiopia
[2]ArbaMinch University, College of Natural Resource Management,
ArbaMinch, Ethiopia

RESEARCH SUMMARY

The Ethiopian highlands witnessed one of the worst forms of land degradation because of rampant deforestation for several centuries. Resettlement has always remained a priority policy option to address land degradation. In order to assess impacts of resettlements and refugees on the natural vegetation, case studies were conducted in resettlement and refugee sites in the Kafa and Gambella areas. The objectives were to quantify the magnitude of deforestation and to analyze impacts on the diversity of the vegetation. Arial photographs and satellite images were used to quantify and analyze land use land cover changes. Vegetation survey was conducted in the refugee site. Results show that land use land cover changes/dynamics were generally from vegetation to non-vegetation, mainly from natural forest to cultivated land. Population density was the driving factor for accelerated deforestation. Forests declined by a rate of 27 to 3792 ha per year while cultivated land expanded by 42 to 2869 ha. Forests in close proximity to resettlements and refugee sites showed reduced number of species, poor structure and density. The regeneration potential of some of the key species is hindered in the resettlement and refugee areas. The study generally shows the natural vegetation in the resettlement and refugee areas are under immense pressure of degradation and policy interventions are necessary to prevent and control further degradation.

In: Environmental and Agricultural Research Summaries …   ISBN: 978-1-63117-090-4
Editor: Lucille T. Cacioppo   © 2014 Nova Science Publishers, Inc.

Chapter 67

THE TRENDS AND DRIVERS OF DEFORESTATION: A CROSS-COUNTRY SEEMINGLY UNRELATED REGRESSION ANALYSIS FOR THE REDD+ POLICIES

*Richard J. Culas**

School of Agricultural and Wine Sciences, Charles Sturt University,
New South Wales, Australia

RESEARCH SUMMARY

Policies for Reducing Emissions from Deforestation and Forest Degradation, known as REDD, and enhancing forest carbon stocks, known as REDD+, could provide a way for tackling global warming and climate change. In this regard several proposals were designed, yet their implementation poses significant methodological problems. One of those problems can be the *interactions* between the *direct* and *indirect* causes (drivers) of deforestation. Deforestation is a transformation of forestland for various land uses. This chapter therefore analyses trends in world deforestation in relation to different geographical regions and its drivers. A cross-sectional econometric model, *recursive in nature*, is estimated in two stages for addressing the interaction between the causes. Firstly, the *direct* causes of deforestation are regressed on *indirect* causes, by *Seemingly Unrelated Regression* (SUR) estimation to account for the correlations between the direct causes. Secondly, the SUR estimates of the direct causes are used for the regression of deforestation equation. The statistical evidences show prevalence of omitted variables for the indirect causes, as well as correlations between the direct causes. The SUR estimates are therefore efficient than OLS estimates. The results are discussed, in relation to Asian, African and Latin American regions, to provide guidance for designing effective REDD+ policies.

---

* E-mail address: rculas@csu.edu.au; Address: PO Box 883, Orange, NSW 2800, Australia

In: Environmental and Agricultural Research Summaries …   ISBN: 978-1-63117-090-4
Editor: Lucille T. Cacioppo   © 2014 Nova Science Publishers, Inc.

Chapter 68

STUDY OF THE COVERAGE OF PLANTS AND THE EVALUATION OF DEFORESTATION

Sira Allende[1], Carlos Bouza[1] and Amita D. Chakraborty[2]
[1]Universidad de La Habana, Cuba
[2]Nosharkart College, India

RESEARCH SUMMARY

Deforestation is naturally connected with plant-coverage. In this paper we consider the study of the coverage through the estimation or prediction of indexes, considering that samples of sites are selected. Their biasedness is characterized as well as some convergence results. The behavior of the analyzed estimators and predictors is studied. We used data provided by a large sample collected for a project on Pest Control in Sugar Cane, developed in Cuba, and investigation Ordering of Territorial Ecological Classification, carried out in the State of Guerrero, Mexico. Monte Carlo experiments are developed for evaluating the effectiveness of the inferential models proposed. A superpopulation predictor appeared as the best alternative for further studies.

In: Environmental and Agricultural Research Summaries …   ISBN: 978-1-63117-090-4
Editor: Lucille T. Cacioppo   © 2014 Nova Science Publishers, Inc.

Chapter 69

MATHEMATICAL MODELLING OF MALARIA USING DIFFERENTIAL EQUATIONS

Nita H. Shah and Jyoti Gupta

Department of Mathematics, Gujarat University, Ahmedabad,
Gujarat, India

RESEARCH SUMMARY

Malaria is the most common mosquito borne viral disease widely spread in most parts of the world. According to the *World Malaria Report 2011*, of the World Health Organisation, there were about 216 million cases of malaria (with an uncertainty range of 149 million to 274 million). Malaria mortality rates have fallen by more than 25% globally since 2000 and by 33% in the WHO African Region.

So, today we are faced with the need to predict the transmission dynamics of vector-borne diseases with greater accuracy and more often with limited empirical data.

Here, we developed a SEIRS model for the dynamics and transmission of malaria starting with the mathematical model developed by Ngwa and Shu. We converted the differential equations in terms of susceptible, exposed, infectious and removed. Then we established a relation for the threshold parameter, "basic reproduction number", R_0.

All the differential equations are simulated simultaneously using MATLAB. The results of simulation show the behaviour of each compartment with respect to all the parameters.

We calculated sensitivity index of R_0 to all the 16 parameters of the model. This analysis shows that most sensitive parameters are mosquito birth rate Ψ_v, density dependent death rate of mosquitoes μ_{1v} and mosquito biting rate σ_v. This means that suddenly reducing the density of mosquito population (by means of spraying some insecticide or so) will not help in controlling transmission of malaria. We need to take steps for controlling mosquito birth rate and to induce mosquito death rate. This way our model provides the direction for determining proper control strategies.

In: Environmental and Agricultural Research Summaries …   ISBN: 978-1-63117-090-4
Editor: Lucille T. Cacioppo   © 2014 Nova Science Publishers, Inc.

Chapter 70

A META-ANALYSIS STUDY OF DEFORESTATION DUE TO GRAZING

Carlos Bouza[1] and Jose F. Garcia[2]
[1]Universidad de La Habana, Cuba
[2]Universidad Juárez Autónoma de Tabasco, México

RESEARCH SUMMARY

We present a methodology for studying deforestation by combining different data. It is based on meta-analysis for evaluating the odds and risks of two grazing methods for establishing the deforestation in pastures lands. Data collected from 172 studies are used for evaluating which methods are less aggressive to the pastures.

In: Environmental and Agricultural Research Summaries …   ISBN: 978-1-63117-090-4
Editor: Lucille T. Cacioppo   © 2014 Nova Science Publishers, Inc.

Chapter 71

A DYNAMIC LANDSCAPE OF FOREST REGENERATION IN A DEFORESTING FOREST FRONTIER

Sean Sloan[*]

Department of Resource Management and Geography,
University of Melbourne, Melbourne, Victoria, Australia
The Climate Adaptation Flagship, The Commonwealth Scientific
and Industrial Research Organisation, Davies Laboratory, Australia
The Centre for Tropical Environmental and Sustainability Science,
School of Marine and Tropical Biology, James Cook University,
Cairns, Queensland, Australia

RESEARCH SUMMARY

This chapter describes nascent trends in forest conservation and regeneration within a Panamanian agricultural frontier previously characterised by forest conversion. Drawing upon household surveys, archival analysis, interviews, and satellite-image analysis, its focuses on the interactions amongst settlers concerned with agricultural livelihoods, community institutions concerned with forest conservation and restoration within watersheds, and corporate timber interest concerned with plantation reforestation. In this context, forest conservation and regeneration depends on the harmonious yet accidental convergence of lesser, self-interested forest-use trends amongst these agents of change. Where such harmonious convergence is impeded, neither conservation nor regeneration is possible, and the inertia of deforestation overtakes all gains in this respect. Opportunistic land sales by settlers and commercial reforestation incentives have promoted corporate timber interests to the fore of reforestation, yet a lack authority on the part of community institutions and high costs imposed by settlers have hindered forest restoration within community lands. Disharmonies limiting forest conservation and restoration reflect economic realities favouring

[*]E-mail address: sean.sloan@jcu.edu.au, Website: www.jcu.edu.au/mtb/staff/az/JCU_ 089792.html.

household deforestation; yet their resolution requires institutional, rather than economic, intervention, such as tenure reform. Without such institutional reforms in such contexts as Eastern Panama, forests are doomed regardless of economic conditions.

In: Environmental and Agricultural Research Summaries …   ISBN: 978-1-63117-090-4
Editor: Lucille T. Cacioppo   © 2014 Nova Science Publishers, Inc.

Chapter 72

TREE TRUNK DIAMETER ESTIMATION IN RAIN FOREST ECOLOGY: ANALYSIS AND OPTIMAL CONTROL

R. Dorville[1,], A. Omrane[2,†] and E. Robo-Petit[3,≠]*

[1] Laboratoire CEREGMIA, IUFM de Guyane, Cayenne
[2] Laboratoire CEREGMIA, Universit'e Antilles-Guyane,
I.E.S.G Campus de Trou-Biran, Cayenne (French Guiana)
[3] Universit'e de Polynésie Française,
IUFM, FAA'A Tahiti (Polynésie Française)

RESEARCH SUMMARY

We discuss about a mechanical problem related to the evaluation of the dimensional variations of tree trunk diameter, in tropical forest, where some data is missing. In particular, the optimal control question is studied rigorously. Within a cost function, the control problem is formulated within the mechanical tree trunk variation model which requires boundary conditions to solve all equations. We give a characterization of the optimal measurement function (the optimal control) for the tree trunk problem.

[*] E-mail address: rene.dorville@guyane.univ-ag.fr
[†] E-mail address: aomrane@univ-ag.fr
[≠] E-mail address: eleda.petit@iufm.upf.pf

In: Environmental and Agricultural Research Summaries …   ISBN: 978-1-63117-090-4
Editor: Lucille T. Cacioppo   © 2014 Nova Science Publishers, Inc.

Chapter 73

BIOLOGICAL REMOVAL OF NITROGEN COMPOUNDS FROM WASTEWATERS: CONVENTIONAL AND NON-CONVENTIONAL PROCESSES

Catarina S. A. Canto[1], Suzana M. Ratusznei[1],
José A. D. Rodrigues[1,*], Marcelo Zaiat[2]
and Eugenio Foresti[2]

[1]Escola de Engenharia Mauá, Instituto Mauá de Tecnologia (IMT),
Praça MauáSão Caetano do Sul, SP, Brazil
[2]Departamento de Hidráulica e Saneamento, Escola de Engenharia de São Carlos,
Universidade de São Paulo (USP), São Carlos, SP, Brazil

RESEARCH SUMMARY

The disposal of domestic and industrial wastewaters containing large concentrations of nutrients, such as nitrogen and phosphor, is one of the main factors responsible for eutrophication of water bodies. This process results in disorderly growth of aquatic plants on the water surface causing reduction in the concentration of dissolved oxygen in these bodies and impairing maintenance of aerobic aquatic life. It is therefore very important to develop treatments that remove these nutrients, in addition to removing organic material and solids.

There are several methods for removing nitrogen from wastewaters. However, the methods involving lower costs and improved efficiency in removing nitrogen and carbonaceous material are those that utilize the biological reactions of the nitrogen cycle as well as of the environmental and physicochemical conditions regulating this process. Aerobic nitrification and heterotrophic denitrification processes are the most commonly used effective and economical methods for nitrogen removal from domestic and industrial wastewaters.

Nitrification is characterized by the oxidation of ammonium nitrogen to nitrite by *Nitrosomonas* bacteria, followed by the oxidation of nitrite to nitrate by *Nitrobacter* bacteria. Denitrification is the biologic conversion of nitrate to more reduced forms (like N_2, N_2O and

---

* To whom all correspondence should be addressed. E-mail: rodrigues@maua.br.

NO) under anoxic conditions, i.e., in the absence of oxygen and having a carbon source as electron donor. Many microorganisms participate in the anoxic process. These bacteria can use several energy sources, such as organic compounds (organotrophic), inorganic compounds (lithotrophic) and light (phototrophic).

Usually, when effluents from secondary treatment systems contain low concentrations of organic material, addition of an electron donor is required for denitrification to occur. The most commonly used electron donors include methanol, ethanol, acetate and methane. Most recently inorganic compounds, such as sulfide, have been used as electron donors in autotrophic denitrification processes.

Two types of bacteria have been identified as being responsible for autotrophic denitrification using sulfur compounds as electron donors: *Thiobacillus denitrificans* and *Thiomicrospira denitrificans*. These bacteria are chemolithotrophic and in anoxic environments oxidize reduced sulfur compounds (like sulfide, sulfite, thiosulfate and elemental sulfur) to sulfate using nitrate (or nitrite) as electron receptor. This alternative is of great interest as it allows simultaneous elimination of highly polluting nitrogen and sulfurous compounds.

This text deals with the removal of nitrogen from domestic and industrial wastewaters using conventional (autotrophic nitrification and heterotrophic denitrification) and non-conventional biological processes (autotrophic denitrification). With regard to the conventional processes the removal efficiency and stability of organic material and ammonium nitrogen are dealt with by assessing the effect of the following parameters: applied volumetric nitrogen load, feed strategy (continuous, batch or fed-batch), C/N ratio, reactor type, type of biomass immobilization (granular or on inert support) and carbon source used as electron donor in the denitrification process. With respect to the non-conventional processes the utilization potential of sulfur compounds as electron donors in the denitrification process is dealt with by assessing factors such as N/S ratio, effect of type of electron acceptor (nitrite or nitrate), influent organic material concentration and effluent sulfate concentration.

The approach of these experimental studies, albeit privileging fundamental kinetics, bioreactor calculations and mass transfer, always maintain the objective to provide information for full-scale use of the investigated technological configurations.

In: Environmental and Agricultural Research Summaries …   ISBN: 978-1-63117-090-4
Editor: Lucille T. Cacioppo   © 2014 Nova Science Publishers, Inc.

Chapter 74

DENITRIFICATION: PROCESSES, REGULATION AND ECOLOGICAL SIGNIFICANCE

Mehran Andalib,[1]*Ahmed Eldyasti,[2] George Nakhla,[1,2]
and Jesse Zhu[1]

[1]Department of Chemical and Biochemical Engineering,
The University of Western Ontario, London, Ontario, Canada
[2]Department of Civil and Environmental Engineering,
The University of Western Ontario, London, Ontario, Canada

RESEARCH SUMMARY

In order to fulfill the increasingly stringent discharge standards, new technologies and operational strategies have been elaborated for the removal of nitrogen from wastewater. Denitrification is considered as the second stage of conventional nitrogen removal from wastewater. The detection of new organisms is making the nitrogen cycle increasingly complicated, to the point that traditional descriptions of nitrification (ammonia is oxidized to nitrate via nitrite) as the first stage, denitrification (conversion of nitrate and nitrite to nitrogen gas) as the second stage, and nitrogen fixation are rather simplistic and insufficient for explanation of nitrogen pathways in real life. Nitrate or nitrite may be denitrified, reduced to the form of ammonia (either assimilatory or dissimilatory) or converted to organic nitrogen along with increase the nitrous oxide (N_2O) and nitrogen gas (N_2). True understanding of denitrification requires an extensive knowledge of biological nitrogen cycle to design the most efficient denitrification process.

The development of biological nitrogen removal processes in different countries is based on the regulations of their municipalities. The impact of regulations on biological nitrogen removal processes has also been studied. This chapter reviews the various types of denitrification processes, and discusses the ecological significance and the regulation limitations.

---

* Corresponding author: Tel.: +1 519 697 1533. E-mail address: mandalib@uwo.ca (M. Andalib).

In: Environmental and Agricultural Research Summaries …   ISBN: 978-1-63117-090-4
Editor: Lucille T. Cacioppo   © 2014 Nova Science Publishers, Inc.

Chapter 75

EFFECT OF BIOAUGMENTATION ON THE ENHANCED BIOLOGICAL DENITRIFICATION IN SUBSURFACE WASTEWATER INFILTRATION SYSTEM (SWIS) AND BIOFILTER

Zou Jinlong[1], Dai Ying[2], Yu Xiujuan[1] and Xing Zi-Peng[1]

[1]Key Laboratory of Functional Inorganic Materials Chemistry,
Ministry of Education, School of Chemistry and Materials Science,
Heilongjiang University, Harbin, China
[2]School of Civil Engineering,
Heilongjiang Institute of Technology, Harbin, China

RESEARCH SUMMARY

With the shortage of available water resources in the world, the excessive presence of nitrogen in water environment has caused serious alterations of the natural nutrient cycle between the living world and the soil, water, and atmosphere. Biological nitrogen removal has already become an important concern throughout the world, especially in densely populated areas, such as some developing countries, that rely primarily on self-purification of receiving water body (watercourses, lakes, or sea) for treatment of nitrogenous wastewater. The efficiencies of biological nitrogen removal are affected by a wide range of interrelated physicochemical-biological factors, which needs us to study clearly. This chapter gathers our latest research results on biological nitrogen removal with a focus on such two topics as: the simultaneous nitrification and denitrification (SND) in biofilters and the enhanced biological denitrification in subsurface wastewater infiltration system (SWIS) through bioaugmentation. (1) Self-made sludge-ceramsite was tested as carrier in biofilter to investigate its biogenic stimulating properties for obtaining high biomass concentration, and the performance of Guangzhou ceramsite, Jiangxi ceramsite, and Shanxi activated carbon were provided as a baseline for comparison. Results show that the removal efficiencies of COD and total nitrogen (TN) increase along with the increased COD/NH_4^+-N ratio (4, 5.7, 8, and 10) in the four biofilters. On average, the sludge-ceramsite biofilter converts 79.1%-86.4% of NH_4^+-N

to NO_x^-−N and removes 43.9%-51.0% of TN at COD/NH_4^+−N ratios of 4-10, which are slightly better than the other three biofilters. The well-developed porous structures (0.5 μm<pore size<10.0 μm) of sludge-ceramsite is propitious to develop many microbial communities and to improve the permeable capacity of biofilm layers and the pollutants removal efficiencies, as they determine the pollutants mass transfer and the biological contact-reaction that occur in the aqueous phases, liquid-solid boundary, and biofilm interior. (2) To characterize the effect of amended soil on nitrogen removal in subsurface wastewater infiltration system (SWIS), culture, grass carbon, and zeolite were mixed to produce microbial inoculums, and then the optimal microbial inoculums, nutrient substance, cinder, and original soil were mixed to produce the soils through bioaugmentation. Results indicate that the microbial inoculums (culture+50% grass carbon+50% zeolite) and the amended soil (12.5% microbial inoculums+25% nutrient substrate+12.5% cinder+50% original soil) have the optimal biogenic stimulating properties, and the adsorption capacity of the amended soil are 1.216 mg-P g^{-1} and 0.495 mg-N g^{-1}. The laboratory soil column experiment indicates that the efficient mode of nitrogen removal in lab-scale SWIS is adsorption-nitrification-denitrification and the nitrification/ denitrification can be enhanced by the application of the amended soil. On average, the SWIS filled with amended soil converts 85% of ammonia nitrogen (NH_4^+−N) to NO_x^-−N and removes 49.8%-60.6% of total nitrogen (TN), while the system filled with original soil removes 80% of NH_4^+−N and 31.3%-43.2% of TN at 4 cm d^{-1}-8 cm d^{-1}. Two systems are overloads at 10 cm d^{-1}. It is concluded that the microbial activities and nitrogen removal efficiencies are improved in SWIS after bioaugmentation.

In: Environmental and Agricultural Research Summaries ...   ISBN: 978-1-63117-090-4
Editor: Lucille T. Cacioppo   © 2014 Nova Science Publishers, Inc.

Chapter 76

BIOFILM REACTORS IN DENITRIFICATION PROCESSES

*P. Teixeira and R. Oliveira**

Institute for Biotechnology and Bioengineering,
Centre of Biological Engineering, Universidade do Minho,
Campus de Gualtar, Braga, Portugal

RESEARCH SUMMARY

The traditional physico-chemical processes used in nitrate removal from water and wastewater (ion exchange, reverse osmosis and electrodialysis) have several drawbacks like a residual concentrated waste generating disposal problems, susceptibility to fouling (especially in reverse osmosis) and involve high operational costs. Biological nitrate reduction has been proving to be more economical and a versatile process for nitrate elimination in water and wastewater treatment. Biological denitrification involves the complete reduction of nitrate to molecular nitrogen and is performed primarily by heterotrophic bacteria but can also be achieved by some autotrophs. All those processes can be accomplished in reactors designed to work with adhered biomass in the form of biofilms, with the advantage of a high biomass concentration protected by the exopolymeric matrix, which grants protection to hydraulic shocks, alterations in the feeding stream, temperature variations, etc.

Recently, several new processes and configurations concerning nitrogen removal have appeared in the domain of wastewater treatment. These processes are based on partial nitrification and anoxic ammonia oxidation (ANAMMOX). The ANAMMOX process offers great opportunities to remove ammonia in fully autotrophic systems with biomass retention. No organic carbon is need in such nitrogen removal system, since ammonia is used as electron donor for nitrite reduction. However, as it is a "new process" many challenges yet remain for the optimization and application of ANAMMOX and its combination process in pilot or full-scale plants.

---

* Corresponding author: E-mail: roliveira@deb.uminho.pt.

This review presents the most common types of denitrification biofilm reactors, also comparing their performance in terms of advantages and drawbacks. The most relevant parameters affecting the biological process of denitrification will be discussed as well, such as the effect of temperature, pH, phosphorus concentration, carbon/nitrogen ratio and carbon source.

Our aim is to give the reader an overview of the several nitrogen removal processes to work as a scientific basis for decision making.

In: Environmental and Agricultural Research Summaries …   ISBN: 978-1-63117-090-4
Editor: Lucille T. Cacioppo   © 2014 Nova Science Publishers, Inc.

Chapter 77

Bio-Denitrification of High Strength Landfill Leachate Using Garden Refuse and Pine Bark As Carbon Sources

Cristina Trois and Bjorn Plug*

CRECHE – Centre for Research in Environmental,
Coastal and Hydrological Engineering, School of Civil Engineering,
Surveying and Construction, University of kwaZulu-Natal, Durban, South Africa

Research Summary

Landfill leachate, a toxic by-product formed through the decomposition of organic matter, is harmful to the environment and human health. After nitrification, the concentration of nitrate in discharged leachate may still present a potential threat to the environment. Further denitrification is required to reduce the high concentrations of nitrates in the nitrified effluents to below discharge limits. In the city of Durban (South Africa) municipal solid waste landfill leachate is currently nitrified in Sequencing Batch Reactor plants. After closure of the landfills (in one case expected in 2012) the effluents from the plant will not comply with discharge limits, requiring an ad-hoc treatment. Denitrification, the conversion of nitrates to nitrogen gas, occurs in the presence of a carbon source in an anaerobic environment. Expensive methods are currently employed worldwide; however these tend not to be a viable solution for developing countries. This investigation aimed at identifying an efficient, cost effective, feasible alternative to expensive easily biodegradable carbonaceous materials such as methanol, promoting the use of natural organic sources such as pine bark and garden refuse. These organic substrates contain relatively high amounts of carbon and are readily available in the major Durban landfills. The suitability of two organic substrates as carbon sources for denitrification was assessed using characterisation tests, small-scale batch tests and larger scale columns. The preliminary stage of the research was to comprehensively characterise the substrates (commercial garden refuse and pine bark) through conventional

---

* Corresponding author: troisc@ukzn.ac.za.

testing done on both the solid substrates and their eluates. The batch tests were conducted at 3 nitrate concentration levels: 100, 500 and 2000 mgNO3-N/ℓ. A synthetic nitrate solution was used to simulate the treated landfill leachate. The substrates tested in batches were then selected for large-scale experiments in columns at two nitrate concentrations (500 and 2000 mg/ℓ) and at two different flow rates. Finally durability tests were conducted on previously used substrates of pine bark and immature compost to determine the period for which the substrates could be used as a means for denitrification before replacement was necessary. The CGR RAW substrate had the highest carbon to nitrogen ratio of 90.19 and although the pH value of 5.45 falls just outside the optimum range for denitrification of 6 – 8, it was expected that this would be the best performing substrate. The best performing substrate was the CGR RAW, which achieved full denitrification at the highest nitrate concentration of 2000 mg/ℓ between 9 – 12 days. The column tests reflected promising results at C_o = 500 mg/ℓ during experiment 1, with all 3 achieving full denitrification. Once again the CGR RAW substrate columns reflected the best results. The column at 500 mg/ℓ displayed a HRT of 8.06 days was required whereas the higher concentration of 2000 mg/ℓ required a HRT of 8.40 days. During experiment 2, the CGR RAW substrate column at 500 mg/ℓ was the only one to achieve 100% nitrate removal. A HRT time required for full denitrification is less than 3.54 days. The results of this investigation were modelled to inform the design of a bio-denitrification system. This paper presents an efficient, cost effective, feasible alternative to expensive methods by promoting the use of natural organic sources such as pine bark and garden refuse as carbon sources for bio-denitrification.

In: Environmental and Agricultural Research Summaries …   ISBN: 978-1-63117-090-4
Editor: Lucille T. Cacioppo   © 2014 Nova Science Publishers, Inc.

Chapter 78

DESIGN ECOLOGICAL TREATMENT SYSTEMS FOR NITROGEN REMOVAL THROUGH NITRITATION AND ANAMMOX

Wendong Tao[*]

Department of Environmental Resources Engineering,
College of Environmental Science and Forestry,
State University of New York, Syracuse, New York, US

RESEARCH SUMMARY

As a sustainable alternative to conventional nitrification-denitrification process, partial nitrification (nitritation) and anaerobic ammonium oxidation (anammox) have been integrated to remove nitrogen from ammonia-rich wastewaters over the last decade. When nitritation and anammox are coupled, only about one half of ammonium needs to be oxidized aerobically to nitrite first. Autotrophic anammox bacteria use the remaining ammonium as electron donors instead of organic substrates for heterotrophic denitrification of nitrite under strictly anaerobic conditions. Compared to nitrification-denitrification, the novel nitritation-anammox process requires 60% less of oxygen, produces lower greenhouse gas emission, and generates less waste sludge. Integration of nitritation and anammox has been accomplished in several types of bioreactors at optimum conditions accomplished through high energy and material inputs. Ecological treatment systems such as constructed wetlands and biofilters, however, rely on natural sources of energy and self-organization for ecosystem functions. It is challenging to enhance the novel nitritation-anammox process in passive wastewater treatment processes. Successful integration of nitritation and anammox has the potential to substantially increase nitrogen removal in ecological treatment systems. This paper reviews the factors that influence the nitritation-anammox process, discusses the challenges to integrate nitritation and anammox in ecological treatment systems, and explores design considerations for enhancing the nitritation-anammox process in ecological treatment systems.

---

[*] E-mail: wtao@esf.edu. Tel.: 315-470-4928.

In: Environmental and Agricultural Research Summaries ...   ISBN: 978-1-63117-090-4
Editor: Lucille T. Cacioppo   © 2014 Nova Science Publishers, Inc.

Chapter 79

DENITRIFICATION APPLIED TO WASTEWATER TREATMENT: PROCESSES, REGULATION AND ECOLOGICAL ASPECTS

G. González-Blanco[1], R. Beristain-Cardoso[1], F. Cuervo-López[1], F. J. Cervantes[2], and J. Gómez[1]*

[1]Departamento de Biotecnología,
Universidad Autónoma Metropolitana-Iztapalapa, DF, México
[2]División de Ciencias Ambientales,
Instituto Potosino de Investigación Científica y Tecnológica (IPICyT),
San Luis Potosí, México

RESEARCH SUMMARY

Denitrification is a process occurring in natural environments, such as soil, marine and fresh waters, where the role of nitrogen cycle is relevant. Denitrification is defined as an anoxic biological process, which involves the reduction of nitrate or nitrite to molecular nitrogen. The energy required for this reduction is coming from inorganic or organic compounds oxidation, called lithotrophic and organotrophic denitrification, respectively. This biological process can be carried out by autotrophic, heterotrophic and phototrophic bacteria, which have been isolated from different environments. Denitrification is considered as an important step during nitrogen removal in wastewater treatment. When the wastewater to be treated contains ammonium, sulfur and carbon compounds usually three biological treatment steps might be required for nitrogen removal: (a) anaerobic digestion, for diminishing organic matter content, (b) nitrification step, where ammonium is aerobically oxidized to nitrate and (c) a denitrification step, where nitrate is anoxically reduced to molecular nitrogen. Nonetheless, there are new evidences indicating that the denitrifying process is capable of conducting simultaneous removal of organic matter, sulfur and nitrogen compounds in a single experimental unit (a multipurpose bioreactor). This biological process has been called

---
* E-mail: beristain_3@yahoo.com.mx, becr@xanum.uam.mx

litho-organotrophic denitrification. The coupling of nitrogen cycle with sulfur and carbon cycles and the use of multipurpose bioreactors is of utmost technological relevance. Nevertheless, there are still many experimental activities to be made about the metabolism, regulation and ecological behavior of bacteria of the nitrogen cycle. In this context, this chapter provides a glance on the progress made over the last decades in the understanding of the metabolic capability, regulation and ecological aspects of denitrification for the biotransformation of nitrogen in wastewaters containing sulfurous and carbonaceous compounds.

In: Environmental and Agricultural Research Summaries …   ISBN: 978-1-63117-090-4
Editor: Lucille T. Cacioppo   © 2014 Nova Science Publishers, Inc.

Chapter 80

EFFECT OF SEDIMENT REDOX CONDITIONS ON RELATIVE CONTRIBUTIONS OF BACTERIA AND FUNGI TO DENITRIFICATION: A REVIEW

Dong Cheol Seo [*]

Department of Biological Environment, Sunchon National University,
Jungangno, Suncheon, Jeonnam, Korea
Department of Oceanography and Coastal Sciences,
School of the Coast and Environment,
Louisiana State University, Baton Rouge, Louisiana, US

RESEARCH SUMMARY

Denitrification is the most important N removal mechanism by which fixed N in the biosphere, especially in wetland soils, returns to the atmosphere. In this paper, we review the relative contributions of bacteria and fungi to denitrification, and fungal/bacterial (F/B) and carbon/nitrogen (C/N) biomass ratios in sediment from a swamp forest used for wastewater treatment as influenced by soil redox conditions (Eh) representing a range of anaerobic or near anaerobic conditions. Fungal and bacterial denitrification was determined with SIR inhibition method under a range of redox conditions in sediment from a Louisiana swamp forest used for wastewater treatment (Seo and DeLaune, 2010a; 2010b). Sediment was incubated in microcosms at 6 Eh levels (−200, −100, 0, +100, +250 and +400 mV) ranging from reducing to oxidizing condition. At Eh values of +250 mV and +400 mV (moderately reducing or aerobic conditions), denitrification by fungi and bacteria were 34.3–35.1% and 1.46–1.59% of total denitrification, respectively, indicating that fungi were responsible for most of the denitrification under aerobic or slightly anaerobic conditions. On the other hand, at Eh −200 mV, denitrification rate of fungi and bacteria were 17.6% and 64.9% of total denitrification, respectively, indicating that bacteria were responsible for most of the

[*] Corresponding Author. Department of Biological Environment, Sunchon National University, 413 Jungangno, Suncheon, Jeonnam 540-742, Korea. Tel.: +82 61 750 3297; Fax: +82 61 752 8011. E-mail address: drseodc@gmail.com.

denitrification under strongly anaerobic conditions. Results show fungal denitrification was dominant under moderately reducing and aerobic condition (Eh > +250 mV), whereas bacterial denitrification was dominant under anaerobic condition (Eh < −100 mV). At Eh values between −100 to +100 mV, denitrification by fungi and bacteria were 37.9–43.2% and 53.0–51.1% of total denitrification, respectively, indicating that both bacteria and fungi contributed significantly to denitrification under these redox conditions. Because N_2O is an important gaseous product in sediment, fungal denitrification could be of greater ecological significance under aerobic or moderately reducing conditions. The fungi/bacteria (F/B) ratios varied between 0.71–1.16 for microbial biomass C, and 0.54–0.94 for microbial biomass N. Under moderately reducing conditions (Eh ≥ +100 mV), the F/B ratios for microbial biomass C and N were higher than that for highly reducing conditions (Eh ≤ 0 mV). In moderately reducing conditions (Eh ≥ +100 mV), the C/N microbial biomass ratio for fungi (C/N: 13.54–14.26) was slightly higher than for bacteria (C/N: 9.61–12.07). Under highly reducing redox conditions (Eh ≤ 0 mV), the C/N microbial biomass ratio for fungi (C/N: 10.79–12.41) was higher than for bacteria (C/N: 8.21–9.14). For bacteria and fungi, the C/N microbial biomass ratios under moderately reducing conditions were higher than that in highly reducing conditions.

In: Environmental and Agricultural Research Summaries ...   ISBN: 978-1-63117-090-4
Editor: Lucille T. Cacioppo   © 2014 Nova Science Publishers, Inc.

Chapter 81

MICROBIAL WATER DENITRIFICATION STIMULATED BY ELECTRIC FIELD: A REVIEW

Venko N. Beschkov[*]

Institute of Chemical Engineering,
Bulgarian Academy of Sciences, Sofia, Bulgaria

RESEARCH SUMMARY

One of the most significant problems for the present society is water pollution by different effluents. Nitrate is one of the most severe pollutants, resulted from industry, agriculture and requiring serious treatment. In the recent decades the microbial methods for nitrate reduction to molecular nitrogen were extensively developed. It was discovered that this process could considerably enhanced and stimulated by constant electric field. The nature of this combined effect is still not sufficiently clear. On the other hand this process of treatment could be applied as energy producing one, with electric power generation in microbial fuel cell operation on nitrate reduction by organic pollutants. The present review considers the last achievements and the problems in bio-electrochemical water denitrification and perspectives for microbial fuel cell operation based on this process.

---

[*] Address for correspondence: bioreac@bas.bg.

In: Environmental and Agricultural Research Summaries …   ISBN: 978-1-63117-090-4
Editor: Lucille T. Cacioppo   © 2014 Nova Science Publishers, Inc.

Chapter 82

APPLICATION OF NITRATE REMOVAL BY PADDY FIELDS: AN OVERVIEW

Tomoki Takahashi[1] and Rikiya Nira[2]
[1]National Agriculture Research Center for Tohoku Region,
National Agriculture and Food Research Organization, Akita, Japan
[2]National Agriculture Research Center,
National Agriculture and Food Research Organization, Ibaraki, Japan

RESEARCH SUMMARY

Since the 1980s, the ability of paddy fields to remove nitrate has been a focus of research because of the recognized adverse environmental effects of nitrate loads from excess nitrogen fertilizer applied to upland fields. There is often a significant time-lag between regulating nitrogen application and a decrease in nitrate concentrations in streams in catchment areas that include intensively farmed upland fields. In such regions, one of the most important methods to decrease nitrate loads quickly is nitrate removal by paddy fields, which can remove an average of 0.002–0.70 g-N m-2d-1 under flooded conditions. Quantifying nitrate removal has revealed that it is a function of the nitrate concentration, flood water depth, rate of inflow, temperature, and surface water percolation rate. Extending the paddy field irrigation period has been investigated as a way to increase nitrate removal. Because the amount of nitrate removed by surface flooding decreases considerably at low-temperatures, many studies have focused on monitoring and on methods to increase nitrate removal during winter. It has been found that nitrate removal by percolating water does not decrease considerably during winter. Furthermore, as predicted by a mathematical model, streaming irrigation increases the amount of nitrate removed, based on area. Incorporating organic matter is an alternative proposal to increase nitrate removal rates, because it provides carbon, which is consumed by denitrifying organisms in soils. These results suggest that incorporating organic matter and streaming irrigation are the most effective ways to increase nitrate removal during winter.

Further studies are needed to clarify the trade-offs between nitrate removal and greenhouse gas emission in paddy fields, to quantify nitrate removal in the subsoil under the plow layer, and to identify socioeconomic solutions for conservation and the enhancement of the nitrate removal function of paddy fields.

In: Environmental and Agricultural Research Summaries …   ISBN: 978-1-63117-090-4
Editor: Lucille T. Cacioppo   © 2014 Nova Science Publishers, Inc.

Chapter 83

DENITRIFICATION IN PLANT-BENEFICIAL BACTERIA: GENETIC ASPECTS AND ROLE IN PLANT-BACTERIAL INTERACTIONS

Elena I. Katsy[*]

Laboratory of Microbial Genetics,
Institute of Biochemistry and Physiology of Plants and Microorganisms,
Russian Academy of Sciences, Saratov, Russia

RESEARCH SUMMARY

Denitrifying microorganisms are responsible for the sequential reduction of nitrate to nitrite, nitric oxide, nitrous oxide, and nitrogen. The complete denitrification process is catalyzed by respiratory membrane-bound or periplasmic nitrate reductase; cytochrome cd1 or copper-containing nitrite reductase; heterodimeric NO reductases, receiving electrons from cytochrome c or from menaquinol, or single-component NO reductase, obtaining electrons from quinol; and N_2O reductase. Plants affect the composition of the bacterial communities and proportions of nitrate, nitrate, NO, and N_2O reducers found in the rhizosphere.

Many plant-growth-promoting rhizobacteria (PGPR) are capable of complete or partial denitrification. Data are discussed that show the potential mobility of some denitrification genes and the probability of their horizontal transfer in the populations of rhizosphere bacteria resulting in extension of the microbial adaptive potential. The denitrifying activity of soil microorganisms influences their interaction with plants and seems to provide the rhizosphere bacteria with a competitive advantage for plant colonization.

On the other side, nitrite and NO produced during bacterial denitrification act as nontraditional plant-growth regulators promoting root formation and development. These and some other agroecological aspects of denitrification performed by various PGPR are also considered.

[*] Tel./fax: +7 8452 970383. E-mail addresses: katsy@ibppm.sgu.ru; ei_katsy@mail.ru.

In: Environmental and Agricultural Research Summaries …   ISBN: 978-1-63117-090-4
Editor: Lucille T. Cacioppo   © 2014 Nova Science Publishers, Inc.

Chapter 84

APPLICATION OF MICROBIAL CONSORTIUM TO PLANT-SCALE SEWAGE TREATMENT FOR EFFICIENT NITROGEN REMOVAL

Joong Kyun Kim[1] and Geon Lee[2]
[1]Department of Biotechnology and Bioengineering,
Pukyong National University, Busan, Korea
[2]Research Department, Sejung Biotech Corporation,
Daegeo-1 Dong, Kangseo-Gu, Busan, Korea

RESEARCH SUMMARY

As an alternative method to the efficient removal of nitrogen, a microbial consortium was applied to a sewage treatment plant in which an advanced treatment system was not equipped in parallel. The microbial consortium used in this study was 'Aeroden' (KCTC11400BP) consisting of *Nitrosomonas*, *Notrobacter*, *Bacillus*, *Pseudomonas*, *Paracoccus*, etc. The major strain of this consortium was *Pseudomonas* sp., which showed efficient denitrification activity under aerobic conditions. In lab-scale experiments, the microbial consortium showed potential nitrogen removal activity in various types of wastewaters, including leather wastewater, synthetic resin wastewater, sewage, and livestock wastewater.

The sewage treatment plant used in this study treated approximately 550,000 m^3 of sewage per day. Among the process lines, experiments were carried out in one process line to remove the high nitrogen content from the recycle water. This involved an AO process consisting of an anaerobic tank (506 m^3) and oxic tank (2,160 m^3). Regarding the volume of the recycled water (Q), the volume of the return sludge from the settling tank was 0.3 Q, and that of the nitrified recycle water was 2 Q. The volume of recycled water treated per day was 3,456 m^5. Experiments were carried out seeding the microbial consortium into the oxic tank at a concentration of 0.1% (w/v). The seeded microbial consortium was proliferated for 7 days. For adaptation of the microbial consortium in the process, only 1/2 Q of the recycled water was loaded and operated under a daily input of 0.05% (w/v) microbial consortium for the next 15 days. After this, stabilization of the process was carried out: 1 Q of recycled water was loaded normally and operated under a daily input of 0.01% (w/v) microbial consortium for the first 30 days, followed by operation under a gradually reduced input size of the microbial consortium. During the 215-day operation, influent TN (in the range from 117.9 - 259.7 mg/L) present in the recycled water was treated, and effluent TN was in the range from 33.7 - 105.9 mg/L, with 68.1% average removal efficiency. On average, the concentrations of BOD_5, COD_{Cr}, TP, and SS removed were 90.7, 86.4, 67.7, and 95.8%, respectively. At the same time, odor (such as ammonia, methyl mercaptan, and hydrogen sulfide) emitted from the anaerobic tank was remarkably reduced as the process was stabilized. As a result, about 20% higher efficiency of nitrogen removal was obtained by seeding of the microbial consortium, compared to that of the existing process.

In: Environmental and Agricultural Research Summaries ...   ISBN: 978-1-63117-090-4
Editor: Lucille T. Cacioppo   © 2014 Nova Science Publishers, Inc.

Chapter 85

DENITRIFICATION PROCESSES
FOR WASTEWATER TREATMENT

Ya-Juan Liu, Darren Delai Sun and Yu Liu
School of Civil and Environmental Engineering,
Nanyang Technological University, Singapore

RESEARCH SUMMARY

Nitrate (especially high concentration), one of the most concerned contaminants, may cause serious environmental problems, such as water acidification and *eutrophication*, leading to damaged eco-system. Nitrate can also cause the health problems, e.g. the development of *methemoglobinemia* and blue baby when nitrate or nitrite concentration in drinking water is greater than 10 mg NO_3^--N/L or 1 mg NO_2^--N/L (the maximum contaminant level in National Primary Drinking Water Regulations set by United States Environmental Protection Agency). Wastewaters discharged from the household and industries, such as the oil industry, fertilizer-processing industry, landfill leachates, sewage and erosion of natural deposits often contain high concentration nitrate and nitrite.

In order to protect and preserve the environment and meet the increasingly stringent environmental regulations for nitrogen discharge, the removal of nitrate-nitrogen as well as other nitrogenous contaminants from water and wastewater has become significance and urgency in recent years.

Several technologies including physicochemical (such as ion-exchange process, reverse osmosis, electrodialysis and distillation) and biological processes have been employed to remove nitrate from municipal and industrial wastewater. It has been proven that biological processes are the simplest and most economically sound means for removing nitrate from various types of wastewaters. Denitrification is essential step towards biological nitrogen removal, and is able to produce bacteriologically and chemically safe treated effluent. Therefore, this chapter focuses on the various types of denitrification processes for nitrate removal from wastewater. The theories and applications of heterotrophic denitrification, autotrophic denitrification, aerobic denitrification, short-cut nitrification and denitrification and denitrifying granular sludge are discussed.

In: Environmental and Agricultural Research Summaries ...   ISBN: 978-1-63117-090-4
Editor: Lucille T. Cacioppo   © 2014 Nova Science Publishers, Inc.

Chapter 86

SEABUCKTHORN (*HIPPOPHAE RHAMNOIDES* L.) A GOLDEN BUSH: ITS GENETIC DIVERSITY CHARACTERIZATION AND BREEDING SCOPE

Gyan P. Mishra[1,] Ashutosh A. Murkute,[1] Jitendra Kumar,[1] Manish S. Bhoyar,[1] Rajwant K. Kalia[1,2,*] and R. B. Srivastava[1]*

[1]Defence Institute of High Altitude Research, DRDO, India
[2]Centre for Plant Biotechnology, CCS HAU, Hisar, Haryana, India

RESEARCH SUMMARY

Genetic diversity in seabuckthorn provides a good opportunity for plant breeding and selection while variations in the growth rhythm, height and hardiness provide guidelines for seed and plant transfer as well as plant introduction. Plant breeders can use this information to design their breeding plans to obtain an ideal type with certain growth periods, maturity time and plant height for a particular region or cultivation technology. Till date there is no breeding programme for seabuckthorn improvement in Ladakh. But there is need to improve the existing germplasm through intensive breeding programme which can be done in three ways. First one is research to the natural seabuckthorn resources distributed in Ladakh, and get the superior provenance by provenance trails, and also search some superior families and then established their progeny testing plantations. The second way is introduction of lots of cultivated seabuckthorn varieties from Russia and Mongolia, since most of them are ssp. *mongolica*. Select few varieties for cultivation under Ladakh conditions which are performing better. The third one is hybridization between sub-species (ssp. *sinensis* and ssp. *mongolica*) and superior plant selection in F_1 generation.

Gene based molecular markers can be used for pre-selection in seedling populations to discard unfavourable genotypes at an earlier stage along. Molecular markers can be used to evaluate the wild germplasm for its use in the development of economically viable varieties.

---

[*] Present Address: Horticulture and Landscape Architecture, Purdue University, West Lafayette, IN 47907. e-mail: gyan.gene@gmail.com.

The phylogenetic analysis can be used as guidelines for improving germplasm collection and breeding. The molecular techniques are quick and accurate to identify the variability in natural populations of the plants, especially to evaluate the wild germplasm for its use in the development of economically viable varieties.

In: Environmental and Agricultural Research Summaries …   ISBN: 978-1-63117-090-4
Editor: Lucille T. Cacioppo   © 2014 Nova Science Publishers, Inc.

Chapter 87

STUDIES ON DIVERSITY OF FISHES, AMPHIBIANS AND REPTILES OF THAR DESERT WITH CONSERVATION STATUS

Akhlaq Husain[1]* and Gaurav Sharma[2]•
[1]Hari Vihar, Vijay Park, Dehra Dun, Uttarakhand, India
[2]Zoological Survey of India, Desert Regional Centre, Jodhpur, Rajasthan, India

RESEARCH SUMMARY

The Thar Desert is a large arid region, in the north-western part of India and covering an area of about 2,08,110 km^2 between $24^\circ30'$ - 30° N Latitude and $69^\circ30'$ - 76° E Longitude. This paper deals with 155 species of fishes, 9 species of Amphibians and 80 species of Reptiles in Thar Desert. The distributional pattern and conservation status with an update on nomenclature are also provided.

* E-mail: drakhlaqhusain@gmail.com.
• E-mail: drgaurav.zsi.india@gmail.com.

In: Environmental and Agricultural Research Summaries …   ISBN: 978-1-63117-090-4
Editor: Lucille T. Cacioppo   © 2014 Nova Science Publishers, Inc.

Chapter 88

FLORAL DIVERSITY, THREATS AND CONSERVATION MEASURES: A CASE STUDY FROM NARA DESERT, PAKISTAN

Rahmatullah Qureshi[*]

Department of Botany, Pir Mehr Ali Shah Arid Agriculture University,
Rawalpindi, Pakistan

RESEARCH SUMMARY

Nara Desert is located in Sindh Province, Pakistan between latitudes 26° to 28° north and longitude 68° to 70° east. The study area is a hot sandy desert with the mean minimum and maximum temperatures of 20°C and 45°C, respectively. Aridity is the most distinctive feature of Nara desert with wet and dry years occurring in clusters. The mean rainfall ranges from 88 mm to 135 mm, mostly received during the monsoon. There is a scarcity of water in the Nara desert. The ground water resources are limited and are met at a depth of 50-300 feet from the surface. In spite of its low productivity, this desert upholds a fairly high human and livestock populations (1.05 million (m) and 1.25 m, respectively). This fragile ecosystem supports human and livestock population for food, sheltering and reproduction/breeding place. The area is also presenting a unique landscape for plant diversity. A total of 147 species belonging to 105 genera and 43 families were recorded during the study period. The vegetation over major area is characterized by xeromorphic in nature. The most common plants in this desert are *Calligonum polygonoides, Aerva javanica, Dipterygium glaucum, Crotalaria burhia, Prosopis cineraria, Tamarix aphylla, Capparis decidua, Salvadora oleoides, Leptadenia pyrotechnica, Aristida* spp., *Limeum indicum* and *Stipagrostis plumosa* growing in Crest, Slope and flat habitats, whereas saline/ sodic land and brackish wetland habitat possesses halophytic and hydrophytic floral elements.

The escalating occurrence of prolonged drought, desertification, deforestation and soil erosion are causing serious threats to this area. The most important factors contributing

---

[*] Email: rahmatullahq@yahoo.com.

destruction of natural environment of the Nara desert are habitat destruction and fragmentation, over-exploitation of biological resources by the local inhabitants and overgrazing by the livestock. The contributing agencies which led to the destruction of natural environment of the study area are: infra-structure developments by Oil and Gas exploratory agencies, exercises by the armed forces, overgrazing by the livestock and the traditional uses of plants by the inhabitants coupled with natural calamities. These factors have exacerbated desert encroachment and exerted huge pressures on the ecology of the region. Some possible conservative measures are also discussed for the rehabilitation of degraded ecosystem of this desert.

In: Environmental and Agricultural Research Summaries ...   ISBN: 978-1-63117-090-4
Editor: Lucille T. Cacioppo   © 2014 Nova Science Publishers, Inc.

Chapter 89

SPECIES COMPOSITION AND ABUNDANCE OF BIRD POPULATIONS IN THE THAR DESERT, INDIA

C. Sivaperuman[*]

Zoological Survey of India, Andaman and Nicobar Regional Centre,
Andaman and Nicobar Islands, India

RESEARCH SUMMARY

The Thar Desert is biogeographically the easternmost edge of the Saharan-Arabian Desert zone, comprising 61 per cent of the total geographical area of the State. It is one of the smallest deserts in the world, but it exhibits a wide variety of habitats and biodiversity. This paper based on field surveys conducted during 2000 to 2004 in different habitat like sandy area, stable and shifting type of sand dunes, rocky area, gravel, sewan grass, lakes and tanks of saline and fresh water, canal area and agricultural fields which provide excellent shelter to the avifauna of this region. The species abundance and distribution of bird community have been discussed in details.

[*] Email: c_sivaperuman@yahoo.co.in.

In: Environmental and Agricultural Research Summaries ...   ISBN: 978-1-63117-090-4
Editor: Lucille T. Cacioppo   © 2014 Nova Science Publishers, Inc.

Chapter 90

MOLLUSC FAUNA AND ITS ECOLOGY IN THE INDIAN DESERT

*M. M. Saxena**

Post-Graduate Department of Zoology,
Dungar College, Bikaner, India

RESEARCH SUMMARY

Surface waters in the Indian desert are noted to be specific in terms of their physical-chemical limnology and their community. Mollusc fauna of such waters investigated for about three decades in diverse bodies of water for long periods and for different bio-ecological aspects is discussed in the current chapter with some ecological observations. Overall 13 species of mollusca are recorded from these waters, of which 11 species belong to class Gastropoda and two to Bivalvia. Lakes and village ponds are noted to harbour greater diversity and population of fauna, with predomination of pulmonate snail *Indoplanorbis exustus* and prosobranch snail *Digoniostoma pulchella*. Bivalves are found to be rare and infrequent. Most of the gastropods breed during monsoon and are resistant to extremes of environmental conditions as those of temperature, salinity and aridity through some adaptive mechanisms. These snails in desert region have a far wider tolerance for temperate as compared to their counterparts in the relatively benign environments of adjoining Aravalli and trans-Aravalli waters. Snails *Bellamya bengalensis* and *Indoplanorbis exustus* are noted to host trematode infection. Former snail harbours only *furcocercous* cercariae with greatest infection during monsoon. Latter pulmonate snail is found to host *furcocercous* and *amphistome* cercariae in the months of September, October and June. The infestation intensity, i.e., number of cercariae per snail, is noted as enormously high during June and September (up to 8580/snail) as compared to that in October (120/snail).

---

* E-mail: saxenamm@rediffmail.com.

In: Environmental and Agricultural Research Summaries …   ISBN: 978-1-63117-090-4
Editor: Lucille T. Cacioppo   © 2014 Nova Science Publishers, Inc.

Chapter 91

THE DESERT ENVIRONMENT OF MENDOZA, ARGENTINA: STATUS AND PROSPECTS FOR SUSTAINABLE BEEF CATTLE PRODUCTION

J. C. Guevara[1, 2], and E. G. Grünwald[1, 3]

[1]Argentinean Institute for Arid Land Research (IADIZA-CONICET), Argentina
[2]Faculty of Agricultural Sciences, National University of Cuyo, Argentina
[3]Argentinean Institute of Nivology, Glaciology and Environmental Sciences
(IANIGLA-CONICET), Argentina

RESEARCH SUMMARY

The purpose of this chapter was to characterize the environment of Mendoza devoted to beef cattle production and propose a management practice to improve the productivity and profitability of this activity using the forage that could be produced in about 75,000 irrigated hectares uncultivated at present. This practice consists of early weaning beef calves averaging 70-kg live weight at 60-day-old, feeding them balanced commercial feed and alfalfa hay until they reach 100-kg live weight within a period of 45 days. Subsequently, calves graze alfalfa and are supplied maize silage in pens during night confinement until reaching 320-kg live weight over a period of 314 days. Mendoza lies in the central west of the country with 148,827 km^2. An important portion of Mendoza falls within the central eastern part of the Monte Phytogeographical Province, the most arid rangeland of the country. The Monte vegetation may take various aspects depending chiefly on its degradation status: dense thickets of small trees, open woodlands and savannas with isolated trees, tall shrublands, low shrublands and bare lands. Floristic resources are used by beef cattle, goats, native and exotic wildlife and other herbivores. South American camelids (*Vicugna vicugna* and *Lama guanicoe*) are the most important fauna species of economic use. Exotic fauna is mainly represented by *Lepus europaeus*. Around 9 million of Mendoza's hectares could be devoted to livestock production. The beef cattle stock is currently 547,825, of which 49.2% are cows. Cow–calf operations under rangeland conditions are the dominant production system. Mendoza consumes 464,025 bovines year^{-1}, of which only 7% are locally finished in cultivated pastures and feedlots. Profitability of the proposed strategy was assessed through the internal rate of return (IRR) and the net present value (NPV). Investments, operating costs, and animal prices were taken at November 2010. The production system that combines early weaning with post-weaning strategies was more profitable than traditional post-weaning production system. For the integrated production system, 378 was the minimum number of animals that permits reaching an IRR higher than the opportunity cost of capital (12%). The NPV obtained per animal, in US$, increased from 1.72 for 378 animals to 1,143.7 for 2,000 animals per year. The cultivated area necessary to feed 100 animals was 14.2 ha (10.6 ha for alfalfa hay and 3.6 for maize silage). Meat productivity was about 1550 kg ha^{-1} year^{-1}. The use of the uncultivated irrigated area could permit post-weaning production of about 500,000 calves per year to supply the total meat demand of Mendoza.

In: Environmental and Agricultural Research Summaries …   ISBN: 978-1-63117-090-4
Editor: Lucille T. Cacioppo   © 2014 Nova Science Publishers, Inc.

Chapter 92

DYNAMIC IN RODENT COMMUNITIES' AFFECTS TEMPORAL NICHE

Elke Scheibler

University Stuttgart, Biological Institute, Dept. Animal Physiology,
Pfaffenwaldring, Stuttgart, Germany

RESEARCH SUMMARY

Life in the desert poses a number of challenges, which are reflected not only in physiological and anatomical adaptations, but also in behavior. What are the characteristics of such a life? Undoubtedly, at least the low primary production of vegetation with a patchy distribution is one of the limitations for the animals. However, not only plants but also animals appear in unpredictable abundance. Therefore, in terms of a social or solitary way of life, it is both for solitary-living animals difficult to find a partner, on the other hand, group living is not the exclusive one solution because of unstable food resources. Finally, on the level of behavior, different strategies have emerged in state; solitary lifestyle or living in unstable social communities is regarded as the most frequently used option. Besides these important intra-specific relationships, the occurrence of heterospecifics requires another strategy. In the case of sympatric species, the coexistence exists for long-term periods, or permanently, and is therefore more important because it implies competition for resources. Our study model is the desert hamster, *Phodopus roborovskii,* living in Gobi desert. Here we find this common species in communities together with the gerbils, jerboas, ground squirrels and other hamster species or some more rare species. Coexistence is an omnipresent situation for nearly all species. Because of the variety of living together, the peculiarity of coexistence appears diverse. Schoener hypothesized the phenomenon of temporal resource partitioning for animals living under limited conditions, which is the case in desert habitats. Establishing its own niche is the most promising way for a peaceful coexistence with species with similar demands if at least one partner shows adaptability for food and in terms of climatic forces. The time factor appears here as an ecological factor with the particularity that other factors like temperature, occurrence of predators, light, etc. are closely associated to it. Moreover, the interspecific contact and the competition as consequence in turn acts as non-photic zeitgeber, where the role as modulator or as a possibility for compensation in constant light conditions is well known. An important characteristic of a temporal niche is its plasticity; because it is not constant it is rather a question of adaption toward current ecological and evolutionary forces and is therefore a dynamic strategy that includes fitness maximization and reduction of fitness loss. For example, changes in species' composition and ratios may vary within days, and we observed a change in the circadian rhythm within days, which demands a complex answer of physiological processes. Beyond that, a significant change in species ratio may happen for diverse reasons like predators, change of land use and grazing, ripeness of local plants, illumination by the moon, weather and, especially, humidity, wind, etc. Needless to say, a change of only a single one of these parameters affects species; the power of impact varies by the time of the year in terms of states of reproduction, dispersal of the young and foraging before winter of all sympatric species. Desert habitats are suited to investigation of the mechanisms allowing animals to survive under harsh conditions because here we have a manageable number of species and ecological parameters and a high level of challenges towards the animals.

In: Environmental and Agricultural Research Summaries ...   ISBN: 978-1-63117-090-4
Editor: Lucille T. Cacioppo   © 2014 Nova Science Publishers, Inc.

Chapter 93

ENCYRTIDAE (INSECTA: HYMENOPTERA: CHALCIDOIDEA) FROM THAR DESERT, INDIA

Sarfrazul Islam Kazmi[*]
Zoological Survey of India, Kolkata, India

RESEARCH SUMMARY

The Thar Desert is one of the smallest deserts and exhibits a wide variety of habitat and biodiversity. The analysis of literature shows that knowledge of distribution and diversity of family Encyrtidae is inadequate in this region on the ground of utterly insufficient survey. The family, Encyrtidae, is second largest among chalcidoidea whose members are used in the biological control of insect pests are mostly primary internal parasitoids and hyper-parasitoids of coccoidea (Homoptera), Lepidoptera, Diptera, Coleoptera and also attack on aphids and psyllids. The present study deals with thirty one genera and forty species of Encyrtidae from the Thar Desert.

[*] E-mail: kazmizsi@gmail.com.

In: Environmental and Agricultural Research Summaries …   ISBN: 978-1-63117-090-4
Editor: Lucille T. Cacioppo   © 2014 Nova Science Publishers, Inc.

Chapter 94

EULOPHIDAE AND EUPELMIDAE (INSECTA: HYMENOPTERA: CHALCIDOIDEA) OF INDIAN THAR DESERT

P. Girish Kumar* and S. I. Kazmi*

Zoological Survey of India, Kolkata, West Bengal, India

RESEARCH SUMMARY

Eulophid and eupelmid fauna of Indian Thar desert was studied during 2000 to 2004. Eight species of chalcidoid wasps were recorded, of these, 6 species of Eulophidae namely *Neotrichoporoides nyemitawus*, *Neotrichoporoides viridimaculatus*, *Oomyzus scaposus*, *Elasmus brevicornis*, *Elasmus johnstoni*, *Notanisomorphella flaviventris* and 2 species of Eupelmidae *viz.* *Anastatus tenuipes* and *Eupelmus australiensis*. The genus *Oomyzus* Rondani, *Notanisomorphella* Girault and *Eupelmus* Dalman and the species *Neotrichoporoides viridimaculatus* (Fullaway), *Oomyzus scaposus* (Thomson), *Notanisomorphella flaviventris* (Girault) and *Eupelmus australiensis* (Girault) were reported for the first time from Rajasthan.

---

* E-mail: kpgiris@gmail.com.
* E-mail: kazmizsi@gmail.com.

In: Environmental and Agricultural Research Summaries …   ISBN: 978-1-63117-090-4
Editor: Lucille T. Cacioppo   © 2014 Nova Science Publishers, Inc.

Chapter 95

COLEOPTERA (INSECTA) FAUNA FROM THAR DESERT OF RAJASTHAN, INDIA

S. I. Kazmi and N. Tak*

Zoological Survey of India, Kolkata, India

RESEARCH SUMMARY

This paper deals with 56 genera and 89 species of beetles distributed under 12 Families, Order Coleoptera. The family Meloidae with 4 genera and 7 species, family Scarabaeidae with 19 genera and 20 species, family Cicindelidae with 1 genera and 3 species, family Curculionidae with 4 genera and 10 species, family Tenebrionidae with 5 genera and 6 species, family Chrysomelidae with 1 genera and 1 species, family Hydrophylidae with 6 genera and 13 species, family Dytiscidae with 5 genera and 17 species, family Haplidae with 1 genera and 1 species, family Carabidae with 3 genera and 3 species, family Coccinellidae with 6 genera and 7 species and with family Elateridae1 genera and 1 species.

* E-mail: kazmizsi@gmail.com.

In: Environmental and Agricultural Research Summaries ...   ISBN: 978-1-63117-090-4
Editor: Lucille T. Cacioppo   © 2014 Nova Science Publishers, Inc.

Chapter 96

COLLEMBOLA (HEXAPODA) FROM THAR DESERT, INDIA

G. P. Mandal and S. I. Kazmi•*

Zoological Survey of India, Kolkata, India

RESEARCH SUMMARY

This paper deals with taxonomic studies of collembolan (Hexapoda) based on a collection made in the project of faunal diversity from the following districts of Jodhpur, Sriganganagar, Jalore, Barmer, Hanumangarh, Bikaner, Churu, Siker and Jhunjunu. The present study deals with seven species of collembola under seven genera of four families.

* E-mail: gpmandal.zsi@gmail.com.
• E-mail: kazmizsi@gmail.com.

In: Environmental and Agricultural Research Summaries …   ISBN: 978-1-63117-090-4
Editor: Lucille T. Cacioppo   © 2014 Nova Science Publishers, Inc.

Chapter 97

LEPIDOPTERA (INSECTA) FAUNA FROM THAR DESERT OF RAJASTHAN, INDIA

*N. Tak and S. I. Kazmi**

Zoological Survey of India, Kolkata, West Bengal, India

RESEARCH SUMMARY

This paper deals with 35 genera and 48 species of Lepidoptera distributed under 11 Families. The Family Noctuidae with 12 genera and 13 species, Geometridae with 1 genera and 2 species, Papilionidae with 3 genera and 4 species, Lycaenidae with 3 genera and 3 species, Pyralidae with 2 genera and 2 species, and Danaidae with 3 genera and 4 species, Pieridae with 4 genera and 12 species, Hisperiidae with 1 genera and 1 species, Satyridae 1 genera and 1 species, Arctiidae with 2 genera and 3 species and with Nymphalidae 3 genera and 3 species

---

* Email: kazmizsi@gmail.com.

In: Environmental and Agricultural Research Summaries …   ISBN: 978-1-63117-090-4
Editor: Lucille T. Cacioppo   © 2014 Nova Science Publishers, Inc.

Chapter 98

THE ROLE OF ENVIRONMENTAL FACTORS IN SHAPING DIATOM FRUSTULE: MORPHOLOGICAL PLASTICITY AND TERATOLOGICAL FORMS

Elisa Falasco[*] and Guido Badino
DBAU, University of Turin, Turin, Italy

RESEARCH SUMMARY

Environment factors play an important role in driving morphological variations of diatom frustule. Adaptation to local physico-chemical changes translates into morphological plasticity, leading to structural variation of the valve toward the best solution in facing adverse conditions. Such phenotypic variations, that must be considered as an aspect of the gene expression within a species or population, mainly affect the cell size, the length:width ratio in pennate diatoms and the diameter in centrics, while always maintaining the normal outline of the valves; moreover, changes can involve pore openings and virgae, fibulae and anchorage structures.

In contrast, teratological forms, that can be induced by acute or chronic environmental stresses, do not have a genetic basis and are a consequence of alterations of the individual biochemical processes leading to valve formation. Diatom teratological forms usually have a deformed outline of the valve, a different striation pattern, loss of areolae and sometimes interruption of the raphe slit, all these modifications potentially altering cell movement and physiological mechanisms.

This chapter summarizes the results of the most important studies conducted on the morphological variability and teratological forms carried out from 1890 up to date, with the aim to provide a tentative attribution of the morphological variations to a series of environmental factors.

---

[*] Author for correspondence: Elisa Falasco
E-mail elisa.falasco@unito.it
phone number: +39 0116704520
fax number: +39 0116704508

In: Environmental and Agricultural Research Summaries …   ISBN: 978-1-63117-090-4
Editor: Lucille T. Cacioppo   © 2014 Nova Science Publishers, Inc.

Chapter 99

MARINE DIATOM COMMUNITIES: TAXONOMICAL VARIABILITY, PHYSIOLOGICAL PLASTICITY AND ROLE IN THE CARBON CYCLING AT COASTAL UPWELLING AREAS

Jesús M. Mercado, Soluna Salles and Dolores Cortés
Centro Oceanográfico de Málaga, Instituto Español de Oceanografía,
Puerto Pesquero Fuengirola, Málaga, Spain

RESEARCH SUMMARY

Diatoms dominate the phytoplankton communities in the most productive oceanic areas, i.e., coastal ecosystems and geostrophic front. Consequently, their contribution to marine primary productivity at global scale is estimated to be 30% to 40%. Furthermore, this group forms the basis of the food web that characterizes these regions and sustains the most important fisheries on the planet. Recent studies indicate that the diatom genome diversity could be the secret of its success and dominance in the oceans as this genomic potential would explain its high response capacity to sudden environmental changes. Accordingly, the high physiological plasticity of the diatoms has been demonstrated from laboratory studies. However, the studies demonstrating this acclimation capacity in natural assemblages are scarce. In the present report, diatom communities inhabiting the Alboran Sea (the westernmost basin in the Mediterranean) are characterized both taxonomically and physiologically by using data collected from different research surveys performed for the last 14 years. Four main type-communities dominated by diatoms were identified. The community 1 was co-dominated by *Thalassiosira*, *Chaetoceros*, *Nitzschia*, *Thalassionema* and *Leptocylindrus*. The community 2 was characterized by the dominance of *Pseudo-nitzschia* and *Chaetoceros*. The community 3 was clearly characterized by a high abundance of *Leptocylindrus* while the community 4 was dominated by *Chaetoceros* accompanied by *Leptocylindrus* and *Pseudo-nitzschia*. The analysis of the hydrological conditions indicates that the four communities grew at high nutrient concentrations. Besides, the communities 1 and 2 were isolated close to the lower limit of the mixed layer while the communities 3 and 4 grew in the surface layer, within the mixed layer. Consequently, the cells making up the communities 3 and 4 can be considered R-strategists. The physiological performance of the four communities was different. Thus, the differences in chlorophyll a specific absorption coefficients and primary productivity rates were significant statistically, especially between communities 3 and 4. These differences could be due partially to the higher S/V obtained for the community dominated by *Leptocylindrus*, which should improve its resource utilization rates per unit volume. However, these shape traits do not explain fully the photosynthetic performance of the two communities, suggesting that the differences could be a consequence of the taxonomical composition beyond the shape constraints.

In: Environmental and Agricultural Research Summaries ...   ISBN: 978-1-63117-090-4
Editor: Lucille T. Cacioppo   © 2014 Nova Science Publishers, Inc.

Chapter 100

A NOVEL DIATOM CLASSIFICATION METHOD BASED ON PATTERN TREES BY USING DIFFERENT MEMBERSHIP FUNCTIONS

Andreja Naumoski[*]

University "Ss. Cyril and Methodius", Faculty of Electrical Engineering
and Information Technologies, Skopje, Macedonia

RESEARCH SUMMARY

The diatoms are very useful bio-indicators of the environment. They are an indicator of wide range of physico-chemical parameters, like the water quality and the trophic status parameters of the ecosystem. According to this, they can be classified into one class of a certain abiotic parameter. Without a domain expert knowledge, by using classical statistical approaches such as canonical correspondence analysis (CCA) and principal component analysis (PCA), it is possible to find a model for a diatom-indicator relationship with a certain degree of prediction accuracy. Although these techniques provide very useful insights into data, they are limited in terms of interpretability. By using classical decision trees, an obvious progress in a direction of interpretability is made. However, decision trees have several drawbacks, namely they are not resistant to over fitting and are not robust to data change, which is one of the essential properties of the ecological data.

In order to overcome these drawbacks, in this chapter, a novel method for diatom classification is proposed. The method induces pattern trees by using several evenly fuzzy membership functions. In this chapter, novel fuzzy membership functions are proposed by modifying some existing ones, in order to make more accurate models. An intensive study of the influence of the fuzzy membership functions and the number of membership functions used per attribute on the classification accuracy is made. The experiments show that some of the proposed fuzzy membership functions have outperformed the trapezoidal, triangular and Gaussian membership functions.

---

[*] E-mail: andrejna@feit.ukim.edu.mk

Since the ecological preferences of the known diatom organisms present the relation between the diatom and the indicators (certain trophic state or water quality class), we have transformed the physico-chemical parameters into water quality and trophic state classes. Then, pattern trees based on the water quality and trophic state classes are induced in the same manner.

The method is fully automated and produces model trees, which can be further transformed into rules. These rules are verified by the existing ecological preferences for the known diatoms in the literature, and add new knowledge about the unknown diatoms. Some of the obtained model trees will be presented and discussed in the chapter.

The proposed method is compared against several classification methods like C4.5, Boosted C4.5, Bagging C4.5, k-Nearest Neighbour and etc. The results show that the proposed method obtained high accuracy for diatom classification, maintain compact model structure, is resistance to over fitting, robust to data change and produces easily interpreted models.

In: Environmental and Agricultural Research Summaries ...   ISBN: 978-1-63117-090-4
Editor: Lucille T. Cacioppo   © 2014 Nova Science Publishers, Inc.

Chapter 101

DIATOM FLORA OF LAKES, PONDS AND STREAMS OF KURIL ISLANDS

T. A. Grebennikova[*]

Pacific Institute of Geography FEB RAS, Vladivostok, Russia

RESEARCH SUMMARY

An analysis of diatoms of the fresh-water bodies (lakes, streams, hot springs) in islands of the North (Shiashkotan, Kharimkotan, Onekotan, Simushir, Matua), Middle (Ketoi, Rasshua) and South (Kunaschir, Iturup, Shikotan, Zelenyy, Tanfilyeva and Iuriy) Kuriles was carried out. In the water bodes studied, more than 500 taxons of diatoms were identified. The peculiarities of forming the diatoms associations in the multitype water bodies were considered and it was shown that the abundance of diatoms, their species composition and ecological structure of complexes were first of all related to local conditions of water bodies differing in the water structure, depth, mineralization, alkalinity and temperature.

---

[*] E-mail: tagrebennikova@mail.ru

In: Environmental and Agricultural Research Summaries ...   ISBN: 978-1-63117-090-4
Editor: Lucille T. Cacioppo   © 2014 Nova Science Publishers, Inc.

Chapter 102

RECONSTRUCTION OF PALAEO-ENVIRONMENTAL CHANGES BASED ON ECOLOGICAL INFORMATION OF DIATOMS IN SHALLOW MARINE SEDIMENTS: EXAMPLE OF A HOLOCENE DELTA SEQUENCE ON THE NOBI PLAIN, CENTRAL JAPAN

Yuichi Niwa, Yoshie Saegusa and Toshihiko Sugai
Department of Natural Environmental Studies, Graduate School of Frontier Science,
The University of Tokyo, Kashiwa, Chiba, Japan

RESEARCH SUMMARY

Ecological information about diatoms is useful for reconstruction of palaeo-environments influenced by marine transgression and regression. Each diatom has a different habitat, especially regarding salinity. In the coastal region, salinity changes occur controlled by marine transgression and regression. And, these salinity changes cause changes of diatom assemblages. If diatoms are in the sediments deposited under the influence of marine transgression and regression, reconstruction of palaeo-environmental changes based on ecological information of diatoms can be done.

We analyzed diatom assemblages from sediment cores from the Nobi Plain, central Japan. Five diatom assemblage zones were identified: (1) at the beginning of the Holocene, freshwater species were dominant; (2) then, marine and brackish-marine species increased, indicating transgression; (3) in the middle Holocene, proportions of marine and brackish-marine species became almost constant, with marine species dominant; (4) marine species began to be replaced by freshwater species, indicating marine regression as a result of delta progradation; and (5) freshwater species again became dominant.

These diatom assemblages correlate with previously defined lithological units: zone 1 and 2 with fluvial to coastal plain deposits, zone 3 with inner bay or prodelta deposits, zone 4 mainly with delta front slope deposits, and zone 5 with delta front platform deposits and delta plain and flood plain deposits. And, the percentage of marine diatom species is almost positively correlated with electrical conductivity (EC—which is considered to be a proxy of salinity, although there are the effects of compaction and grain size distribution), especially in inner bay deposits.

In summary, if there are many diatoms in sediments with good storage condition, we can directly reconstruct salinity with high accuracy. Thus, the ecology of diatoms is useful for reconstruction of palaeo-environmental changes, especially those controlled by marine transgression and regression.

In: Environmental and Agricultural Research Summaries ...   ISBN: 978-1-63117-090-4
Editor: Lucille T. Cacioppo   © 2014 Nova Science Publishers, Inc.

Chapter 103

ECOLOGICAL ROLE OF BENTHIC DIATOMS AS REGULATORS OF INVERTEBRATE PHYSIOLOGY AND BEHAVIOUR

Valerio Zupo[*] *and Chingoileima Maibam*
Stazione Zoologica Anton Dohrn. Functional and Evolutionary
Ecology Laboratory, Punta San Pietro, Ischia, Naples. Italy

RESEARCH SUMMARY

Diatoms play several ecological roles in the marine benthos as well as in the plankton. Some diatoms have a deterrent power against grazers as they produce toxic aldehydes and other compounds able to reduce the viability of planktonic copepod embryos. Correspondingly, diatoms of the genus *Cocconeis* and in particular *C. scutellum parva* and *C. neothumensis*, are able to selectively destroy the androgenic gland (AG) and the testis of the shrimp *Hippolyte inermis*, so determining its early sex reversal, in the field and in the laboratory. These effects are due to a specific apoptogenic activity affecting the shrimp's AG in a very narrow temporal window. Extracts of these diatoms also trigger the quick apoptosis of selected cancer cells. The still unknown active compound might have, therefore, interesting biotechnological applications. In addition, it was demonstrated that among the wound-activated compounds characterizing several benthic diatoms, also a large set of volatile organic compounds (VOC) exists. VOCs produced by *Cocconeis spp.* after wounding influence the behaviour of several benthic invertebrates, acting as a repellent or attractant according to the life strategy of individual species. In this chapter we review our knowledge about the "regulatory" influences of diatom metabolites on benthic invertebrates, discussing their role as both physiologic modulators and infochemicals.

---

[*] E-mail: vzupo@szn.it

In: Environmental and Agricultural Research Summaries …   ISBN: 978-1-63117-090-4
Editor: Lucille T. Cacioppo   © 2014 Nova Science Publishers, Inc.

Chapter 104

LIVING MARINE BENTHIC DIATOMS AS INDICATORS OF NUTRIENT ENRICHMENT: A CASE STUDY IN THE GULF OF TRIESTE

Tamara Cibic[1] and Oriana Blasutto[2]*

[1] Dipartimento di Oceanografia Biologica, Istituto Nazionale di Oceanografia e di
Geofisica Sperimentale, Trieste, Italy
[2] Regional Environmental Protection Agency- FVG, Palmanova, Udine, Italy

RESEARCH SUMMARY

Benthic diatom assemblages were studied to highlight their response to different nutrient concentrations. Three sublittoral sites of the Gulf of Trieste (Italy) were investigated: St. C1 (a marine sanctuary), St. AA1 (subjected to river flows) and St. Duct (nearby an underwater sewage duct). Nutrients were analysed in the overlying water. Benthic diatom abundance was estimated by microscopic analyses. Diversity indices were calculated and k-dominance curves were applied to abundance data. A cluster analysis on species was performed. Principal component analysis was computed on species abundance, nutrients and samplings. Fuzzy set theory was applied to obtain the degrees of membership between each species and each nutrient. St. Duct was characterised by ammonium (NH_4^+) and phosphate (PO_4^{3-}) enrichment. The highest richness and diversity were obtained at St. C1, whereas St. Duct was characterised by the highest dominance. *Navicula* and *Nitzschia* were the most abundant genera at all the investigated stations. *Paralia sulcata* was the most abundant benthic species at St. C1 and St. AA1 (8.2% and 20.0%, respectively), while at St. Duct *Navicula directa* was dominant (51% of the total abundance). The dendrogram separated five groups; one of these comprised only one species, i.e. the tychopelagic *Cylindrotheca closterium*. The fuzzy sets revealed a phosphate loving group which included, among others, *N. directa*, *Thalassiosira*

---

* Correspondence: Tamara Cibic,
Dipartimento di Oceanografia Biologica,
Istituto Nazionale di Oceanografia e di Geofisica Sperimentale,
Via A. Piccard 54, 34151 Trieste, Italy.
E-mail: tcibic@ogs.trieste.it

eccentrica, *Entomoneis alata* and *Nitzschia panduriformis*. The highly silicified *P. sulcata* showed the highest degree of membership with silicate, while the majority of *Nitzschia* species showed the highest ones with nitrite. *C. closterium* did not show high degree of membership with any of the nutrients, seeming to prefer oligotrophic conditions. In nutrient enrichment conditions, total abundance was high, but an enhanced dominance of a single species occurred, leading to a decrease in diversity. In oligotrophic conditions, when diatoms were limited by more than one nutrient, thus not providing a competitive advantage to any single species, high diversity was maintained. This study suggests that not only macrobenthos but also marine benthic diatoms can be useful indicators of nutrient enrichment, representing a potential and innovative tool in biomonitoring.

In: Environmental and Agricultural Research Summaries …   ISBN: 978-1-63117-090-4
Editor: Lucille T. Cacioppo   © 2014 Nova Science Publishers, Inc.

Chapter 105

PROBLEMS AND POTENTIALITIES OF USING DIATOMS AS PALEOCLIMATIC INDICATORS IN CENTRAL ARGENTINA

Gabriela S. Hassan[*], *Eleonor Tietze,*
Claudio G. De Francesco and Paula A. Cristini

CONICET - Instituto de Geología de Costas y del Cuaternario, Universidad Nacional de Mar del Plata, Mar del Plata, Buenos Aires, Argentina

RESEARCH SUMMARY

Paleoclimatologists advocate learning from the past to know the natural and anthropogenically induced climatic shifts that occurred in the history of the Earth, and to estimate future changes in ecological systems related to the projected range of temperature increases. Framed within this context, current rates of global warming are unprecedented based on the last 10,000 years of paleoclimatological evidence. Diatom analysis has played a major role in the reconstruction of these past climate changes, bringing evidences of water and air temperature fluctuations, as well as of climatically driven variations in water chemistry variables. Most of these evidences came from North American and European records, while the number of studies in South America has been considerably lower. Hence, many questions regarding the natural climatic cycles and the strength of human induced changes remain unanswered for vast regions of South America. In Central Argentina, the occurrence of many shallow lakes with sedimentary records encompassing the last 10,000 years, as well as outcropping alluvial sequences of Late Pleistocene and Holocene origin, provide good opportunities for studying these topics. Moreover, the diverse ranges of temperature and precipitation that characterize this region would allow studying the patterns of distribution of modern diatom assemblages against climatically driven environmental variables, as well as to assess the potential application of these modern datasets to the quantitative reconstruction of past climates. In this chapter, we analyze the problems and

---

[*] Corresponding author: E-mail: ghassan@conicet.gov.ar

potentialities regarding to the application of the modern diatom data to assess past climate changes in central Argentina. The main objective is to identify particular lines of research that need to be addressed in order to allow precise quantitative reconstructions of Holocene climatic changes in this region.

In: Environmental and Agricultural Research Summaries …   ISBN: 978-1-63117-090-4
Editor: Lucille T. Cacioppo   © 2014 Nova Science Publishers, Inc.

Chapter 106

PALEOECOLOGICAL SIGNIFICANCE OF DIATOMS IN ARGENTINEAN ESTUARIES: WHAT DO THEY TELL US ABOUT THE ENVIRONMENT?

Gabriela S. Hassan[*]

CONICET - Instituto de Geología de Costas y del Cuaternario,
Universidad Nacional de Mar del Plata,
Mar del Plata, Buenos Aires, Argentina

RESEARCH SUMMARY

Diatoms are an important and often dominant component of the microalgal assemblages in estuarine and shallow coastal environments. Given their ubiquity and strong relationship with the physical and chemical characteristics of their environment, they have been used to reconstruct paleoenvironmental changes in coastal settings worldwide. The quality of the inferences relies upon a deep knowledge on the relationship of modern diatom species and their ecological requirements, as well as on the taphonomic constrains that can be affecting their preservation in sediments. In Argentina, information on estuarine diatom ecology is scattered and fragmentary. Studies on estuarine diatoms from the 20th century have been mostly restricted to taxonomic descriptions of discrete assemblages. Given the lack of detailed studies on the distribution of modern diatoms in local estuarine environments and their relationship with the prevailing environmental conditions, most paleoenvironmental reconstructions were based on the ecological requirements of European diatoms. However, studies on diatom distribution along estuarine gradients from Argentina have increased in recent years, constituting a potential source of data for paleoecologists. In this chapter, the literature on modern estuarine diatoms from Argentina is revised in order to synthesize the available ecological information and to detect possible modern analogues for Quaternary diatom assemblages. The main objective is to build bridges between ecology and paleoecology, and to discuss the reaches and limitations of the different approaches to diatom-based paleoenvironmental reconstructions. Further studies exploring the relationship

---

[*] E-mail: ghassan@mdp.edu.ar

between estuarine diatom distribution and environmental characteristics are necessary in order to increase the precision of paleoenvironmental inferences in the region and to generate new hypothesis for further study.

In: Environmental and Agricultural Research Summaries …   ISBN: 978-1-63117-090-4
Editor: Lucille T. Cacioppo   © 2014 Nova Science Publishers, Inc.

Chapter 107

Bacilli, Green Algae, Diatoms and Red Blood Cells – How Nanobiotechnological Research Inspires Architecture

I. C. Gebeshuber[1,2,3,4,*], M. Aumayr[5], O. Hekele[1], R. Sommer[6], C. G. Goesselsberger[1], C. Gruenberger[1], P. Gruber[3,7], E. Borowan[7], A. Rosic[7] and F. Aumayr[1]

[1]Institut fuer Allgemeine Physik, Technische Universitaet Wien, Wien, Austria
[2]AC2T Austrian Center of Competence for Tribology,
Wiener Neustadt, Austria
[3]TU BIONIK - Center of Excellence Bionik / Biomimetics,
Technische Universität Wien, Wien, Austria
[4]Institute of Microengineering and Nanoelectronics, Universiti Kebangsaan Malaysia
[5]Krems University of Applied Sciences, Krems, Austria
[6]Institute of Hygiene and Applied Immunology, Water Hygiene,
Medical University Vienna, Vienna, Austria
[7]Institut fuer Architektur und Entwerfen, Technische Universitaet Wien, Wien, Austria

Research Summary

Biological processes, structures, functions and materials provide powerful inspiration for novel approaches in architecture. In this chapter, a variety of biological systems are introduced: *Bacillus subtilis*, the green alga *Euglena gracilis*, diatoms and red blood cells. Subsequently results of bionanotechnological research performed (by physicists) on these systems are presented. In the next step, the systems and the results are discussed with an architect, resulting in a multitude of ideas, possible approaches, experiments and projects. Such interdisciplinary access corroborates the power of collaboration across established fields in modern science and technology.

---

[*] Contact details: Email ille.gebeshuber@ukm.my, Phone +60 12 3929233, FAX +60 3 8925 0439.

In: Environmental and Agricultural Research Summaries …   ISBN: 978-1-63117-090-4
Editor: Lucille T. Cacioppo   © 2014 Nova Science Publishers, Inc.

Chapter 108

THE IMPORTANCE OF VIABLE BUT NON-CULTURABLE BACTERIA IN MONITORING MICROBIAL WATER QUALITY

Karina Yew-Hoong Gin and *Shin Giek Goh*

Department of Civil and Environmental Engineering,
Faculty of Engineering,
National University of Singapore, Singapore

RESEARCH SUMMARY

When bacteria are subject to environmental stresses, they are known to enter a physiological state where they maintain activity or viability, but are no longer culturable, i.e. the viable but non-culturable (VBNC) state. Since current standard methods of detection typically rely on culture based methods, the presence of these bacteria often goes undetected. Studies have shown that these bacteria can be resuscitated once the environmental stressors have been removed. In the case of pathogenic bacteria, infectivity can be revived leading to risk of infection when humans are exposed.

Bacteria such as *Escherichia coli* and enterococci are commonly used as fecal indicators to assess the quality and safety of waters. However, studies have shown that these bacteria can also enter the VBNC state, thereby questioning the reliability of the culture based measurement. In this chapter, a review of the VBNC phenomenon is presented, with attention to the factors inducing the VBNC state and the physiological and molecular changes in cells that result. Current methods for detection are discussed and evaluated, with specific reference to enterococcus as a target indicator. The difficulties and limitations of measuring VBNC in natural water environments are still challenges that need to be overcome. Nevertheless, the significance of VBNC cells on environmental monitoring should not be overlooked and their impact on modeling directions will be addressed.

---

* E-mail: ceeginyh@nus.edu.sg

In: Environmental and Agricultural Research Summaries …   ISBN: 978-1-63117-090-4
Editor: Lucille T. Cacioppo   © 2014 Nova Science Publishers, Inc.

Chapter 109

REGIONALIZING HYDROLOGICAL SOIL PROPERTIES IN THE BRAZILIAN CERRADO REGION USING A SEMANTIC IMPORT MODEL APPROACH

Monika Hofmann[1,*], Andreas Hoppe[1],
Joachim Karfunkel[2] and Allan Büchi[2]

[1]Institut für Angewandte Geowissenschaften, Technische Universität Darmstadt, Schnittspahnstr, Darmstadt, Germany
[2]Instituto de Geociências, Universidade Federal de Minas Gerais, Avenida Antônio Carlos, Belo Horizonte, MG, Brazil

RESEARCH SUMMARY

Hydrological soil properties are important input variables for various modeling purposes at catchment scale. Nevertheless, it is difficult to extract these data from standard soil maps since the focus of traditional soil classes are not only their physical and hydrological properties but also chemical parameters and their genesis. Thus, direct mapping of hydrological soil properties for each modeling purpose would be desirable but is often not feasible within restricted time budgets. Soil maps are usually based on analyzed soil profiles that are supplemented by local knowledge of soil-landscape interrelation. This soil-landscape knowledge implicit in the map is difficult to access since the mapping rules are often not explicitly stated. In this study, a transparent procedure combining explicit soil-landscape mapping rules for regionalizing hydrological soil properties is presented. First, field and literature information of local soil-landscape interrelation is visualized by means of typical catenas with the focus on hydrological soil classes. This information is then transferred into soft statements using normal language (e.g. deep permeable soil is typical for flat slopes on high topographic position). These statements are translated into optimality values ranging from 0 to 1 using a Semantic Import Model approach. The optimality values are used to define the typical position of soil properties in the landscape. The whole workflow is

* mb.hofmann@gmx.de.

integrated in a GIS environment that automatically generates hydrological soil property maps out of the combined statements. The derived maps are optimized taking into account all available data and a plausibility analysis based on local knowledge about soil-landscape interrelation. Thus, input statements and their combinations are modified in a recursive process until the output maps are in concordance with the internal soil-landscape model. Using this workflow, a case study of an area of 430 km² in the Brazilian cerrado region north of the city Belo Horizonte in Minas Gerais has been chosen. As a result, various maps of hydrological soil properties including effective field capacity, dominant flow processes (infiltration, subsurface storm flow, Hortonian or saturation excess surface flow) and weathering depth are created. These hydrological soil property maps can be later used for catchment hydrological modelling, prediction of linear erosion risk or groundwater vulnerability estimation. Since they are based on transparent mapping rules stored in a GIS environment, they can be adapted easily for specific input requirements of different watershed models and uptdated if new information is available.

In: Environmental and Agricultural Research Summaries …   ISBN: 978-1-63117-090-4
Editor: Lucille T. Cacioppo   © 2014 Nova Science Publishers, Inc.

Chapter 110

EPHEMERAL GULLY AND GULLY EROSION IN CULTIVATED LAND: A REVIEW

Antonina Capra [*]

Department of AGRARIA, Mediterranean University of Reggio Calabria,
Reggio Calabria, Italy

RESEARCH SUMMARY

Soil erosion has been recognized as the major cause of land degradation worldwide. The quantification of soil erosion is an important requirement for representing land degradation processes. One of the crucial points attracting an increased amount of attention in recent years is constituted by the possible discrimination of the different forms of soil erosion. In these contexts, relatively few studies have been conducted on channel erosion that still require improvement and elucidation, though most research and models proved to be very effective in providing useful information about surface erosion rates (rill-interrill).

Erosion due to concentrated flow is severe on many unprotected farm fields across different countries of the world. The presence of various gully types (ephemeral, permanent, etc.) can be observed in different land uses and climatic conditions.

The formation and development of channels, called ephemeral gullies, routinely obliterated by tillage and other farm operations, constitute a severe problem in many cultivated fields. In fact, crops are washed out by scour as these small gullies form, and the crops at the lower end of the gully are submerged by the sediments from the ephemeral gullies. These filling operations reduce the long-term productivity of farmlands. Ephemeral gullies rapidly evolve in permanent gullies and contribute to the catchment rill network formation. They constitute effective links for transferring the runoff and sediment from uplands to valley bottoms and contribute to the denudation processes. Ephemeral gullies may also generate new badlands and aggravate the off-site effects of water erosion.

The data available on gully erosion is scarce and usually restricted to small areas in which measurements are carried out over short time periods.

---

[*] E-mail: acapra@unirc.it

The objective of this paper is to review recent studies on the different aspects of gully erosion, which are:

- the morphological characteristics of gullies in comparison to the characteristics of other erosion channel types, including rills and streams;
- the contribution of the gully erosion to overall soil loss and sediment production;
- the analysis of some controlling factors;
- and the models currently available to predict gully erosion.

In: Environmental and Agricultural Research Summaries …   ISBN: 978-1-63117-090-4
Editor: Lucille T. Cacioppo   © 2014 Nova Science Publishers, Inc.

Chapter 111

PROTECTION AND MANAGEMENT
OF KARST WATER SOURCES CATCHMENTS

Nataša Ravbar[*]

Karst Research Institute at SRC SASA, Slovenia

RESEARCH SUMMARY

Among available drinking water resources, groundwater from karst aquifers is becoming more and more valuable for potable, irrigation and other agricultural and industrial use due to its abundance (high flow rate springs up to some tens of m^3/s) and relatively high quality of water. Due to the specific characteristics of karst aquifers (high flow velocities that may exceed several hundreds m/h, turbulent flow, heterogeneous infiltration and underground flow conditions) many important springs are improperly protected. As a key criterion for source protection the transfer time of groundwater flow or distance criteria are often used. However, these criteria are usually not appropriate for protection zoning in karst. In addition, protection zoning should consider hydrologic and hydrogeologic characterization of source and its drainage area. The purpose of this chapter is to present the concept of groundwater vulnerability as an alternative approach for source protection zoning in karst that has in some countries already been adopted by some national water-related policies. In many studies vulnerability assessment has been proved to be practical tool for protection zoning as it offers balance between groundwater protection and economic interests. The resulting maps are useful for practitioners and decision-makers dealing with the protection and management of karst groundwater. However, caution needs to be taken when selecting the appropriate method for vulnerability assessment and when interpreting the results.

---

[*] Email: natasa.ravbar@zrc-sazu.si

In: Environmental and Agricultural Research Summaries …   ISBN: 978-1-63117-090-4
Editor: Lucille T. Cacioppo   © 2014 Nova Science Publishers, Inc.

Chapter 112

DEVELOPING A SPATIAL SUPPORT SYSTEM FOR MONITORING OF WATER QUALITY OF RIVER ISUNWIN CATCHMENT IN OYO TOWN OF OYO STATE, NIGERIA

A. Adediji and I. Lasisi

Department of Geography,
Obafemi Awolowo University, Ife, Nigeria

RESEARCH SUMMARY

The problem of monitoring river water quality especially in the developing nation like Nigeria has been on for some decades now because of its huge capital requirement for instrumentation and setting up of state of art laboratory. Thus, there is the need to set up framework for surface water quality monitoring. In this regard, this study attempts to develop a spatial support system for monitoring the pollution level of urbanized catchment of River Isunwin in Oyo Town, Oyo State, Nigeria. The data used for this study were derived from IKONOS, SPOT 5 and Topo sheet covering the entire catechment area of River Isunwin. 20 water samples were also taken from 10 lcoation (2 samples per location) along the river channel with a view to determine both the physical and chemical quality of the river water. Generally, the data obtained were processed using Arc Gis 9.3 software.

Geospatial Water Pollution Information System (WPIS) was derived for the study basin and also tested by using spatial search to detect the inaccessible dump site within the study catchment. Also, the result of water quality parameters determined showed that the quality of water was low at most of the locations in the upstream and even in the downstream sections of the basin. Hence, the entroplication problem identified impact negatively on the river water quality.

In: Environmental and Agricultural Research Summaries ...   ISBN: 978-1-63117-090-4
Editor: Lucille T. Cacioppo   © 2014 Nova Science Publishers, Inc.

Chapter 113

THE RESPONSE OF PLANTS TO DROUGHT STRESS: THE ROLE OF DEHYDRINS, CHAPERONES, PROTEASES AND PROTEASE INHIBITORS IN MAINTAINING CELLULAR PROTEIN FUNCTION

I. Vaseva,[1] J. Sabotič,[2] J. Šuštar-Vozlič,[3] V. Meglič,[3] M. Kidrič,[2] K. Demirevska,[1] and L. Simova-Stoilova[1]*

[1]Department of Plant Stress Molecular Biology,
Institute of Plant Physiology and Genetics,
Bulgarian Academy of Sciences, Sofia, Bulgaria
[2]Department of Biotechnology, Jožef Stefan Institute, Ljubljana, Slovenia
[3]Crop and Seed Production Department,
Agricultural Institute of Slovenia, Ljubljana, Slovenia

RESEARCH SUMMARY

Abiotic stresses with a dehydration component (drought, salt, and freezing) involve, as a common feature, increased numbers of inactive proteins – denatured, aggregated or oxidatively damaged. Maintaining proteins in their functional conformation, preventing aggregation of non-native proteins, refolding of denatured proteins to their native conformation and removal of non-functional and potentially harmful polypeptides are all vital for cell survival under dehydration stress. To achieve this, plants respond to drought by synthesis of protective proteins such as dehydrins and chaperones and by degradation of irreversibly damaged proteins by proteases. Here we review the important cellular functions of dehydrins, chaperones, proteases and protease inhibitors, together with their role in the response to drought, that make them potential biochemical markers for assessing drought tolerance.

---

* Corresponding author, email: lsimova@mail.bg.

In: Environmental and Agricultural Research Summaries …   ISBN: 978-1-63117-090-4
Editor: Lucille T. Cacioppo   © 2014 Nova Science Publishers, Inc.

Chapter 114

PHYSIOLOGICAL AND MOLECULAR BASES OF DROUGHT TOLERANCE IN WHEAT (*TRITICUM* L.) GENOTYPES

J. A. Aliyev[*]

Institute of Botany, Azerbaijan National Academy
of Sciences, Baku AZ, Azerbaijan

RESEARCH SUMMARY

Several thousand wheat (*Triticum* L.) genotypes were grown in field conditions under normal water supply and a severe water deficit. *Triticum durum* L. genotypes distinguish by higher tolerances to water shortage than those of *Triticum aestivum* L. Under severe soil drought conditions during a period of the early spring tillering stage until the end of grain filling, grain yield and protein losses in numerous genotypes constitute within 25-65%. Ear photosynthesis plays a crucial role in crop accumulation and protein synthesis in grain. In tolerant to water stress genotypes, more than 60% of grain yield and protein synthesis is due to ear photosynthesis. Under dry conditions, the afternoon depression of leaf photosynthesis increased and the rate of dark respiration decreased. The rate of photosynthesis of 7- and 8-layered leaves in all genotypes in the evening, and especially in the morning hours, is higher. Photosynthetic rates of 7- and 8-layered leaves decreased greatly at the end of the milk ripeness and beginning of wax ripeness. Under the effect of drought and leaf aging, leaf area and accumulation of dry biomass shorten by more than half. After two weeks of drought, the intervarietal differences in photochemical activity, expressed in the higher reduction in extensive varieties in comparison with the intensive ones, are observed. Activities of Calvin cycle enzymes (phosphoglycerate kinase, NADP-glyceraldehyde dehydrogenase) decrease with strengthening of drought, especially in sensitive genotypes. Such a decline occurs more rapidly in the ear elements at the early stages of development of generative organs. Activity of enzymes of C_4 cycle (PEP-carboxylase, NAD- and NADP-malate dehydrogenase, aspartate aminotransferase) in C_3 plants under soil drought in leaves and ear elements increases

---

[*] E-mail:aliyev-j@botany-az.org

significantly and the pyruvate orthophosphate dikinase is activated. The correlation between the genetically determined tolerance of wheat genotypes and level of antioxidant enzymes activity was revealed. Fv/Fm ratio changes differently in various wheat genotypes during the growing season under drought. Plant architectonics and various photosynthetic traits are of essential importance in tolerance together with the root system and stress proteins controlled by certain genes. There is a correlation between tolerance of genotypes and overexpression of 60, 40.5 and 28-24.5 kDa proteins from the thylakoid membrane of wheat. 920 bp fragment was revealed in tolerant genotypes using RAPD markers P6 and P7, associated with drought tolerance. The gliadin and glutenin contents increased under drought conditions compared to a variant of optimal water supply, and maintenance of albumin and globulin proteins is reduced in all studied genotypes. Precise screening for drought tolerance of wheat genotypes using functional markers showed that the transcription factor genes *Dreb1*, that cis-regulate drought tolerance, are localized only on the third chromosome of A genome (3A) in 11 genotypes, whereas in the tolerant genotype Barakatli-95, these genes were revealed both in A and B genome.

In: Environmental and Agricultural Research Summaries ...   ISBN: 978-1-63117-090-4
Editor: Lucille T. Cacioppo   © 2014 Nova Science Publishers, Inc.

Chapter 115

EXPERIMENTAL METHODOLOGIES FOR CHARACTERIZATION OF IMPACTS OF DROUGHT ON SEASONAL AND ANNUAL TIMESCALES IN PORTUGUESE FORESTS

Abel Rodrigues[1] and Gabriel Pita[2]

[1] Unidade de Silvicultura e Produtos Florestais (Unit of Silviculture and Forest Products), INRB (IP), Quinta do Marquês, Oeiras, Portugal
[2] Instituto Superior Técnico (Technical University of Lisbon), IST, Lisboa, Portugal

RESEARCH SUMMARY

The increase in global average temperature, linked to climate change, at the surface of the globe in the twentieth century was 0.4 to 0.8 °C (IPCC, 2001). Particularly in Mediterranean regions the frequency and severity of droughts, worsened since the 70s due to the increase in atmospheric temperature and decreased precipitation. The drought of 2004 and 2005 was the worst in the Iberian Peninsula during the last 140 years, having been recorded, e.g., reductions in rainfall in the South of Portugal about 45% for long-term average of 1960-1990. Scenarios for climactic evolution in Portugal based on global scale models point out to air temperature increases of 3 °C to 7 °C and precipitation losses of 20% to 40% till the end of the century. Available scientific evidence indicates that forests interact with water resources over the full spectrum of timescales. The control of water use by forests is mainly determined by climate, soil water availability and physiological and aerodynamic factors. Of these, perhaps the best understood are the aerodynamic controls.

The role of forest ecosystems, especially in seasonally dry climates, is essential to the development of water and carbon cycles closely interlinked and contributive to the dynamics of climate change. Over the past 20 years, research on a global scale have been made to understand the influence of forest ecosystems in the various processes involved in the problems of drought such as the quantification of atmospheric evaporation, precipitation, water storage and runoff. The interaction of drought with other components of forest ecosystems such as carbon sequestration has also been addressed.

In Portugal, forests occupy an area of approximately 3,2 million ha. The three dominant species in the country are maritime pine, cork oak and eucalypt. For these species, quantifications of atmospheric water vapor fluxes and Penman-Monteith decoupling coefficients were made in plots located in central and southern Portugal by application of eddy covariance and aerodynamic methods. Studies of mass balances of rainfall interception by pine and eucalyptus canopies were also done. For the period 2002-2010 a case study of temporal evolution of carbon sequestration and efficiency of water use in an eucalypt site, is reported. In this site decreases of in annual gross primary production and carbon balance were *circa* 50% and 40% in 2005, when the effects of drought in 2004-2005 were more evident.

In: Environmental and Agricultural Research Summaries …   ISBN: 978-1-63117-090-4
Editor: Lucille T. Cacioppo   © 2014 Nova Science Publishers, Inc.

Chapter 116

DROUGHT AND ARTHROPOD PESTS OF CROPS

Allan T. Showler[*+]
Kika de la Garza Subtropical Agricultural Research Center,
USDA-ARS IFNRRU, Weslaco, Texas, US

RESEARCH SUMMARY

In addition to making otherwise arable regions less, or nonarable, from lack of life-sustaining water, water deficit also affects the extent to which crops are afflicted by arthropod pests. The effects of drought on host plant availability and nutritional value influence arthropod pests of crops in a variety of ways that can benefit or detract from crop production. In the arid Sahel region of Africa (roughly from Mauritania to Sudan), for example, the effect of variable rainfall is associated with desert locust, *Schistocerca gregaria* (Forskål), plagues that can devastate crop production from the Cape Verde Islands to India. Water deficit stress can also lead to host plant accumulations of proteins, carbohydrates, free amino acids, and other nutrients that favor insect growth and development, sometimes leading to outbreaks, as in the cases of bark beetles in forests, and accelerated insect infestation in field crops. Insects can also benefit from drought when dry conditions suppress or exclude predator and parasite populations that would otherwise help mediate populations of pests. Water deficit in host plants can be unfavorable to insect pests because decreased plant turgor hinders fluid uptake by plant-sucking arthropods, desiccation of insects exposed to ambient heat can occur, and increases in secondary defensive plant compounds (*e.g.*, phenolics) and lignification of plant tissues may render the plant unsuitable. Strategies to ameliorate drought-associated pest problems, including use of drought tolerant crop varieties, soil amendments to improve water retention, heightened surveillance, and the use of more efficient irrigation practices are discussed.

[*]Allan T. Showler, Ph.D., USDA-ARS IFNRRU, 2413 East Highway 83, Weslaco, Texas 78596 USA, (956) 969-4882 (phone), (956) 969-5024 (fax), allan.showler@ars.usda.gov
[+]Mention of trade names or commercial products in this publication is solely for the purpose of providing specific information and does not imply recommendations or endorsement by the U.S. Department of Agriculture.

In: Environmental and Agricultural Research Summaries …   ISBN: 978-1-63117-090-4
Editor: Lucille T. Cacioppo   © 2014 Nova Science Publishers, Inc.

Chapter 117

PLANT DROUGHT TOLERANCE: SOME GENETICS AND AGRONOMICS RELEVANT ASPECTS FOR BREEDING IN FORAGE SPECIES

Gerardo Tapia[*], Hernán Acuña and Luis Inostroza
Instituto de Investigaciones Agropecuarias,
INIA, Centro Regional de Investigación Quilamapu. Casilla, Chillán, Chile

RESEARCH SUMMARY

The agronomic effects of drought on forage species and grassland are related with productivity and pasture persistence. The water shortage produce a growth reduction caused by decreased turgor at cellular level, changes in membrane fluidity and composition, decrease of photosynthetic electron transport, changes in solute concentration and metabolism in general. Plants have developed several mechanisms for tolerate drought stress in additive action and synergy. They are the origin for morphological adaptations, which will give place to a stable acclimation for drought tolerance. In grasses, water stress produce decrease in leaf growth and the number of tillers, in white clover result in a severe reduction in stolon elongation. The roots architecture, mass and depth, for specie, in particular, can be determinant in its response to water stress. Reduction of soil water availability in pastures also produces changes in fertilizer use efficiency, nutritive value, incidence of pests and diseases, and grazing animals performance.

Morphological modifications reduce water loss which are associated to changes in leaf anatomy as presence of trichomes, decrease of leaf area or loss of any leaves, change in position respect to radiation, increase of cuticle thickness and decrease of stomatal density. Leaves can modify cuticle thickness or compositions thanks to a phenotypic plasticity given for regulation of cutin pathway biosynthesis and transport of lipidic component to a leaf surface.

---

[*] Corresponding author: gtapia@inia.cl

In this section the agronomical aspects of drought stress in forage plants are presented. The cuticle formation in plant is a matter revised specifically centered in the effect over drought tolerance and considered as a character for plant breeding selection. Additionally, advances in forage perennial legumes for increasing drought tolerance will be discussed and some results of the Forage Breeding Program of INIA-Chile will be presented as example.

In: Environmental and Agricultural Research Summaries ...   ISBN: 978-1-63117-090-4
Editor: Lucille T. Cacioppo   © 2014 Nova Science Publishers, Inc.

Chapter 118

THE IMPACTS OF EXTREME DROUGHT AND CLIMATE CHANGE ON PLANT POPULATION DYNAMICS AND EVOLUTION

Robert C. Godfree[1]

Centre for Australian National Biodiversity Research, CSIRO Plant Industry,
Canberra, ACT, Australia

RESEARCH SUMMARY

One of the key predictions of climate change is that, in some regions, droughts are likely to increase in frequency and severity. This will have significant implications for the long-term viability of plant populations, especially where water availability plays a key role in delineating species ranges. However, while drought and overall aridity are known to be strong determinants of plant species distributions at the landscape level, much less is known about the ways in which plant populations respond to changes in drought regime, or the long-term impacts that extreme droughts have on plant community composition, structure, and function. While it is known that drought can cause significant re-structuring of plant communities, relatively few studies have quantified the environmental and biological factors that promote plant survivorship under acute moisture stress, especially in topoedaphically heterogeneous landscapes. The capacity for evolution to rescue plant populations faced with increasingly severe drought from extinction is also poorly understood. This places severe restrictions on our ability to predict the impacts of climate change on plant populations in many environments worldwide.

In this paper I attempt to shed light on these questions by first providing a review of the evidence obtained from a range of different plant communities, and then by considering data from a semi-arid grassland ecosystem in south-eastern Australia in which the demographic responses of plant populations to extreme drought have recently been quantified. The results of this work suggest that populations of grassland plants may undergo rapid collapse when faced with prolonged, extreme drought, and that species persistence under such conditions can depend on the presence of small-scale topoedaphic refugia which reduce mortality and

---

[1] Email: Robert.Godfree@csiro.au; Tel: +61 2 6246 4956.

increase population fitness. The role of the seedbank also becomes critical if drought-induced mortality among established plants is high. I also provide new evidence that under severe drought, individual plant survivorship increasingly reflects local or micro-variation in soil moisture, with drought tolerance traits apparently being rendered effectively selection-neutral. Under such conditions, opportunities for the evolutionary rescue of stressed populations may be low.

Overall, the bulk of evidence suggests that, if faced with increased drought stress under climate change, many grassland populations, species and ecosystems will undergo rapid changes in size and distribution. However, the specific nature of these responses is likely to involve the complex interplay between drought severity, local variation in topography and soils, grazing pressure, atmospheric CO_2 concentration, and the capacity for evolutionary advance in drought-affected plant populations. Untangling these effects will continue to be a fruitful and exciting area of future research.

In: Environmental and Agricultural Research Summaries ...   ISBN: 978-1-63117-090-4
Editor: Lucille T. Cacioppo   © 2014 Nova Science Publishers, Inc.

Chapter 119

CHEMICAL COMPOSITION OF URBAN DUSTS IN SLOVENIA

Robert Šajn, Gorazd Žibret[*] and Jasminka Alijagić
Geological Survey of Slovenia, Ljubljana, Slovenia

RESEARCH SUMMARY

The chemical composition of urban dusts in Slovenia (Europe) is the topic of this contribution. Urban dusts are important substances in the environment because they can be an important pathway for toxic metals into the human body. The goal of this work is the presentation of the chemical composition of selected urban deposits (dusts) and their relation to spatial macrolocation (rural/urban environments), geological background, topsoil composition, dominant natural/anthropogenic factors and other influential factors. The evaluation was done on the basis of 83 sampling locations, where attic dust, household dust and topsoil were sampled. Twenty-three of them were placed in towns; others ware placed in natural environments in Slovenia.

In the work, distributions of 41 chemical elements were evaluated. According to the multivariate statistics, the dominant geochemical associations of elements were recognized. Their areal distribution in sampled materials across the countryside and larger towns in Slovenia was determined using the universal kriging method. The geochemical properties of household and attic dust were compared with topsoil and evaluated in terms of their elemental contents and correlation coefficients. The proportion of anthropogenic impact to toxic metal concentrations in urban sediments was assessed. As based on comparisons of household dust, attic dust and topsoil using the multivariate statistical method (factor and cluster analysis), four patterns of elemental distributions were established.

The two natural geochemical associations, Ti-V-Al-Th-Sc-Fe-Y-Nb-Co-Mn-La and Ba-Na-La, are mainly influenced by the weathering of crust or soil. The association Pb-Zn-Cd-Sb-Mo-Hg-Sn-Cu represents the chemical elements anthropogenically introduced into the environment. Distribution of this association represents the consequences of the influence of

---
[*]E-mail: gorazd.zibret@geo-zs.si; +386-1-2809-757.

Pb and Zn smelters in the past. High Hg is a consequence of centuries of lasting operation of the Idrija mercury mine and smelters and of military activities during the First World War, known as Soča (Insonzo) front line. The fourth association of Ni-Cr-Co is influenced by natural and anthropogenic factors. Distribution is mainly influenced by lithology, but it can also be attributed to the anthropogenic influence as a result of iron processing.

An alarming fact is that high contents of Cd, Cu, Hg, Pb, Sn and Hg were measured in household dust. These concentrations exceed their corresponding values in natural sediments by more than twenty times. The urban sediments, especially household dust, are substances to which the humans are exposed on a daily basis. Dust particles containing toxic metals can enter human organisms by being swallowed or inhaled. Several authors established significant associations between the heavy metal contents in household dust and concentrations in body liquids (blood, urine). Thereof direct hazards to population in Slovenia may be derived. High contents of toxic metals in urban dust are potentially dangerous, especially to children. Small infants are the most endangered group because of their higher intake of dust compared to adults and owing to their higher sensitivity to the influence of toxic metals.

In: Environmental and Agricultural Research Summaries …   ISBN: 978-1-63117-090-4
Editor: Lucille T. Cacioppo   © 2014 Nova Science Publishers, Inc.

Chapter 120

DISTRIBUTION OF HEAVY METALS IN ATTIC AND DEPOSITED DUST IN THE VICINITY OF COPPER ORE PROCESSING AND FERRONICKEL SMELTER PLANTS IN THE REPUBLIC OF MACEDONIA

Trajče Stafilov[1,], Robert Šajn[2], Biljana Balabanova[3]*
and Katerina Bačeva[1]

[1]Institute of Chemistry, Faculty of Science,
Sts. Cyril and Methodius University, Skopje, Macedonia
[2]Geological Survey of Slovenia, Ljubljana, Slovenia
[3]Faculty of Agriculture, Goce Delčev University, Štip, Macedonia

RESEARCH SUMMARY

A comprehensive monitoring was applied to assess the environmental pollution in the Republic of Macedonia. Large amounts of fine dust are generated during blasts and excavations of mining minerals and from highly technological industrial processes, whereas they are distributed in the air by the winds. For that issue characterization of heavy metals content in attic dust and total deposited matter was performed. The significant emission sources that contribute to atmospheric pollution with heavy metals on the territory of the Republic of Macedonia appear to be all mines and smelter plants. In one of the region three collection stations were placed for monthly monitoring of heavy metals content in total deposited dust is near a copper mine in the Radoviš region and the second location is in the vicinity of the smelter plant known for its ferronickel industrial activity in the Kavadarci region. In both locations two most affected villages and the nearest town was monitor within one year. Characterisation of contents showed higher content of heavy metals in deposited dust, which is due to distribution of fine particles from mine and smelter plant respectively, in air and their deposition in settlements in the close vicinity.

---

[*] E-mail: trajcest@pmf.ukim.mk.

Attic dust samples were also used in order to determine and monitor long-term air pollution with heavy metals around the copper mine and the ferronickel smelter plant. The total contents of about 20-40 elements were analysed by inductively coupled plasma - mass spectrometry (ICP-MS), inductively coupled plasma - atomic emission spectrometry (ICP-AES) and electrothermal atomic absorption spectrometry (ETAAS). Basic statistical methods and multivariate exploratory (factor and cluster analysis) techniques were applied for data processing. The results of the study of spatial distribution of different trace elements over these regions show some areas with critically high content of some elements. It was found that high contents of those anthropogenic elements are deposited in the close vicinity of the mine and the smelter plant.

In: Environmental and Agricultural Research Summaries ...   ISBN: 978-1-63117-090-4
Editor: Lucille T. Cacioppo   © 2014 Nova Science Publishers, Inc.

Chapter 121

METHODS FOR THE CHARACTERISATION AND CONTROL OF DUST IN MATERIALS HANDLING APPLICATIONS WITH A SPECIFIC FOCUS ON PASSIVE DUST CONTROL IN TRANSFER CHUTES

T. J. Donohue, C. A. Wheeler, A. W. Roberts, X. L. Chen and A. Katterfeld
TUNRA Bulk Solids, University of Newcastle, NSW, Australia

RESEARCH SUMMARY

Dust control is a widespread problem affecting the mining industry in Australia and most parts of the world where the mining of natural resources is taking place. Due to the ever increasing focus on the health and safety of personnel, as well as environmental concerns, the problem of dust control is certainly an important one that needs total attention. Within the mining industry, the majority of dust problems arise from the transportation of the material being mined. However there are also problems associated with product that is exposed to the environment during storage, such as in large stockpiles. In this chapter current technology is presented and discussed that addresses both the characterisation of dust and different avenues for classifying a material in terms of "dustiness". In addition, analysis techniques currently available for use in the design of materials handling equipment are also presented. The particular emphasis is on passive dust control measures with the focus on transfer chutes, as it is well known the transfer of material from one conveyor to another is a major cause of dust problems. The work presented herein includes a series of case studies that seek to highlight the challenges involved in the design of plant equipment to handle dusty materials.

In: Environmental and Agricultural Research Summaries ...   ISBN: 978-1-63117-090-4
Editor: Lucille T. Cacioppo   © 2014 Nova Science Publishers, Inc.

Chapter 122

BLOWING DUST AND DUST STORMS IN THE ARABIAN PENINSULA WITH PARTICULAR REFERENCE TO THE ARABIAN GULF

M. P. de Villiers
Weather Services International, Europe,
Birmingham, UK

RESEARCH SUMMARY

Dust lifted into the atmosphere can be carried far afield and, apart from disruption to human activities, can have serious and life threatening implications. The Arabian Peninsula is a major dust producing region. This chapter briefly discusses the health and environmental effects of dust storms and, in more detail, the dynamics and the two atmospheric mechanisms that cause dust storms and allow dust to be raised in suspension for prolonged periods in the atmosphere. Particular reference is made to blowing dust and dust storms during the summer and winter Shamals, as well as those caused by the Kaus wind, the less frequent Nashi wind and the usually short lived thunderstorm associated dust storm. Seasonal and diurnal distribution and frequency is discussed. Attention is drawn to the importance of numerical weather prediction models and a simple dust forecast index proposed. The latest advances in satellite imagery for dust detection are discussed and a dust storm forecasting methodology is presented.

In: Environmental and Agricultural Research Summaries …   ISBN: 978-1-63117-090-4
Editor: Lucille T. Cacioppo   © 2014 Nova Science Publishers, Inc.

Chapter 123

SOURCES OF DUST: THEIR CONTROL AND HAZARD IN KUWAIT

Adeeba Al-Hurban[*]

Earth & Environmental Sciences Dept.,
Faculty of Science, Kuwait University, State of Kuwait

RESEARCH SUMMARY

Dust and dust storms are always associated with widespread consequences, hazards and complications on the environment, public health, soil quality, economy … etc. Rates of dust fallout deposition on multiple large scale areas throughout the world significantly indicates the adverse effect of dust storms on the deposition of soil particles in arid and semi-arid areas. Soil erosion, sediment suspension and sediment deposition are considered to be the major processes that are involved in a dust storm and could contribute in a diversity of environmental hazards. Soil quality, particularly its fertility, can be directly affected by soil erosion due to the deterioration of its nutrient contents. Deflation of clay and silt particles by the wind action is the major contributor to the high sand content of soil. Suspended particles during a dust storm directly affect the atmospheric environmental quality and greatly reduce the visibility in some severe cases to less than 0.5meter, which results in traffic accidents and their consequent complications. Sediment deposition and sand approach results in considerable economics losses in the urban areas, different utilities' plants, field crops and cultivated areas, and disruption of communications. The factors playing a significant role in dust storms and dust fallout could be the environment type, geomorphology and relief differences.

[*] Tel: 0096524985951 / 7143; Fax: 0096524987143; E-mail: q8geo@hotmail.com or Adeeba@kuc01.kuniv.edu.kw

In: Environmental and Agricultural Research Summaries ...   ISBN: 978-1-63117-090-4
Editor: Lucille T. Cacioppo   © 2014 Nova Science Publishers, Inc.

Chapter 124

PHOTOCHEMICAL AND CLIMATE IMPLICATIONS OF AIRBORNE DUST

Jonathan E. Thompson

Department of Chemistry and Biochemistry,
Texas Tech University, Lubbock, Texas, US

RESEARCH SUMMARY

Airborne mineral dusts suspended in earth's atmosphere can have dramatic effects on climate, regional photochemistry and human life. In this chapter, both the direct and indirect climate forcing effects of dust will be discussed. Physical models for treating light scattering and absorption by dusts will be considered. Since dust absorbs light in the ultraviolet and blue portion of the electromagnetic spectrum, its presence can reduce actinic flux and alter atmospheric photochemistry. This phenomenon will be considered from the perspective of common atmospheric pollutant gases. Finally, the chemistry occurring at / on dust surfaces will be considered and their significance discussed.

In: Environmental and Agricultural Research Summaries ...   ISBN: 978-1-63117-090-4
Editor: Lucille T. Cacioppo   © 2014 Nova Science Publishers, Inc.

Chapter 125

DUST EXPLOSIONS: PROTECTION OF SILOS BY VENTING

Alberto Tascón[1] and Pedro J. Aguado[2]

[1]Departamento de Agricultura y Alimentación,
Universidad de La Rioja, Spain
[2]Departamento de Ingeniería y Ciencias Agrarias,
Universidad de León, Spain

RESEARCH SUMMARY

It is well-established that dust explosions represent a serious hazard in many process industries and silo facilities. Many catastrophic cases have been reported, and statistics show that the number of incidents per year is still significant. Venting is the most common protective measure used in silos in order to prevent the appearance of unacceptably high internal pressures. However, the installation of venting devices is not always simple, and technical complications frequently arise. Furthermore, the cost of protection by venting must be taken into account. Vent areas in silos should be large enough to prevent damaging overpressures, but not so large that the use of venting becomes impracticable. Thus, vent area sizing is a critical issue. To calculate vent area size, standards EN 14491 (2006) and NFPA 68 (2007) are commonly used in Europe and North America, respectively, but in certain situations, they are contradictory.

The aim of this study was to analyze dust explosion venting in silos by comparing the above venting standards and also conducting CFD simulations. The pressures and associated vent areas in these numerical simulations were compared to those contemplated in the standards. In addition, some calculations were carried out for venting devices with inertia. The simulated explosion pressures showed the expected trends for the associated vent areas and agreed reasonably well with the values contemplated in NFPA 68 (2007).

For low overpressure values, the differences were significant compared to those vent areas predicted by standard EN 14491 (2006). Numerical simulations could serve as a powerful tool for helping engineers to design explosion protection and calculate the structure of vented silos. However, the results of numerical simulations should be extrapolated with caution since they are absolutely dependent on the flow characteristics and the dust concentration of the initial dust cloud.

In: Environmental and Agricultural Research Summaries …   ISBN: 978-1-63117-090-4
Editor: Lucille T. Cacioppo   © 2014 Nova Science Publishers, Inc.

Chapter 126

CONTAMINATION OF DUST PARTICLES BY HEAVY METALS: THE ROLE OF SOURCES AND TRANSPORTATION PATHWAYS

Aurela Shtiza[1,] and Artan Tashko[2]*
[1]Katholieke Universiteit Leuven,
Geo-Institute, Heverlee, Belgium
[2]Universiteti Politeknik, Fakulteti Gjeologji-Miniera,
Tirana, Albania

RESEARCH SUMMARY

The dust composition due to the impact of industry and traffic in the some Albanian cities are subject of this investigation. 42 dust samples from the house lofts or green house gutters, where undisturbed dust deposition has occurred for a period of about 30 years, were investigated from the vicinity of three industrial sites (i.e. Burrel: a ferrochromium smelter; Elbasan: a metallurgical complex; Porto-Romano: a former chemical plant).

The characterization of the dust samples consisted in assessing the elemental and speciation analysis, by means of atomic absorption spectroscopy (AAS) and X-ray diffraction. The elemental concentration of the dust samples from these industrial sites, were compared with local background dust concentrations. The geochemical signature indicated that the contamination of dust by Cr, Fe, Ni, Co, Mn and to a lesser extent by Zn and Pb in the samples from the industrial sites (42 in total) is apparent when total concentrations are compared with the background values (three samples). The time these industrial sites have been active, played an important role in the geochemical signature of the dust accumulated, especially for chromium, iron, cobalt, nickel. An additional source dominated of aluminium, potassium, and sodium indicates that a natural source, not linked to the industrial processes, but most probably from pulverized clay-rich soils also contributes to the composition of the dust particles in the investigated sites. Additionally the composition of the dust indicates that the industrial activities

---

* E-mail address: aurela_shtiza@yahoo.com; Tel: +3216327797; Fax: +3216322980

are the main source of the contamination especially with the heavy metals. The composition of dust particles is ruled by the intensity of the industrial activity as confirmed by XRD and SEM-EDX, while the distribution is dominated from the prevailing winds. In the dust particles collected outside the ferrochromium smelter/stalk chimney, was seen that ferrochromium was the main species relating to the industrial activity, chromite and quartz were also detected most likely relating to the technological process use in the industrial plants as well as to its performance.

Maps for the spatial distribution show the spreading of the contaminants in relation to the pollution sources and the influence of the prevailing winds in transportation and deposition in distance from these investigated industrial sites. Although with a limited data set of samples, it is clear that the prevailing winds are the dominant factor in the transportation of the dust particles in distance from the industrial site.

Moreover, from the air contamination history, as recorded by the age of the dust samples it can be concluded that the air quality has been severely affected, mainly during the 1980's, due to the intensive industrial activity in these industrial sites. Knowing that the health related issues, due to the quality of air are strongly related to asthma, these studies might be an initial step in applying some on-site risk management measures minimise the dust release and to filter the gases and dusts released from these industrial sites. Obviously these conclusions may be useful in the long term health studies in these industrial sites as well as to determine and regulate the air quality in the Albanian cities.

In: Environmental and Agricultural Research Summaries ...   ISBN: 978-1-63117-090-4
Editor: Lucille T. Cacioppo   © 2014 Nova Science Publishers, Inc.

Chapter 127

ASSESSING THE QUALITY OF URBAN ENVIRONMENT BY THE ELEMENTAL CONCENTRATIONS OF FOLIAGE DUST

E. Simon[1], A. Vidic[2], M. Braun[3], I. Fábián[3] and B. Tóthmérész[1]

[1]Department of Ecology, University of Debrecen, Debrecen, Hungary
[2]Department of Conservation Biology, Vegetation Ecology
and Landscape Ecology, University of Vienna, Vienna, Austria
[3]Department of Inorganic and Analytical Chemistry,
University of Debrecen, Hungary

RESEARCH SUMMARY

The sources and pathways of dust play an important role for the global climate and biogeochemical cycles. In that context, the assessment of the elemental concentration of foliage dust elevated to an interesting topic of many scientific studies. Foliage dust may indicate heavy metal contamination and the source of contamination from atmospheric deposition in urban areas. Foliage dust contains heavy metals that may have harmful effects on human health; thus, elemental contents of foliage dust are useful to assess air pollution.

The concentrations of heavy metals in dust samples may vary across cities depending on the density of industrial activities. Our aim is to summarize the sources of dust and heavy metal concentration in dust samples. In a case study we demonstrated that dust is a useful indicator to assess the level of pollution in urban environment. We studied the elemental concentrations in foliage dust along an urbanization gradient in Vienna, Austria.

Samples were collected from urban, suburban and rural areas. We analyzed 10 metals in samples from all three areas: Al, As, Ba, Co, Cu, Fe, Pb, S, Sr and Zn. We found that the elemental concentrations of foliage dust were significantly higher in the urban area than in the rural area for aluminium, barium, iron, lead, phosphor and selenium. Urbanization changed significantly the elemental concentrations of foliage dust and the applied method proved itself as a useful way to monitor the environmental load.

In: Environmental and Agricultural Research Summaries …   ISBN: 978-1-63117-090-4
Editor: Lucille T. Cacioppo   © 2014 Nova Science Publishers, Inc.

Chapter 128

ECO-CITY AND GREEN COMMUNITY: THE EVOLUTION OF PLANNING THEORY AND PRACTICE

Zhenghong Tang and Ting Wei

Community and Regional Planning Program
University of Nebraska – Lincoln, Nebraska, US

RESEARCH SUMMARY

Introduction: The world has been significantly urbanized since the 1900s and world population has grown rapidly in the last century and will continue this trend in the future. Although population growth rate of developed countries is increasing relatively slowly, developing countries face multiple pressures from urban population growth, economic explosion, and land consumption at a terrifying rate. Rapid population growth, global economic expansion, and massive urbanization have caused an exponential growth in the volume of resources consumed and pollution created around the world. Yet, perversely, a significant portion of the growing urban population lives in low-quality communities with no running water, no electricity, no sanitation, no clean air, no health care, no shelter, no transit, no public space, and there are millions who are still living in life-threatening urban environments or unhealthy urban communities. Environmental decline continues to accelerate in many cities in the long-term. Many city dwellers are threatened by overwhelming pollution and unequal community. Since the 1970s, car-dependent development patterns have caused rapid urban sprawl whose effects on local communities include the unavoidably negative conversion of productive agricultural and ecologically fragile lands into built environments such as residential housing and auto-dominated commercial strips and highways. Urban sprawl significantly converts natural lands to built environment, and creates huge pressures on environmental protection, urban infrastructures, urban services, and social equality. Not only does urban sprawl lead to direct or indirect environmental degradation, but, more importantly, it can cause social problems such as racial segmentation and environmental injustice.

In the 21th century, urban planning is facing many challenges and opportunities. In general, rapid urban development and population growth have contributed greatly to serious environmental burdens. Our cities and communities are confronted with many unavoidable environmental and social problems including air pollution, environmental degradation, transportation congestion, health issues, global warming, environmental injustice, and social inequity. Our communities and cities, as mankind's habitat, caused major destruction of the natural environment when creating the living environment. Urban development threatens the ecosystem and human survival. Today's cities consume most of the world's energy and cause significant waste and pollution. Urbanized areas are the centers of production and consumption of most non-agricultural goods and materials. Cities are suffering endless pollution, waste, overcrowding, and inner-city decay (Girardet, 2004). While urban problems are defined broadly, it can be illustrated that urban environmental problems threaten present and future populations, by human-induced damage to the natural and built environments. The sources of urban environmental problems include: 1) localized community environmental problems generated by the community itself such as noise, indoor air pollution and household waste water; 2) urban-regional environmental problems that may mainly affect the city, such as river water quality; and 3) regional-strategic environmental burdens that have cross-boundary, long-term impacts, such as biodiversity, ecosystem, and climate change. As many environmental problems require community participation, an increasing number of voices are calling for more locally-driven environmental approaches. It is important to link Research Summary environmental problems with responsible local initiatives in a coherent fashion. In short, it would seem that helping cities to address the goals of eco-city and green community will contribute to sustainable development.

All these problems provide opportunities for planners to create and maintain healthy environments and natural systems while conserving energy, water, soils, and important natural resources and reducing waste and cleaning up pollution and brownfield sites. Some planners have made significant progress in infill development, transit-oriented development, and compact development. The principles of mixed-use commercial and residential development have been accepted in many cities around the world. Environmental justice has become an important concern in the siting of controversial land use projects. Urban planning has paid special attention to the protection of sensitive natural areas and the creation of open green spaces. In short, urban planning has become an important element in addressing environmental challenges.

Planning emerges out of a series of crises, such as health crises (e.g. diseases), social crises (e.g. riots), and other crises (e.g. hazards). In the 19th century urban public health became a focus of concern in the planning field. In 1876, Benjamin Ward Richardson published an important book "*Hygeia, City of Health.*" This book proposed that planning should address air pollution control, water quality purification, sewage treatment, public laundries, public health inspectors, and other important health issues. The concerns proposed in this book stimulated the Parks Movement in the 19th century which grew out of landscape architecture, garden design, and community design. It emphasized shifting planning from private to public settings. Frederick Law Olmsted, also a key person in the parks movement, designed numerous park projects including Prospect Park, Chicago's Riverside subdivision and World's Fair design, Buffalo's park system, the park near Niagara Falls, and the Boston park system. His works integrated "naturalistic" design or "organic" design and addressed social-psychological impacts. The milestone of the parks movement is Central Park created in

1857 in New York City. The parks movement is the original starting point of eco-city and green community. The goal of the parks movement was to separate transportation modes, support active and passive uses of urban lands, collect urban water, and promote moral pastimes. Many of those ideas are still important topics in current planning for eco-city and green community development.

The Garden City movement was an important element in the development of eco-city and green community. Many researchers believe that this movement was ad hoc, but the Garden City movement was indeed planned. The concepts and principles in this movement greatly influence the development of modern city planning which rapidly spread from Europe to the United States and other countries. Ebenezer Howard was the key person in the Garden City Movement which proposed three concepts: 1) town level with higher wages, many jobs and amusement; 2) country level with natural beauty, low rent, and good air quality; 3) town-country level with a combination of the above. He emphasized using greenbelts to separate the central city which would be an ideal, self-contained city within the core area and the surrounding greenbelt. This idea is widely used in many countries to discourage metropolitan sprawl and industrial centralization. In England, his Garden City ideas were implemented in two towns, Letchworth and Welwyn in the early 1990s. Currently hundreds of cities throughout the world claim to be garden cities. However, many of Howard's original Garden City ideas have failed to be implemented. Many residential homes have been developed in suburbs causing urban sprawl with local residents commuting to work from suburbs to downtown because local industries and businesses do not provide adequate job opportunities.

The sustainable development concept emerged in the 1980s. No event did more to push sustainable development into the mainstream of worldwide policy debates than the 1987 release of the report of the World Commission on Environment and Development, commonly known as the Brundtland Commission. The Bruntland report for the U.N. defines sustainable development as "*development that meets the needs of the present without compromising the ability of future generations to meet their own needs*" (The World Commission, 1987). The report succeeded remarkably well at calling global attention to the need for sustainable development and developing a common formulation of this concept. The second conference, held in Rio de Janeiro, in 1992, produced a lengthy declaration known as Agenda 21 that laid out sustainable development principles in many different areas. Moreover, it raised a point of "Local Agenda 21." This mandate for "Local Agenda 21" planning has stimulated a large number of local planning initiatives, especially in the U.S., Europe, and a number of developing nations. In the planning field, Philip Berke and Maria Conroy (2000) defined sustainable development as "... *a dynamic process in which communities anticipate and accommodate the needs of current and future generations in ways that reproduce and balance social, economic, and ecological systems, and link local actions to global concerns.*" Sustainable development emphasizes harmony with nature, livable built environment, and local-based economy. The dream of eco-city and green community has been included as a part of the sustainable development campaign.

The concept of eco-city and green community is different from traditional planning models since it incorporates important ecological principles in its design and functions. The idea and techniques of eco-city and green community can help communities understand how to become more sustainable by changing behaviors that contribute to resource utilization and conservation. Eco-city and green community can maximize the quality of life, minimize total lifecycle costs, and reduce transportation demand. The implementation of eco-city and green community covers urban structure, transportation systems, energy and material flows, and other socioeconomic sectors. Urban planning for eco-city or green community provides a general framework for understanding the urban function of the natural and built environment. Urban planners for eco-city or green community need to consider that the physical structure of the community is an interconnected system which includes land demands, land use types, urban growth boundaries, open spaces, and density. Transportation systems are a major factor in the development of eco-city and green community and cover physical and virtual movement of people, goods and data. Energy system has become an important concern in this campaign which addresses the movement or flow of energy and materials in the urban system. Last, the socioeconomic context includes human and economic activities that relate to urban growth.

Perhaps the eco-city and green community effort is not the only way to solve urban environmental problems; but it is probably one of the most likely ways to lead to a solution for a future sustainable society. The concept of eco-city and green community has been proposed as the backbone for sustainable development in the United Nations report of "Our Common Future" (1987). The idea of eco-city and green community addresses the core concept of sustainability and redefines wealth with natural capital such as clear air, fresh water, clean seas, and healthy ecosystems, etc. Eco-city and green community can provide future generations with a stock of natural and social capital which can exceed our own inheritance. Actually, cities and communities are the most appropriate places to implement sustainable development. At the same time, no place can receive more potent and beneficial rewards from the eco-campaigns than our cities and communities. Some researchers have proposed urban ecosystem ideas to treat urban development issues. Since the core of eco-city and green community is a healthy and ecologically friendly society, cities themselves must be viewed as integrated ecological systems that are also connected with regional and global ecosystems. The idea of eco-city and green community should inspire urban planners and policy makers to design urban related policies. It provides a fundamental approach to change city development patterns and thus eventually change human behaviors through collaborative efforts of governments and the private sectors. While governments implement the concepts of eco-city and green community, private developers, who build for purely commercial returns, can change their behaviors from pure commercial commitment to more responsible environmental and social commitment to citizens and the quality of life. Berke (2008) has pointed out that a collaborative, comprehensive, systematic approach is needed to develop eco-city and green community campaigns.

The History and Evolution of Eco-city and Green Community: This section illustrates the evolution of eco-city and green community. It first provides an overview of major planning theories and planning history to highlight research relating to the concept of eco-city and green community and present the definition of eco-city and its derivation. Although there is not a concrete definition of the terms "eco-city" or "green community", it still represents the goal – a direction for sustainable city development. The section then explores the historical development of the eco-city and green community. Major planning theories and historical achievements have laid the groundwork for sustainable urban form models. Understanding particular historical themes – which continue to be echoed today – is important in order to understand how cities and communities can become more sustainable in the future. Based on the historical overview and theoretical discussion, we have also reviewed urban models that can provide insights for eco-city and green community development. It continues to question the proper eco-city models, compares different physical urban forms models and classifies the qualities of the eco-city system model. This section offers insights into physical models which may be more sustainable for urban ecology, land conservation, and transport. In so doing, the linear metabolism city model, the compact city model, the macro-structure of alternative city models, and dense city models are explored. After comparing and contrasting these models, the dense city model was determined to be the appropriate model in many aspects. The concept of eco-city and green community dispels the widely held view that sustainable urban development is a key step for achieving long-term global sustainability.

In: Environmental and Agricultural Research Summaries ...   ISBN: 978-1-63117-090-4
Editor: Lucille T. Cacioppo   © 2014 Nova Science Publishers, Inc.

Chapter 129

MAKING ECO-CITIES A REALITY: SOME KEY DIMENSIONS FOR ECO-CITY DEVELOPMENT WITH BEST PRACTICE EXAMPLES

Jeffrey R. Kenworthy

Curtin University Sustainability Policy Institute,
Curtin University, Perth, Western Australia

RESEARCH SUMMARY

Making existing cities and new urban development more ecologically based and more livable is becoming an increasingly mainstream planning objective as cities try to fulfil their local, national and global responsibilities for greater sustainability. The pressures of global climate change and the sceptre of peaking world oil production are two powerful forces at work in cities today. But also at work are a host of other local imperatives to ensure greater ecological orientation in urban development and environmental improvements, better social development of the city and the need to maintain a good economic base for the city. This paper discusses ten critical responses to the issue of eco-city development by way of some useful examples of each response from some cities around the world. A previously developed simple conceptual model involving ten key planning and transport factors for more ecologically based urban development is used as the basis of the chapter. The ten factors cover (1) compact, mixed use urban form, (2) protection of the city's natural areas and food producing capacity, (3) priority to the development of superior public transport systems and conditions for non-motorised modes, with minimal road capacity increases, (4) environmental technologies aiming for closed loop physical systems, (5) well defined higher density, human-oriented centres, (6) a greatly enhanced public realm throughout the city, (7) sustainable urban design principles, (8) economic growth based on creativity and innovation, (9) vision-oriented rather than "predict and provide planning" and (10) decision making within a sustainability framework involving genuine public engagement. Each one of these pursuits is briefly summarised and illustrated with some examples of best practice from around the world.

In: Environmental and Agricultural Research Summaries ...   ISBN: 978-1-63117-090-4
Editor: Lucille T. Cacioppo   © 2014 Nova Science Publishers, Inc.

Chapter 130

COMPARISON OF PLANNING THE SUSTAINABLE ECO-CITY IN READING AND TAIPEI

Szu-Li Sun
University of Reading Business School, England

RESEARCH SUMMARY

Both Taipei City in Taiwan and Reading town in England have put significant efforts on policy-making and implementation aimed at developing a sustainable Eco-city. This paper aims to explore how the sustainable Eco-city policy was deployed and interpreted at a local city level in different contexts (political, cultural and economic), with particular emphasis on land use and transportation. The research strategy involves cross-national comparison. It discusses and compares the local and global contexts of the two empirical studies to help understand how sustainable eco-city policy is deployed at a local city level. It investigates the issues surrounding policy formulation, the structure of the planning process and the outcomes of over a decade of (variable) policy implementation.

The evaluation is based on a theoretical propositions of the sustainable eco-city concept with four principles (environment, futurity, equality and participation), developed from Szu-Li Sun's PhD thesis. It is used to investigate the evidence, although local interpretation of the principles is acknowledged and incorporated. In order to collect the evidence, the interviews in the two cases were conducted. As a result, the discussion will identify some of the vital factors which influence the planning process and outcomes.

In: Environmental and Agricultural Research Summaries ...   ISBN: 978-1-63117-090-4
Editor: Lucille T. Cacioppo   © 2014 Nova Science Publishers, Inc.

Chapter 131

PRESERVATION OR DEVELOPMENT – TDR AND THE APPLICABILITY TO URBAN GREENBELT OF SEOUL

Yunwoo Nam
Community and Regional Planning,
University of Nebraska, Lincoln, Nebraska, US

RESEARCH SUMMARY

Over the world, many cities are often faced with the challenge of trying to encourage the development and expansion of built-up areas, while, simultaneously protecting the historical resources and natural environment. The conflict between preservation and transition is a critical issue when considering eco-cities and sustainable development. This chapter responds to the growing interests in the encouragement of urban growth strategies that are sustainable environmentally and socially. Two programs, TDR and Greenbelt, are introduced and discussed.

One of innovative smart growth management tools used to reduce the conflicts between these seemingly incompatible objectives is called 'Transfer of Development Rights (TDR)'. This technique allows development rights, which are unused on one parcel of land to be separated from that parcel and transferred to another parcel. The TDR program can be used to achieve numerous land use goals ranging from growth management to the preservation of open space, historic landmarks, natural areas, and agricultural land. In American planning practice, a TDR program has been a useful tool to reduce the financial inequalities that stem from land use regulation and a compromise means of compensation to the landowners.

Another tool of urban growth management is known as 'Greenbelt' policy. The greenbelt is an urban containment strategy to designate areas of open space surrounding the rapidly growing city. It is designed as a growth management program against urban sprawl to direct the most development into existing urban areas inside the boundary and to preserve ecosystem. In an urban environment, a green space is crucial for the well-being of residents due to its diverse ecological functions, such as air pollution filtration and the biodiversity conservation.

In Korea, the greenbelt system was introduced in 1971, and has been a main target of arguments over environmental protection and urban development. The designation of the boundary lines was decided on political reasons, rather than as an outcome of environmental impact assessment or land use surveys. It also has compensation problems for the loss of individual property rights regulated by the government for the purpose of public interests.

The TDR principle may be applicable to other countries' situations, especially Seoul's greenbelt case. In principle, TDR creates a market oriented mechanism as an alternative to regulatory approach of zoning. It provides incentives for compliance. It motivates the conservation on private lands by compensating land owner's opportunity costs of sacrificing development. This chapter reviews the theory and practice of TDR, discusses the key factors of a successful program, and explores the potential for its use to conserve natural areas in Seoul metropolitan area.

This chapter mainly consists of two parts: introducing TDR as an innovative growth management program and the applicability of TDR approaches for Seoul's greenbelt case. In the first part, I review the American experiences of TDR from a theoretical perspective as well as a managerial perspective. In the second part, I review Seoul's greenbelt policy, discuss unexpected effects, and explore the potential of TDR applicability for environmental planning and open space preservation.

In: Environmental and Agricultural Research Summaries ...   ISBN: 978-1-63117-090-4
Editor: Lucille T. Cacioppo   © 2014 Nova Science Publishers, Inc.

Chapter 132

DESIGN THINKING: A POTENTIAL PLATFORM FOR THE 'REFLECTIVE PRACTITIONER AND PRACTICAL SCHOLAR' TO SPEAK?

Erin Bolton

Community and Regional Planning Program
University of Nebraska, Lincoln, Nebraska, US

RESEARCH SUMMARY

As a planning student, I am the proverbial child of two divorced, bickering parents – the planning academic and the planning practitioner. As a result of this separation, there appears to be conflict and confusion in planning.

In 2003, Fainstein et al. stated that the practical scholar and the reflective practitioner ought to at least be able to speak to one another. Well, just as David C. Perry suggested a spatial approach as "a mode of thought" for planners to "make space," I'm proposing design thinking not only as a "mode of thought," but one that provides common ground for both the practical scholar and the reflective practitioner to discuss, evaluate, and envision better, or more just and sustainable, cities. To do so, I note the desires of planning theorists in *Readings in Planning Theory* and show how design thinking satisfies, creates, or makes room for them. I feel this is important because perhaps if practitioners and theorists could talk and interact more efficiently, they may have a greater impact on important issues of sustainability (i.e. addressing inherent conflicts underlying sustainability outlined by Campbell in 1996).

In: Environmental and Agricultural Research Summaries …   ISBN: 978-1-63117-090-4
Editor: Lucille T. Cacioppo   © 2014 Nova Science Publishers, Inc.

Chapter 133

TRANSPORTATION FOR GREEN COMMUNITIES: WHAT ARE THE COUNTIES DOING?

Praveen K. Maghelal
Department of Public Administration,
University of North Texas, Texas, US

RESEARCH SUMMARY

The field of transportation and urban planning has been aware and interested in the objectives of creating green communities for about two decades now. Several policies and legislations have been enacted that directly or indirectly recommend transportation and urban planners to deal with the air pollution in their communities.The Clean Air Act (CAA) of 1990 recommended that Metropolitan Planning Organizations (MPOs) should attain the Air Quality standards through network-based models and appropriate land use planning. The Surface Transportation Act of 1991 required the MPOs to plan in consultation with other agencies and indicators to plan efficient travel by all modes. The Intermodal Surface Transportation Efficiency Act (ISTEA) of 1991, the Transportation Equity Act for the 21st Century (TEA-21) of 1998, and the Safe Accountable Flexible Efficient Transportation Equity Act: A Legacy for Users (SAFETEA-LU) of 2005 has build upon the growing need to address the need for a healthy green community. These Acts have focused on accommodating all modes to transportation and reducing the Vehicle Miles Traveled (VMT) by individuals through integrated Land Use Planning.

Although not directly linked to transportation, the issues of deteriorating urban (both environmental and community) health were noticed even before the 1990s. The Clean Air Act of 1955 and its subsequent amendments (CAAAs) have focused on reducing the significant impact of air pollution on the environmental and community health. The Clean Air Act of 1970 actually identified the automobile as a major contributor to the air pollution. Subsequently, the transportation planning agencies were called upon to meet the air quality goals with efficient land use planning.

The Primary reason for this integrated effort was the impact of air pollution on the environment and the individuals of the community. Transportation accounts for 24% of Green

House Gas Emissions and 55% of Nitrogen Oxide (NOx) (Bloomberg and Aggarwal, 2008). Reduction in these emissions can have direct impact on public health. Since the air pollutions is directly associated with the respiratory and other chronic diseases, efforts to reduce the air pollution is eminent. For example, the UN Intergovernmental Panel on Climate Change (IPCC) reports that it is important to deal with this issue because, it will "directly shape the health of populations such as education, health care, public health initiatives and infrastructure and economic development" (IPCC Report 4, pg. 48). Several urban and transportation planning approaches have been proposed in the past and recent years to deal with the issue of air pollution

In: Environmental and Agricultural Research Summaries ...   ISBN: 978-1-63117-090-4
Editor: Lucille T. Cacioppo   © 2014 Nova Science Publishers, Inc.

Chapter 134

GREEN URBAN PATTERN AND ENVIRONMENTAL DESIGN IN HONG KONG

Shaojing Tian
Community and Regional Planning Program
University of Nebraska, Lincoln, Nebraska, US

RESEARCH SUMMARY

More than half of the population in the world lives in urban area. Urban environment has experienced a rapid growth and influx of population, and borne the major function of the operation of society and economy. We witnessed the rapid development of East Asian cities including Hong Kong, Tokyo, and Shanghai. Among them, Hong Kong is the most iconic vertical city in the world with attractive ridgeline and collective skyline of skyscrapers as symbols of modern urbanism. As a harbor city, Hong Kong has grown from a colony trading port more than a hundred years ago to the world's leading financial and commercial center. Always being compared with New York City, Hong Kong is viewed as the place where many of the visionary ideas proposed by 1920's New York architects came true. Even today, Hong Kong has surpassed New York in terms of the number of high-rises, population density, and efficiency of public transit services. Besides the accomplishment it achieved in economic and social growth, as the most densely populated and concentrated city in the world, its urban form, land use pattern, and impact to the coastal ecological environment with its unique location merit further study and review on it.

In: Environmental and Agricultural Research Summaries … ISBN: 978-1-63117-090-4
Editor: Lucille T. Cacioppo © 2014 Nova Science Publishers, Inc.

Chapter 135

GREEN AGENDA IN INDIAN CONTEXT: REFLECTIONS FROM ECO-CITY EXPERIENCES IN PURI, INDIA

Akhilesh Surjan[*] and Prasanta Kumar Mohapatra[†]
United Nations University, Japan

RESEARCH SUMMARY

Urban growth in India is complimented by both perils and promises. 'Eco-City' and 'Green Community' largely remains alien concepts for Indian cities; however, there are some pilot efforts to steer attention on these notions. This paper begins with reviewing Indian policies and plans towards urban development and environmental improvement which may be considered as precursor to Eco-City ideas. Further, field realities from the city named Puri, which was selected to develop as Eco-City in the beginning of this century, have been summarized. A brief qualitative analysis of key issues and concerns of Puri city reflects that it stands as an ideal candidate city to be developed as Eco-City. The paper concludes that, institutional players although played important role to impose Eco-City principles while addressing Puri's concerns, but lacked long term vision and necessary support mechanism to translate Eco-City into a reality with earlier envisioned multiplier effect.

[*] Akhilesh Surjan is Lecturer in Global Change and Sustainability Program, United Nations University – Institute for Sustainability and Peace (UNU-ISP), 53-70, Jingumae 5-chome, Shibuya-ku, Tokyo, Japan. Email: akhilesh.surjan@yahoo.com
[†] Prasanta Kumar Mohapatra is Project Engineer, Orissa Water Supply and Sewerage Board, Water Works Road, Puri (Orissa), India. E-mail: prasant_mohapatra@hotmail.com

In: Environmental and Agricultural Research Summaries …   ISBN: 978-1-63117-090-4
Editor: Lucille T. Cacioppo   © 2014 Nova Science Publishers, Inc.

Chapter 136

INTERNATIONAL CASE STUDIES OF GREEN CITY AND URBAN SUSTAINABILITY

Ting Wei and Zhenghong Tang
Community and Regional Planning Program
University of Nebraska, Lincoln, Nebraska, US

RESEARCH SUMMARY

Many old cities have manifested a culture of sustainability from generation to generation. Historically, many traditional cities grew and prospered by having a sustainable supply of food and other products from the surrounding countryside. Some old China cities utilized waste matter as fertilizer for agricultural production which helped to maintain a self sustainable system. Medieval European cities such as Siena or Dinkelsbuehl, as well as many Asian cities, had concentric rings of market gardens, forests, orchards, farm and grazing land. In some areas this situation continues today. Mont-Saint-Michel is a typical early example of the "Dense City" model. Located in northern France, it has stable high density from center to boundary and a distribution of services and facilities throughout the whole city. It was a "walking city" with short distances making for intensive social interaction. That is, work places, living areas and public places or social places are near each other or overlapping. Such cities have high population densities which encourage a social mix and interaction, the major characteristic of traditional cities.

The story of Tokyo is equally as interesting so it will be useful to discuss it in some detail. It was originally called Edo; its history dates back to the 10th century BC. Novelist Eisuke Ishikawa has researched the Edo Period and describes it as a highly sustainable society. He found that when Edo was first established, great piles of rubbish disfigured it and created very unhealthy conditions. However by about 1790, the residents of Edo had created an extremely clean, hygienic and sanitary urban environment. Nevertheless, in the absence of mass production and consumption, the economy grew by only 0.3 per cent a year. The sustainable utilization of limited resources in a continuous circular system had become the norm with widespread reuse and recycling of waste materials. "End-of-life" goods were not discarded; instead, tens of thousands of specialized traders and craftsmen were engaged in their reuse and recycling. They repaired old pans, pots and kettles. Ceramic repairers glued broken pieces of pottery. Others fixed tubs, barrels, lanterns, locks, inkpads, wooden footwear, umbrellas or mirrors. There were some 4,000 old clothes dealers in the city. Candle wax buyers even collected candle drippings and made them into new candles. This exemplified another type of sustainable city.

Modern cities can learn a great from these traditional cities. For instance, the compact city form can learn from the Medieval European city. Edo city is somewhat similar to the linear metabolism city model. However, present day cities cannot simply import unchanged traditional experiences into the 21st century. Urban planners must select their most applicable forms to incorporate into modern theory to build more sustainable cities.

Presently, most cities in the world have realized the importance of sustainable development. Some have made significant progress in developing sustainability in their environmental plans, transportation, residential areas, health facilities and sustainable initiatives. Such examples include Curitiba (Brazil), Portland (USA), London, UK, and Wellington (New Zealand). This essay chose Curitiba, Brazil and London, UK, for the following case studies since both have used modern techniques in their own way to achieve some degree of sustainability. Their eco- systems will be evaluated in terms of the above-mentioned qualities.

In: Environmental and Agricultural Research Summaries ...   ISBN: 978-1-63117-090-4
Editor: Lucille T. Cacioppo   © 2014 Nova Science Publishers, Inc.

Chapter 137

ARTIFICIAL NEURAL NETWORK SIMULATION OF SPATIAL DISTRIBUTION OF ARTHROPODS: A MULTI-MODEL COMPARISON

WenJun Zhang[1,2] and *GuangHua Liu[3+]*
[1] Research Institute of Entomology, School of Life Sciences,
Sun Yat-sen University, Guangzhou, China
[2] International Academy of Ecology and Environmental Sciences, Hong Kong
[3] Guangdong AIB Polytech College, Guangzhou, China

RESEARCH SUMMARY

Probability distribution functions have been widely used to model the spatial distribution of arthropods. Aggregation types (i.e., randomly distributed, uniformly distributed, aggregately distributed, etc.) of arthropods can be detected based on probability distribution functions, but the abundance at given location is not able to be predicted by them. This study aimed to present an artificial neural network to simulate spatial distribution of arthropods. Response surface model and spline function were compared and evaluated against the neural network model for their simulation performance.

The results showed that the artificial neural network exhibited good simulation performance. Simulated spatial distribution was highly in accordant with the observed one. Overall the neural network performed better in the case of lower total abundance of arthropods. Response surface model could fit the spatial distribution of arthropods but the simulation performance was worse than neural network. Cross validation revealed that neural network performed better than response surface model and spline function in predicting spatial distribution of arthropods. Confidence interval of predicted abundance could be obtained using randomized submission of quadrate sequences in the neural network simulation. It is concluded that artificial neural network is a valuable model to simulate the spatial distribution of arthropods.

---

[*] Correspondence: zhwj@mail.sysu.edu.cn.
[+] Correspondence: ghliu@gdaib.edu.cn.

In: Environmental and Agricultural Research Summaries ...   ISBN: 978-1-63117-090-4
Editor: Lucille T. Cacioppo   © 2014 Nova Science Publishers, Inc.

Chapter 138

MULTISPECTRAL VEGETATION INDICES IN REMOTE SENSING: AN OVERVIEW

George P. Petropoulos[1,] * and Chariton Kalaitzidis[†,2]*

[1] Department of Natural Resources Development & Agricultural Engineering,
Agricultural University of Athens, Athens, Greece,
[2] Department of Geoinformation, Mediterranean Agronomic Insitute of Chania,
Alsyllio Agrokipiou, Crete, Greece

RESEARCH SUMMARY

Remote sensing has generally demonstrated a great potential in mapping spatial patterns of vegetation. By employing the amount of reflected radiation at particular regions of the electromagnetic spectrum, it is possible to make estimates on certain characteristic of vegetation. The use of radiometric vegetation indices is a fast and efficient method for vegetation monitoring, exploiting information acquired from remote sensing data. These indices are dimensionless radiometric measures that generally function as indicators of relative abundance and activity of green vegetation.

Throughout the years, a large number of multispectral vegetation indices have been formulated. Each has variable degree of efficiency in estimating one or more vegetation parameters such as, health status, nutrient or water deficiency, crop yield, vegetation cover fraction, leaf area index, absorbed photosynthetically active radiation, net primary production and above-ground biomass. Additionally some of them also consider atmospheric effects and/ or the soil background for an enhanced retrieval. The present chapter aims in providing an overview on the use of radiometric vegetation indices developed over the last few decades, utilizing spectral information acquired from multispectral optical remote sensing sensors. This overview is preceded an introduction to some important principles of remote sensing relevant to the vegetation spectral response is made available, as this was considered necessary to better understand the context of the present overview.

* Email: petropoulos.george@gmail.com
† Email: harry.kalaitzidis@gmail.com

In: Environmental and Agricultural Research Summaries …   ISBN: 978-1-63117-090-4
Editor: Lucille T. Cacioppo   © 2014 Nova Science Publishers, Inc.

Chapter 139

DEVELOPMENT OF A DECISION SUPPORT SYSTEM FOR THE ESTIMATION OF SURFACE WATER POLLUTION RISK FROM OLIVE MILL WASTE DISCHARGES

Anas Altartouri[1,*], Kalliope Pediaditi[2,3,†], George P. Petropoulos[2,4,≠], Dimitris Zianis[2,δ] and Nikos Boretos[5]

[1] School of Science and Technology, Aalto University, Lahti, Finland
[2] Department of Environmental Management,
Mediterranean Agronomic Institute Chania,
Alsyllion Agrokepion, Chania, Crete, Greece
[3] Ministry of Environment, Energy and Climate Change, Athens, Greece
[4] Department of Natural Resources Development & Agricultural Engineering,
Agricultural University of Athens, Athens, Greece
[5] Department of Information Systems and Technology,
Mediterranean Agronomic Institute Chania,
Alsyllion Agrokepion, Chania, Crete, Greece

RESEARCH SUMMARY

According to the Water Framework Directive (WFD, 2000/60/EC), Integrated River Basin Management Plans (RBMP) are required at different scales, in order to prevent amongst other things, water resource deterioration and ensure water pollution reduction. An integrated river basin management approach underpins a risk-based land management framework for all activities within a spatial land-use planning framework. To this end, a risk assessment methodology is required to identify water pollution hazards in order to set

* Email: anas.altartouri@aalto.fi
† Email: dzianis_2000@yahoo.com
≠ Email: kalliapediaditi@hotmail.com
δ Email: petropoulos.george@gmail.com

appropriate environmental objectives and in turn design suitable mitigation measures. Surface water pollution as a result of Olive Mill Waste (OMW) discharge is a serious hazard in the olive oil producing regions of the Mediterranean. However, there is no standardised method to assess the risk of water pollution from olive mill waste for any given river basin. The present chapter shows the results from a study conducted addressing the above issue by designing a detailed risk assessment methodology, which utilises GIS modelling to classify within a watershed individual sub-catchment risk of water pollution occurring from olive mill waste discharges. The chapter presents the proposed criteria and calculations required to estimate sub-catchment risk significance and comments on the methods potential for wider application. It combines elements from risk assessment frameworks, Multi Criteria Analysis (MCA), and Geographic Information Systems (GIS). MCA is used to aggregate different aspects and elements associated with this environmental problem, while GIS modeling tools helped in obtaining many criterion values and providing insight into how different objects interact in nature and how these interactions influence risk at the watershed level. The proposed method was trialed in the Keritis watershed in Crete, Greece and the results indicated that this method has the potential to be a useful guide to prioritise risk management actions and mitigation measures which can subsequently be incorporated in river basin management plans.

In: Environmental and Agricultural Research Summaries …   ISBN: 978-1-63117-090-4
Editor: Lucille T. Cacioppo   © 2014 Nova Science Publishers, Inc.

Chapter 140

ANALYSIS OF GREEN OAK LEAF ROLLER POPULATION DYNAMICS IN VARIOUS LOCATIONS

L. V. Nedorezov[*]

The Research Center for Interdisciplinary Environmental Cooperation (INENCO)
of Russian Academy of Sciences, Saint Petersburg, Russia

RESEARCH SUMMARY

Publication is devoted to the problem of population time series analysis with various discrete time models of population dynamics. Applications of various statistical criterions, which are normally used for determination of mathematical model parameters, are under the discussion. With a particular example on green oak leaf roller (Tortrix viridana L.) population fluctuations, which had been presented in publications by Rubtsov (1992), and Korzukhin and Semevskiy (1992) for three different locations in Europe, the possibilities of considering approach to the analysis of population dynamics are demonstrated. For approximations of empirical datasets the well-known models of population dynamics with a discrete time (Kostitzin model, Skellam model, Moran – Ricker model, Morris – Varley – Gradwell model, and discrete logistic model) were applied. For every model the final decision about the possibility to use the concrete model for approximation of datasets are based on analyses of deviations between theoretical (model) and empirical trajectories: the correspondence of distribution of deviations to Normal distribution with zero average was checked with Kolmogorov – Smirnov and Shapiro – Wilk tests, and existence/absence of serial correlation was determined with Durbin – Watson criteria. It was shown that for two experimental trajectories Kostitzin model and discrete logistic model give good approximations; it means that population dynamics can be explained as a result of influence of intra-population self-regulative mechanisms only. The third considering empirical trajectory needs in use more complicated mathematical models for fitting.

---

[*] E-mail address: l.v.nedorezov@gmail.com.

In: Environmental and Agricultural Research Summaries …   ISBN: 978-1-63117-090-4
Editor: Lucille T. Cacioppo   © 2014 Nova Science Publishers, Inc.

Chapter 141

INDIVIDUAL-BASED MODELLING
OF PLANKTONIC ORGANISMS

Daniela Cianelli,[1,2]* Marco Uttieri[1]* and Enrico Zambianchi[1]*
[1] Department of Environmental Sciences, University of Naples "Parthenope",
Centro Direzionale di Napoli Isola C4, Naples, Italy
[2] ISPRA – Institute for Environmental Research and Protection, Rome, Italy

RESEARCH SUMMARY

In the last decades, numerical modelling has gained increasing consensus in the scientific world, and particularly in the framework of behavioural and population ecology. Through numerical models it is possible to reconstruct what is observed in the environment or in the laboratory and to get a more in-depth comprehension of the factors regulating the phenomena under examination.

Numerous approaches have been developed in this framework, but probably one of the most promising is the individual-based modelling. With this type of approach it is relatively straightforward to investigate aspects related to the ecology of a population starting from the characterisation of processes taking place at the scale of the individual organism.

This contribution is intended to provide a general view of the main features of the individual-based models and of their peculiarities in comparison to other modelling strategies. Special emphasis will be given to applications in the field of phyto- and zooplankton ecology and behaviour, and results from the available literature on this topic will be used as examples.

In: Environmental and Agricultural Research Summaries ...   ISBN: 978-1-63117-090-4
Editor: Lucille T. Cacioppo   © 2014 Nova Science Publishers, Inc.

Chapter 142

THE EFFECTIVENESS OF ARTIFICIAL NEURAL NETWORKS IN MODELLING THE NUTRITIONAL ECOLOGY OF A BLOWFLY SPECIES

Michael J. Watts[1], Andre Bianconi[2*], Adriane Beatriz S. Serapiao[3], Jose S. Govone[3] and Claudio J. Von Zuben[2]

[1] School of Earth and Environmental Sciences, The University of Adelaide, Australia
[2] Departamento de Zoologia, Instituto de Biociências – Unesp – São Paulo State University, Rio Claro-SP, Brazil
[3] DEMAC – Unesp – São Paulo State University, Brazil

RESEARCH SUMMARY

The larval phase of most blowfly species is considered a critical developmental period in which intense limitation of feeding resources frequently occurs. Furthermore, such a period is characterised by complex ecological processes occurring at both individual and population levels. These processes have been analysed by means of traditional statistical techniques such as simple and multiple linear regression models. Nonetheless, it has been suggested that some important explanatory variables could well introduce non-linearity into the modelling of the nutritional ecology of blowflies. In this context, dynamic aspects of the life history of blowflies could be clarified and detailed by the deployment of machine learning approaches such as artificial neural networks (ANNs), which are mathematical tools widely applied to the resolution of complex problems. A distinguishing feature of neural network models is that their effective implementation is not precluded by the theoretical distribution of the data used. Therefore, the principal aim of this investigation was to use neural network models (namely multi-layer perceptrons and fuzzy neural networks) in order to ascertain whether these tools would be able to outperform a general quadratic model (that is, a second-order regression model with three predictor variables) in predicting pupal weight values (outputs) of experimental populations of Chrysomya megacephala (F.) (Diptera: Calliphoridae), using

* Email address: drebianconi@yahoo.com.br

initial larval density (number of larvae), amount of available food, and pupal size as input variables. These input variables may have generated non-linear variation in the output values, and fuzzy neural networks provided more accurate outcomes than the general quadratic model (i.e. the statistical model). The superiority of fuzzy neural networks over a regression-based statistical method does represent an important fact, because more accurate models may well clarify several intricate aspects regarding the nutritional ecology of blowflies. Additionally, the extraction of fuzzy rules from the fuzzy neural networks provided an easily comprehensible way of describing what the networks had learnt.

In: Environmental and Agricultural Research Summaries …   ISBN: 978-1-63117-090-4
Editor: Lucille T. Cacioppo   © 2014 Nova Science Publishers, Inc.

Chapter 143

Development and Utility of an Ecological-Based Decision-Support System for Managing Mixed Coniferous Forest Stands for Multiple Objectives

Peter F. Newton[1*]

[1] Canadian Wood Fibre Centre, Canadian Forest Service,
Natural Resources Canada, Sault Ste. Marie, Ontario, Canada

Research Summary

An ecological-based decision-support system and corresponding algorithmic analogue for managing natural black spruce (Picea mariana (Mill) BSP.) and jack pine (Pinus banksiana Lamb.) mixed stands was developed. The integrated hierarchical system consisted of six sequentially-linked estimation modules. The first module consisted of a key set of empirical yield-density relationships and theoretically-based functions derived from allometry and self-thinning theory that were used to describe overall stand dynamics including temporal size-density interrelationships and expected stand development trajectories. The second module was comprised of a Weibull-based parameter prediction equation system and an accompanying composite height-diameter function that were used to recover diameter and height distributions. The third module included a set of species-specific composite taper equations that were used to derive log product distributions and volumetric yields. The fourth module was composed of a set of species-specific allometric-based composite biomass equations that were used to estimate mass distributions and associated carbon-based equivalents for each above-ground component (bark, stem, branch and foliage). The fifth module incorporated a set of species-specific end-product and value equations that were used to predict chip and lumber volumes and associated monetary equivalents by sawmill type (stud and randomized length mill configurations). The sixth module encompassed a set of species-specific composite equations that were used to derive wood and log quality metrics

---

* Correspondence: peter.newton@nrcan.gc.ca

(specific gravity and mean maximum branch diameter, respectively). The stand dynamic and structural recovery modules were developed employing 382 stand-level measurements derived from 155 permanent and temporary sample plots situated throughout the central portion of the Canadian Boreal Forest Region, the taper and end-product modules were developed employing published results from taper and sawmill simulation studies, and the biomass and fibre attribute modules were developed using data from density control experiments.

The potential of the system in facilitating the transformative change towards the production of higher value end-products and a broader array of ecosystem services was exemplified by simultaneously contrasting the consequences of density management regimes involving commercial thinning treatments in terms of overall productivity, end-product yields, economic efficiency, and ecological impact. This integration of quantitative relationships derived from applied ecology, plant population biology and forest science into a common analytical platform, illustrates the synergy that can be realized through a multi-disciplinary approach to forest modeling.

In: Environmental and Agricultural Research Summaries ...   ISBN: 978-1-63117-090-4
Editor: Lucille T. Cacioppo   © 2014 Nova Science Publishers, Inc.

Chapter 144

ECOLOGICAL NICHE MODELS IN MEDITERRANEAN HERPETOLOGY: PAST, PRESENT AND FUTURE

A. Márcia Barbosa[1,2]*, Neftalí Sillero[3],
Fernando Martínez-Freiría[4] and Raimundo Real[5]

[1] 'Rui Nabeiro' Biodiversity Chair, CIBIO (Centro de Investigação em Biodiversidade
e Recursos Genéticos) – University of Évora, Évora, Portugal
[2] Department of Life Sciences, Imperial College London,
Silwood Park Campus, Ascot (Berkshire) UK
[3] CICGE (Centro de Investigação em Ciências Geo-Espaciais),
Faculty of Sciences, University of Porto, Porto, Portugal
[4] CIBIO (Centro de Investigação em Biodiversidade e Recursos Genéticos) – University
of Porto, Instituto de Ciências Agrárias de Vairão,
R. Padre Armando Quintas, Vairão, Portugal
[5] Biogeography, Diversity and Conservation Lab, Department of Animal Biology,
Faculty of Sciences, University of Málaga, Málaga, Spain

RESEARCH SUMMARY

We present a review of the concepts and methods associated to ecological niche modeling illustrated with the published works on amphibians and reptiles of the Mediterranean Basin, one of the world's biodiversity hotspots for conservation priorities. We start by introducing ecological niche models, analyzing the various concepts of niche and the modeling methods associated to each of them. We list some conceptual and practical steps that should be followed when modeling, and highlight the pitfalls that should be avoided. We then outline the history of ecological modeling of Mediterranean amphibians and reptiles, including a variety of aspects: identification of the ecological niche; detection of common distribution areas (chorotypes) and other biogeographical patterns; analysis and prediction of species richness patterns; analysis of the expansion of native and invasive species; integration of molecular data with spatial modeling; identification of contact zones between related taxa; assessment of species' conservation status; and prediction of future conservation problems, including the effects of global change. We conclude this review with a discussion of the research that still needs to be developed in this area.

In: Environmental and Agricultural Research Summaries …   ISBN: 978-1-63117-090-4
Editor: Lucille T. Cacioppo   © 2014 Nova Science Publishers, Inc.

Chapter 145

SOME ASPECTS OF PHYTOPLANKTON AND ECOSYSTEM MODELLING IN FRESHWATER AND MARINE ENVIRONMENTS: CONSIDERATION OF INDIRECT INTERACTIONS, AND THE IMPLICATIONS FOR INTERPRETING PAST AND FUTURE OVERALL ECOSYSTEM FUNCTIONING

V. Krivtsov[1,2] and C. F. Jago[1]*

[1] School of Ocean Sciences, Bangor University, Menai Bridge, Anglesey, UK
[2] Department of Ecology, Kharkov State University,
Kharkov, USSR (Ukraine)
School of Ocean Sciences, University of Wales, Bangor,
Marine Science Laboratories, Menai Bridge, Bangor, Gwynedd, UK

RESEARCH SUMMARY

Numerical techniques (e.g. correlation, multiple regression and factor analysis, path analysis, methods of network analysis, and, in particular, simulation modelling) may be very helpful in investigations of indirect relationships in aquatic ecosystems. Here we give a brief overview of some examples of the relevant studies, and focus on 1) a case study of a freshwater eutrophic lake, where statistical analysis of the datasets obtained within a comprehensive monitoring programme, and sensitivity analysis by a mathematical model 'Rostherne', helped to reveal the previously overlooked relationships between Si and P biogeochemical cycles coupled through the dynamics of primary producers, and 2) give an overview of how the coupling of physical, chemical, and biological processes in the marine ecosystem models offers a basis for investigations of indirect interactions in continental shelf

---

[*] Corresponding author. Present address: SBE, Institute for infrastructure and environment, Heriot-Watt University, Edinburgh EH14 4AS, UK.
E-mail: e96kri69@netscape.net.

seas. Complex aquatic ecosystem models provide a numerical simulation of biogeochemical fluxes underpinned by coupling physical forcing functions with definitions simulating biological and chemical processes, and offer a potential for quantitative interpretation of sediment proxies in the stratigraphic record. Combination of models and sediment proxies, calibrated by training sets, can provide information on water column structure, surface heating, mixing, and water depth, thus providing a basis for reconstruction of the past, and predicting the future environmental dynamics.

In: Environmental and Agricultural Research Summaries ...   ISBN: 978-1-63117-090-4
Editor: Lucille T. Cacioppo   © 2014 Nova Science Publishers, Inc.

Chapter 146

MODELING POPULATION DYNAMICS, DIVISION OF LABOR AND NUTRIENT ECONOMICS OF SOCIAL INSECT COLONIES

Thomas Schmickl[*] and Karl Crailsheim

Artificial Life Laboratory of the Department of Zoology
Karl-Franzens University Graz, Graz, Austria

RESEARCH SUMMARY

In the evolution of social insects, the colony and not the (often sterile) individual worker should be considered the major unit of selection. Thus, social insect colonies are considered to be 'super-organisms', which have – like all other organisms – to perform behaviors which affect their outside environment and which alter their own future internal status. The way these behaviors are coordinated is by means of communication, which is either direct or indirect and which involves information exchange either by transmitting signals or by exploiting cues. Therefore, social insect colonies perform information processing in a rather similar way as multicellular organisms do, where behaviors result from the exchange of information among their sub-modules (cells). In many cases, self-organization allows a colony to evaluate massive amounts of information in parallel and to decide about the colony's future behavioral responses. Many feedback systems that govern self-organization of workers have been investigated empirically and theoretically. Here, we discuss models which have been proposed to explain division of labor and task selection in social insects. We demonstrate how the collective regulation of labor in eusocial insect colonies is studied by means of top-down modeling and by bottom-up models, often analyzed with multi-agent computer simulations.

---
[*] Tel: +43 316 380 8759, Fax: +43 316 380 9875.

In: Environmental and Agricultural Research Summaries …   ISBN: 978-1-63117-090-4
Editor: Lucille T. Cacioppo   © 2014 Nova Science Publishers, Inc.

Chapter 147

OBSERVATION AND CONTROL IN DENSITY- AND FREQUENCY-DEPENDENT POPULATION MODELS

Manuel Gámez

Department of Statistics and Applied Mathematics
Almería University, Spain

RESEARCH SUMMARY

The paper is a review of a research line initiated two decades ago. At the beginning, the research was concentrated on basic qualitative properties of ecological and population-genetic models, such as observability and controllability. For population system, observability means that, e.g. from partial observation of the system (observing only certain indicator species), in principle the whole state process can be recovered. Recently, for different ecosystems, the so-called observer system (or state estimators), have been constructed that enables us to effectively estimate the whole state process from the observation. The methodology of observer design can be also applied to estimate unknown changes in ecological parameters of the system. Clearly, both observation (i.e. monitoring) and control are important issues in conservation ecology. For an ecological system, in an appropriate setting, controllability implies that a disturbed ecosystem can be steered beck to an equilibrium state by an abiotic human intervention. Recent research concerns the effective calculation of such control functions. While the considered ecological models are density-dependent, observability and controllability problems also naturally arise in frequency-dependent models of population genetics. As for the frequency-dependent case, observation systems typically occur in case of phenotypic observation of genetic processes; control systems can be used to model e.g. artificial selection. In this survey, in addition to the basic methodology and its applications, the recent developments of the field are also reported.

In: Environmental and Agricultural Research Summaries ...   ISBN: 978-1-63117-090-4
Editor: Lucille T. Cacioppo   © 2014 Nova Science Publishers, Inc.

Chapter 148

ENVIRONMENTAL NOISE AND NONLINEAR RELAXATION IN BIOLOGICAL SYSTEMS

B. Spagnolo[1]*, D. Valenti[1]°, S. Spezia[1], L. Curcio[2], N. Pizzolato[1],
A. A. Dubkov[3], A. Fiasconaro[1,4], D. Persano Adorno[1],
P. Lo Bue[5], E. Peri[5] and S. Colazza[5]

[1] Dipartimento di Fisica, Group of Interdisciplinary Physics
Università di Palermo and CNISM, Unità di Palermo, Palermo, Italy
[2] Dipartimento di Ingegneria Elettrica, Elettronica
e delle Telecomunicazioni, Palermo, Italy
[3] Radiophysics Department, Nizhniy Novgorod State University,
Nizhniy Novgorod, Russia
[4] Departamento de Fisica de la Materia Condensada,
Universidad de Zaragoza, Zaragoza, Spain
[5] Dipartimento di Scienze Entomologiche, Fitopatologiche,
Microbiologiche, Agrarie e Zootecniche, Università di Palermo,
Palermo, Italy

RESEARCH SUMMARY

We analyse the effects of environmental noise in three different biological systems:
(i) mating behavior of individuals of Nezara viridula (L.) (Heteroptera Pentatomidae);
(ii) polymer translocation in crowded solution; (iii) an ecosystem described by a Verhulst
model with a multiplicative Lévy noise. Specifically, we report on experiments on the
behavioral response of N. viridula individuals to sub-threshold deterministic signals in the
presence of noise. We analyze the insect response by directionality tests performed on a
group of male individuals at different noise intensities. The percentage of insects which react
to the sub-threshold signal shows a nonmonotonic behavior, characterized by the presence of
a maximum, for increasing values of the noise intensity. This is the signature of the non-

* E-mail address: bernardo.spagnolo@unipa.it
° E-mail address: davide.valenti@unipa.it

dynamical stochastic resonance phenomenon. By using a "hard" threshold model we find that the maximum of the signal-to-noise ratio occurs in the same range of noise intensity values for which the behavioral activation shows a maximum. In the second system, the noise driven translocation of short polymers in crowded solutions is analyzed. An improved version of the Rouse model for a flexible polymer has been adopted to mimic the molecular dynamics, by taking into account both the interactions between adjacent monomers and introducing a Lennard-Jones potential between non-adjacent beads. A bending recoil torque has also been included in our model. The polymer dynamics is simulated in a two-dimensional domain by numerically solving the Langevin equations of motion. Thermal fluctuations are taken into account by introducing a Gaussian uncorrelated noise. The mean first translocation time of the polymer center of inertia shows a minimum as a function of the frequency of the oscillating forcing field. In the third ecosystem, the transient dynamics of the Verhulst model perturbed by arbitrary non-Gaussian white noise is investigated. Based on the infinitely divisible distribution of the Lévy process we study the nonlinear relaxation of the population density for three cases of white non-Gaussian noise: (i) shot noise, (ii) noise with a probability density of increments expressed in terms of Gamma function, and (iii) Cauchy stable noise. We obtain exact results for the probability distribution of the population density in all cases, and for Cauchy stable noise the exact expression of the nonlinear relaxation time is derived. Moreover starting from an initial delta function distribution, we find a transition induced by the multiplicative Lévy noise from a trimodal probability distribution to a bimodal probability distribution in asymptotics. Finally we find a nonmonotonic behavior of the nonlinear relaxation time as a function of the Cauchy stable noise intensity.

In: Environmental and Agricultural Research Summaries …   ISBN: 978-1-63117-090-4
Editor: Lucille T. Cacioppo   © 2014 Nova Science Publishers, Inc.

Chapter 149

LANDSCAPE STRUCTURAL MODELING: A MULTIVARIATE CARTOGRAPHIC EXEGESIS

Alessandro Ferrarini

Department of Evolutionary and Functional Biology,
University of Parma, Parma, Italy

RESEARCH SUMMARY

Landscape modelling is founded on the idea that the patterning of landscape elements strongly influences ecological characteristics, thus the ability to quantify landscape structure is a prerequisite to the study of landscape function and change over time as well. For this reason, much emphasis has been placed until now on developing methods to quantify landscape structure.

Unfortunately, on one side landscape (i.e., landcover or landuse) and vegetation maps are very complex mosaics of thousands of patches, and this makes the interpretation of their structure very challenging. On the other side, methods developed so far to quantify landscape structure just return numerical results, that are not linked to cartographic outputs. Last, landscape pattern indices are numerous, and the need for a synthetic representation is more and more impelling.

I provide here the description and application of a novel approach to landscape structural modelling based on the combined use of GIS (Geographical Information Systems) and multivariate statistics. First, landscape structure of the study area (Ceno valley, Italy) is analyzed through 5 patch-based, non-redundant indicators (area, isolation, compactness, shape complexity, interspersion) with indirect link to functional aspects. Second, PCA (principal component analysis) is used in order to synthesize structural indicators, and cartographic output is given. Third, KCA (k-means cluster analysis) is applied in order to group landscape patches into homogeneous clusters, and again GIS output is supplied. Last, LDA (linear discriminant analysis) is employed to provide evidence for the differences among clusters.

This modelling approach provides the chance for a deep and cost-effective exegesis of landscape structure, with promising consequences on conjecture formulation about functional aspects as well.

In: Environmental and Agricultural Research Summaries ...   ISBN: 978-1-63117-090-4
Editor: Lucille T. Cacioppo   © 2014 Nova Science Publishers, Inc.

Chapter 150

BASIC CONCEPTS FOR MODELLING IN DIFFERENT AND COMPLEMENTARY ECOLOGICAL FIELDS: PLANTS CANOPIES CONSERVATION, THERMAL EFFICIENCY IN BUILDINGS AND WIND ENERGY PRODUCING

Mohamed Habib Sellami
Laboratory of Thermal Radiation, Department of Physics,
Faculty of Science Tunis, University Tunis El Manar, Tunisia

RESEARCH SUMMARY

Our days, the climatic change, manifested by strong and brutal precipitation, violent wind and long drought, has as direct consequence to damage the plant canopies (forests, sylviculture, oasis, pastoral lands and agricultural fields) so menacing the human feeding either from plants or animals (caprine, ovine, bovine, cameline..), exhausting the water resources, increasing the need for energy in buildings used for all activities (industrial, agricultural and services). Which solution the ecological modelling is capable to participate with, at short and long dated, in order to buffer the climatic change effect and to assume the need of food and clean energy for human? In this chapter we will present the basic concepts to model the plant architecture (species, densities, positions and orientation) the most adaptable to the sudden calamity, the energy use efficiency in building (material of construction, isolation system, organisation of accessories and apparatus), and the produce of clean energy from the wind velocity (founding wind sources and evaluating regional wind potential offshore and inshore, conceptualising wind turbine and testing their efficiencies)

In: Environmental and Agricultural Research Summaries …   ISBN: 978-1-63117-090-4
Editor: Lucille T. Cacioppo   © 2014 Nova Science Publishers, Inc.

Chapter 151

BIOAVAILABILITY AND RISK ASSESSMENT OF ARSENIC IN HOMEGROWN VEGETABLES

Emese Sipter[1] and Gabriella Máthé-Gáspár[2]*

[1]Semmelweis University, Department of Labor and Environmental Health,
Budapest, Hungary
[2]Research Institute for Soil Science and Agricultural Chemistry of the Hungarian
Academy of Sciences, Budapest, Hungary

RESEARCH SUMMARY

Mining and mining activities are the major source of metal pollution. In most cases the main pollutants are cadmium, lead, mercury, copper and arsenic. The main exposure pathways of these toxic metals are the soil ingestion and ingestion of homegrown vegetables. Risk assessment of arsenic and toxic metals are often based on total or pseudo-total soil concentrations and does not take the bioavailability into account.

Previous studies suggest that soil metals are not always as well absorbed as soluble forms, therefore use of default data are overestimate the real hazard. However these data are differed, using various phytoextraction tests or in vivo studies are found in the literature, but other pot or field experiments also found differences in accumulating capacity of vegetables. The calculation processes of human health risk also should be modified for better approach.

Using of plant concentrations or extractable metal concentrations in new equations can refine the human health risk assessment of arsenic.

---

* Email: esipter@mail.bme.hu

In: Environmental and Agricultural Research Summaries …   ISBN: 978-1-63117-090-4
Editor: Lucille T. Cacioppo   © 2014 Nova Science Publishers, Inc.

Chapter 152

EFFECTS AND AFTER-EFFECTS OF 20 YEARS OF REDUCED TILLAGE PRACTICES ON SOIL PROPERTIES AND CROP PERFORMANCE IN THE SEMI-ARID SUBTROPICS IN AUSTRALIA

B. J. Radford[*] and C. M. Thornton

Queensland Department of Environment and Resource Management,
Queensland, Australia

RESEARCH SUMMARY

A long-term tillage experiment was designed to assess the effect of tillage frequency and intensity on rainfed grain production and quality in the semi-arid subtropical environment of central Queensland, Australia. There were four tillage treatments: traditional tillage (TT), stubble mulch tillage (SM), reduced tillage (RT) and no till (NT), each with and without applied fertiliser (N+Zn). On completion, after 20 years of treatment application, all treatments were managed using no till and appropriate fertiliser (N+Zn) application for a further 5 years.

During the 20 years when tillage treatments were being applied, the reduced tillage treatments (NT, RT and SM) outyielded TT in fewer than half of the 22 crops grown. Mean yields without fertiliser were 2.0 t/ha (TT) and 2.6 t/ha (NT) while mean yields with fertiliser were 1.9 t/ha (TT) and 2.9 t/ha (NT). During the subsequent 5 years of no till with fertiliser, the former reduced tillage treatments outyielded the former TT in each of the 5 crops grown. For example, the long-term NT gave an average yield of 3.3 t/ha while the short-term NT, which was formerly TT, produced only 2.1 t/ha - a 57% yield increase. This increase was due to both increased soil water storage and higher water use efficiency (WUE). Both were attributed to the development of improved soil structure, higher population densities of soil macrofauna and slightly higher soil organic carbon content. High WUE in NT was also attributed to a beneficial effect resulting from slow early growth under no till. Results indicate

---

[*] Corresponding author: Email: bruce.radford@derm.qld.gov.au.

it takes at least 20 years to attain the full soil benefits (physical, chemical and biological) of a no-till system. The large yield responses from the three reduced tillage treatments, during and after treatment application, were realised in part because cropping frequency exceeded the appropriate level for traditional tillage. Increased cropping frequency also results in higher levels of groundcover, which reduces soil erosion and creates a more sustainable farming system. A high-yielding, viable cropping system can also contribute towards environmental sustainability by reducing the need for further land clearing.

In: Environmental and Agricultural Research Summaries ...   ISBN: 978-1-63117-090-4
Editor: Lucille T. Cacioppo   © 2014 Nova Science Publishers, Inc.

Chapter 153

VARIABILITY AND ECOLOGICAL SIGNIFICANCES OF SECONDARY METABOLITES IN TERRESTRIAL BIOSYSTEMS

Nabil Semmar[1, 2], Saïd Nouira[1] and Muhammad Farman[3]*

[1]ISSBAT, Institut Supérieur des Sciences Biologiques Appliquées de Tunis, Tunisia
[2]Laboratory of Clinical Pharmacology, Medical School of Marseilles, Marseilles, France
[3]Department of Chemistry, Quaid-i-Azam University, Islamabad, Pakistan

RESEARCH SUMMARY

Since plants are immobile, they must put up with the conditions in which they find themselves. Therefore, to maximize the acquisition of the basic resources, plants have evolved elaborate mechanisms capable of detecting incoming physical, chemical and biological signals. For that, Secondary metabolites (SMs) represent a vast catalogue of plant compounds characterized by very diversified physico-chemical and biological activities. They are believed to aid plant fitness by preventing herbivory and pathogen attack, attracting symbiotic micro-organisms, limiting diverse physico-chemical stresses, as well as aiding reproduction through providing pollinator attraction as either floral scent or coloration. Therefore, their chemical analyses in different plant organs can provide precious information for surveying ecosystems. Providing such information consists in correlating spatial and/or temporal variations in absolute or relative amounts of secondary metabolites with plant physiological states, biological interaction signals, or responses to different abiotic factors. For example, (i) the presence-absence of SMs help to elucidate induction factors. Moreover, (ii) continuous variations in amounts of SMs can help to detect ecological gradients representing complex phenomena that are not easily measurable. (iii) Variations in ratio between SMs allow to identify different metabolic profiles in relation to different environmental conditions, etc. (iiii) Beyond the static aspect of these variations, temporal

---

* Email: nabilsemmar@yahoo.fr.

changes of these phytochemical responses can provide important information on dynamic or rhythmic processes that manage the biological interactions between species.

In: Environmental and Agricultural Research Summaries …   ISBN: 978-1-63117-090-4
Editor: Lucille T. Cacioppo   © 2014 Nova Science Publishers, Inc.

Chapter 154

PESTICIDES: A BOON OR THREAT TO FERTILE AGRICULTURAL LANDS

Vandita Sinha[*]*, Vartika Rai and P. K. Tandon*
Department of Botany, University of Lucknow
Lucknow, Uttar Pradesh, India

RESEARCH SUMMARY

Modern farming is based on many chemicals to produce and preserve large quantity of high-quality food. Fertilizers, pesticides, cleaners and crop preservatives are the major categories which are now abundantly used in agriculture for increasing production. But, each of these chemicals poses a hazard. Like most of the pesticides are degraded very slowly by atmospheric and biological factors leading to the development of resistant strains of pests, contamination of environment and food chain and thereby causing serious ecological imbalance. However, in many countries range of pesticides has been banned or withdrawn for health or environmental reasons; even though their residues are detected till date in the various kinds of materials like food grains, fodder, milk, etc. The majority of chemical insecticides consist of an active ingredient (the actual poison) and a variety of additives, which improve efficacy of its application and action. All these formulations degrade over time. The chemical by-products that form as the pesticide deteriorates can be even more toxic than the original product.

Often stockpiles of pesticides are poorly stored and toxic chemicals leak into the environment, turning potentially fertile soil into hazardous waste. Once pesticides enter soil, it spread at rates that depend on the type of soil and pesticides, moisture and organic matter content of the soil and other factors. A relatively small amount of spilled pesticides can therefore create a much larger volume of contaminated soil. The International Code of Conduct on the Distribution and Use of Pesticides states that packaging or repackaging of pesticides should be done only on licensed premises where staff is adequately protected against toxic hazards. Now many agencies come forward to prevent the contamination and

---

[*] Email: sinha_vandita@yahoo.com

accumulation of pesticide in the environment. For example FAO has issued the International Code of Conduct on the Distribution and Use of Pesticides. In addition, the organization works to improve pesticide regulation and management in developing countries. In order to prevent accumulation of pesticides, WHO works to raise awareness among regulatory authorities and helps to ensure that good regulatory and management systems for health sector pesticides are in place. UNIDO is supporting cleaner and safer pesticide production with moves towards less hazardous products based on botanical or biological agents. Wider use of these products will result in reductions in the imported chemicals that contribute to obsolete pesticide stockpiles. The World Bank has established a binding safeguard policy on pest management which stipulates that its financed projects involving pest management follow an IPM approach.

In: Environmental and Agricultural Research Summaries ...   ISBN: 978-1-63117-090-4
Editor: Lucille T. Cacioppo   © 2014 Nova Science Publishers, Inc.

Chapter 155

A REVIEW OF AMENDMENT-ENHANCED PHYTOEXTRACTION OF SOIL CONTAMINANTS

A. Johnson[*] and N. Singhal

Department of Civil and Environmental Engineering,
University of Auckland, Auckland, New Zealand

RESEARCH SUMMARY

Organic and metallic contaminants can accumulate in soils where they may remain strongly bound to mineral and organic matter, limiting their removal. Phytoextraction is the use of plants to mobilise, capture and take up contaminants from soil. Plant roots, driven by transpiration, draw in water and dissolved substances that can be transported to the aerial biomass, forming the basis for a natural remediation system. Contaminant removal processes can be enhanced by the application of amendments to promote plant growth, increase contaminant bioavailability, reduce soil toxicity or improve intrinsic plant uptake mechanisms. Potential chemical amendments include chelating agents, organic and amino acids, surfactants, hormones and inorganic compounds. In addition, biosolids, minerals, compost and industrial wastes can be applied as bulk amendments. Biological amendments include inoculations of microorganisms, as well as compounds naturally released by plant roots. Differing uptake routes and mechanisms for organic and ionic contaminants exist within plant tissues, which may be altered in the presence of soil amendments.

Complications arise when amendment-mediated mobilisation of contaminants from soil increases the bioavailability of substances to levels that are potentially toxic for plants and soil biota. Additionally, rapid leaching of contaminants from the soil can result in plumes of mobilised contaminants migrating further afield. Predicting the influence of soil amendments on contaminant uptake by plants has proved challenging due to the diversity of physical, chemical and biological processes to be considered in addition to the inherent variability that exists in natural systems. This paper presents an overview of plant physiology and the routes of contaminant uptake as well as the potential benefits and limitations of using soil amendments to enhance phytoextraction. While amendments can offer some benefits for

[*] Corresponding author: Tel: +64-9-3737599 ext 84512; Fax: +64-9-3737462; Email: a.johnson @auckland.ac.nz.

contaminant removal from soil, their influence is often dependent on factors such as site conditions, contaminants present and plant species involved. Implementation of phytoremediation technologies, as with other remediation approaches, remains site-specific and therefore requires an understanding of these factors.

Chapter 156

APPLICATION OF ANALYTICAL PYROLYSIS-MASS SPECTROMETRY IN CHARACTERIZATION OF ANIMAL MANURES

Jim J. Wang[1,], Syam K. Dodla[1] and Zhongqi He[2]*

[1]School of Plant, Environmental and Soil Sciences, Louisiana State University
Agricultural Center, Baton Rouge, Louisiana, US
[2]USDA-ARS, New England Plant, Soil and Water Laboratory, Orono, Maine, US

RESEARCH SUMMARY

Analytical pyrolysis-mass spectrometry (Py-MS), principally in the format of pyrolysis-field ionization mass spectrometry (Py-FIMS) or pyrolysis-gas chromatography/mass spectrometry (Py-GC/MS), is a technique capable of providing information on complex organic matter at the molecular level. Unlike C-13 nuclear magnetic resonance (NMR) spectroscopy which provides an average structure of the whole organic material, analytical pyrolysis with mass spectrometry characterizes individual molecular composition through thermal "extraction" (pyrolysis) of the complex organic matter followed by either direct detection by MS or separation through GC then detection by MS. The technique provides a "fingerprint" that can be used to characterize a sample and statistically compare it to others. Besides the use mostly as a qualitative tool, its ability to quantitatively compare samples with similar organic and inorganic matrices makes analytical pyrolysis a powerful tool. Both Py-FIMS and Py-GC/MS have been widely used for the characterization of organic matter of various environmental matrices including aquatic and terrestrial natural organic matter (NOM), microorganisms, soils, and municipal wastes. The major advantages of this technique in organic matter characterization as compared to other traditional techniques are (1) relatively small sample size (usually in the sub milligram range), (2) virtually negligible sample preparation except for grinding and (3) short analysis time (typically one hour or less). Also, Py-GC/MS is much more affordable as compared to solid state NMR spectroscopy.

---

* Corresponding Author: jjwang@agcenter.lsu.edu

Though used widely, there have been only limited studies investigating the chemistry of animal manures using Py-FIMS or Py-GC/MS. In this chapter, we review the current literature on the use of analytical pyrolysis in organic manure characterization and present molecular composition data of cattle manure and poultry litter as characterized by Py-GC/MS.

In: Environmental and Agricultural Research Summaries ...   ISBN: 978-1-63117-090-4
Editor: Lucille T. Cacioppo   © 2014 Nova Science Publishers, Inc.

Chapter 157

STRUCTURAL AND BONDING ENVIRONMENTS OF MANURE ORGANIC MATTER DERIVED FROM INFRARED SPECTROSCOPIC STUDIES

Zhongqi He[1*], *Changwen Du*[2] *and Jianmin Zhou*[2]

[1]USDA-ARS, New England Plant, Soil, and Water Laboratory,
Orono, Maine, US
[2]Institute of Soil Science, Chinese Academy of Sciences,
Nanjing, China

RESEARCH SUMMARY

The structure of natural organic matter can be investigated using various spectroscopic methods. Infrared spectroscopy is a relative simple, yet important, technique. Infrared spectra can be obtained, often nondestructively, on samples in all three states of matter-gases, liquids, and solids, although most samples are examined in the solid form for natural organic matter studies. For a given sample, there will usually be various different sampling techniques that can be used in obtaining the spectrum, thus permitting a researcher to choose one that may be dictated by available accessory equipment, personal preference, or the detailed nature of that particular sample.

Infrared spectroscopy, usually in the form of Fourier transform infrared spectroscopy (FTIR), is a technique based on molecular vibrations. There are three types of motions: (i) bond stretching, (ii) bending, and (iii) tensional motions. Internal vibrational modes are usually found in the 400-4000 cm^{-1} infrared range. Several typical vibrations of C-H and oxygen-containing functional groups absorb light in the infrared region, yielding peaks (absorption bands) so that IR spectroscopy is very valuable in the identification of these functional groups and their structural arrangements in natural organic matter and other soil constituents. Thus, an IR spectrum of a sample can be compared to the spectra of known reference materials or to tabulated frequencies from literature so that the presence of

---

[*] Corresponding Author e-mail: zhongqi.he@ars.usda.gov

diagnostic IR bands indicates the occurrence of particular bonding environments (components) in the sample examined. The apparent advantages of this comparative analytic approach are (i) no requirement for detailed understanding of spectroscopy, (ii) amenability to routine analysis by a nonspectroscopist, and (iii) high efficiency of spectral analysis.

Like in other environmental samples, organic matter in animal manures and composts has been characterized by infrared spectroscopy. In this chapter, we review and discuss the structural and bonding environments of animal manure and their changes under different management practices derived from infrared spectroscopic studies. Recently, Fourier transform infrared photoacoustic spectroscopy (FTIR-PAS) has been applied in soil analyses. In this chapter, we also present FTIR-PAS spectral data of three types of animal manure to show that this technique can also be used to characterize organic matter in animal manure.

In: Environmental and Agricultural Research Summaries ...   ISBN: 978-1-63117-090-4
Editor: Lucille T. Cacioppo   © 2014 Nova Science Publishers, Inc.

Chapter 158

CARBON FUNCTIONAL GROUPS OF MANURE ORGANIC MATTER FRACTIONS IDENTIFIED BY SOLID STATE ^{13}C NMR SPECTROSCOPY

Zhongqi He[1]* and Jingdong Mao[2]
[1]USDA-ARS, New England Plant, Soil, and Water Laboratory,
Orono, Maine, US
[2]Department of Chemistry & Biochemistry,
Old Dominion University, Norfolk, Virginia, US

RESEARCH SUMMARY

Similar to infrared (IR) spectroscopy, nuclear magnetic resonance (NMR) spectroscopy is a non-destructive technique that uses the magnetic resonance of nuclei to investigate chemical structural environments around them. NMR was well established for organic chemical applications by 1965. The scope of NMR applications includes solutions (liquids), solids, and intermediate physical states. The great strength of NMR in natural organic matter research is its unique ability to provide information on more complex materials which are characterized by irregular structures, and strong physical links to each other or to mineral matter (Preston, 1996). Many organic matter samples are analyzed using solid state C-13 NMR that presents the following advantages:

1) Some organic matter samples or fractions are not soluble;
2) Solid-state NMR facilitates a much larger sample than solution NMR, enhancing signal and shortening run times. In solution NMR signal intensity is dependent upon the concentration of sample in an NMR tube. Making the organic matter concentration high enough to achieve a strong signal in solution state may lead to aggregation, resulting in lower sensitivity, lower resolution and loss of structural information;

---

* Corresponding author: Zhongqi.He@ars.usda.gov

3) Solid-state NMR generally involves less sample handling. The sample can be analyzed without any pretreatment and extraction, i.e. the sample can be examined as a whole and secondary reaction can be avoided;

4) Solid-state NMR avoids solvent effects on organic matter structures and solvent; artifact peaks that are common problems in solution NMR;

5) Solid-state NMR is non-intrusive, i.e., it does not consume sample. Solution NMR is not. The alteration of sample during solution NMR preparation and analysis would void valuable sample for other analyses;

6) It is easier and more straightforward to detect unprotonated carbons using solid-state techniques;

7) In solution NMR, the fast tumbling of molecules averages the anisotropic interactions, while in solid-state NMR we can take advantage of these anisotropic interactions by using specially developed pulse sequences to extract structural information not obtainable from solution NMR;

8) Solid-state techniques can identify domains and heterogeneities within organic matter structures, which solution NMR cannot

Perhaps, solid state ^{13}C cross-polarization /magic angle spinning (CP/MAS) NMR represents the most common approach for characterizing organic matter. Conte et al. (2004) reviewed relevant literature which applied ^{13}C CP/MAS NMR spectroscopy to the qualitative and semi-quantitative characterization of natural organic matter. Other solid-state ^{13}C NMR techniques, such as advanced spectral-editing techniques and two-dimensional ^1H–^{13}C heteronuclear correlation (2D HETCOR), have also been recently used on investigation of natural organic matter and its components. This chapter first reviews the spectral features and functional groups of organic matter which can be identified by these techniques, and then synthesizes and analyzes the structural information of organic matter in animal manure derived from these techniques.

In: Environmental and Agricultural Research Summaries ...   ISBN: 978-1-63117-090-4
Editor: Lucille T. Cacioppo   © 2014 Nova Science Publishers, Inc.

Chapter 159

ULTRAVIOLET-VISIBLE ABSORPTIVE FEATURES OF WATER EXTRACTABLE AND HUMIC FRACTIONS OF ANIMAL MANURE AND RELEVANT COMPOST

Mingchu Zhang[1,], Zhongqi He[2] and Aiqin Zhao[1]*

[1]Department of High Latitude Agriculture, School of Natural Resources
and Agricultural Sciences, University of Alaska Fairbanks,
Fairbanks, Alaska, US
[2]USDA-ARS, New England Plant, Soil and Water Laboratory,
Orono, Maine, US

RESEARCH SUMMARY

The absorption of electromagnetic radiation in the ultraviolet (UV, 200−400 nm) and visible (400−800 nm) regions is associated with the electronic transitions of the bonding electrons in a matter. The absorption of UV-visible radiation by organic compounds is due to the presence of specific segments or functional groups (chromospheres) which contain unbonded electrons (e. g., carbonyl groups, S, N, or O atoms, and conjugated C-C multiple bonds). Theoretically, the UV/visible absorbance spectrum of a compound is a characteristic which can be used in its identification. However, because the peaks of UV/visible absorbance spectra of natural organic matter are broad, it is difficult to identify a particular compound in a mixture of simple molecules and practically impossible in a complicated organic matter sample such as dissolved organic matter from soils or animal manure. However, the color of natural organic matter did attract the attention of many scientists who have attempted using the UV/visible spectroscopy for organic matter characterization.

Whereas the UV/visible absorbance spectra are generally broad and featureless, the absorption intensity or absorptivity at certain wavelengths of organic matter components varies with the types, sources, environmental factors, and management conditions under which samples are taken. The variations constitute the basis of UV-visible spectroscopic

---

[*] Corresponding Author: mzhang3@alaska.edu

characterization of natural organic matter. For example, the absorbances at 260 and 280 nm have been frequently used to monitor the dissolved organic carbon fractions eluted from size-exclusion high performance liquid chromatography (HPLC) column. Specific absorption at 254 nm (SUVA$_{254 nm}$; i.e., measured absorptivity divided by the dissolved organic carbon concentration) has been an important parameter to assess the aromaticity of dissolved organic matter. The absorbance ratios at 250 and 365 nm (E2/E3), and at 465 and 665 nm (E4/E6), can be used to characterize a variety of properties of organic matter such as molecular weight, aromaticity, and polarity. In this chapter, we first review and synthesize the information on these UV-visible absorptive features of organic matter fractions of animal manure and manure-related compost. We then use two case studies to comparatively analyze the UV/visible absorptivities of the water extractable organic matter (WEOM) fraction of conventional and organic dairy manure, and hay field soil with long-term histories (0–20 years) of poultry litter application.

In: Environmental and Agricultural Research Summaries ...   ISBN: 978-1-63117-090-4
Editor: Lucille T. Cacioppo   © 2014 Nova Science Publishers, Inc.

Chapter 160

Fluorescence Spectroscopic Analysis of Organic Matter Fractions: The Current Status and a Tutorial Case Study

Tsutomu Ohno[1,] and Zhongqi He[2]*

[1]Department of Plant, Soil, and Environmental Sciences,
University of Maine, Orono, Maine, US
[2]USDA-ARS, New England Plant, Soil,
and Water Laboratory, Orono, Maine, US

Research Summary

Fluorescence spectroscopy has been one approach to chemically characterize organic matter (OM) from various sources. One of the chief advantages of fluorescence spectroscopy is its high sensitivity which can provide information on the chemical properties of OM fractions (i.e. water extractable organic matter and humic substances) without any pretreatment. This reduces substantially concerns regarding the introduction of artifacts due to processing steps to concentrate the organic matter. Fluorescence analysis for the characterization of OM fractions has undergone substantial advancement recently with adoption of two techniques. First, it has become common to use excitation-emission matrix (EEM) spectroscopy to generate three-dimensional fluorescence spectra. The EEM method measures the emission (EM) spectra over a range of excitation (EX) wavelengths resulting in a landscape surface defined by the fluorescence intensity at EX and EM wavelength pairs. The EEM approach has been used to characterize OM fractions extracted from a variety of sources relevant to agronomic nutrient management: crop residues, manures, wastewater treatment residues and soils. Although the EEM has greater spectral information density than the traditional fluorescence approaches, the EEM landscape has been typically characterized by "peak picking" the locations of one or more peaks visually observable in the fluorescence

---

* Corresponding author: ohno@maine.edu

intensity landscape. Two fluorophores frequently observed in DOM samples are located near EX 270~280 nm and EM 335~350 and the other at EX 310~325 nm and EM 420~445. These have been characterized as "protein-like" and "humic-like", respectively. Chen et al. (2003) have quantified the EEM spectra by operationally delineating the EEM landscape into five regions and calculating the integrated volume under each region to characterize the DOM. The regions are characterized as aromatic protein-like (two regions), fulvic acid-like, microbial by-product-like, and humic acid-like.

Secondly, the use of the statistical parallel factor analysis (PARAFAC) method has been demonstrated to decompose a suite of EEM landscapes into *chemically meaningful* spectral components. PARAFAC provides a direct estimate of the relative concentration of the OM components present in the data set as well as the excitation and emission spectra of the components. Thus, PARAFAC can be seen as providing the spectral signatures of the individual fluorophores present in complex and heterogeneous OM mixture without needing any kind of separation methodology. Application of PARAFAC to OM extracted from plant biomass, soil, and manures revealed that five fluorophores could be present (Ohno and Bro, 2006). Seven components were identified by Hunt and Ohno (2007) on a set of DOM isolated from crop residues and manures which were subjected to microbial decomposition in laboratory incubation. The potential of application of the EEM-PARAFAC method in characterizing manure OM fractions and their impacts on soil OM composition has not been fully explored.

The objectives of this chapter are: (1) review and discuss fluorescence spectroscopic studies of OM fractions of animal manure; (2) to provide an introduction to PARAFAC for the characterization of fluorescence spectra of OM; and (3) to present as a case study an example workflow of PARAFAC analysis of a set of EEM spectra of dissolved organic matter (DOM, i.e. water extractable OM) samples derived from six animal manures and three relevant soil samples to promote the application of this method in manure OM-relevant studies.

In: Environmental and Agricultural Research Summaries ...   ISBN: 978-1-63117-090-4
Editor: Lucille T. Cacioppo   © 2014 Nova Science Publishers, Inc.

Chapter 161

AMMONIA EMISSION FROM ANIMAL MANURE: MECHANISMS AND MITIGATION TECHNIQUES

Pius M. Ndegwa[1,*], Alexander N. Hristov[2] and Jactone A. Ogejo[3]

[1]Biological Systems Engineering, Washington State University,
Pullman, Washington, US
[2]Dairy and Animal Science Department, Pennsylvania State University,
University Park, Pennsylvania, US
[3]Biological Systems Engineering, Virginia Tech, Blacksburg, Virginia, US

RESEARCH SUMMARY

Ammonia (NH_3) volatilization is one of the most important pathways through which nitrogen (N) is lost from animal manures. Ammonia volatilization is a critical issue because its loss not only reduces the fertilizer-value of the manure but, in most cases, also has negative impacts on the environment. Agriculture is believed to be the largest source of global NH_3 emission, with the majority of emissions (~80%) estimated to originate from animal manures. Potential adverse consequences associated with NH_3 emission to the environment include: respiratory diseases caused by exposure to high concentrations of secondary fine particulate aerosols formed from NH_3 (commonly referred to as $PM_{2.5}$); nitrate contamination of drinking water; eutrophication of surface water bodies manifested in harmful algal blooms and decreased water quality; vegetation and ecosystem changes caused by excess N deposition; and soil acidification through nitrification and leaching. Reducing NH_3 emissions from animal manures can ultimately mitigate these environmental impacts. In order to design effective techniques for reducing NH_3 loss from animal manures, it is important to first understand the fundamental mechanisms involved in such emissions. This Chapter is divided into two sections. Section 6.2 presents processes and mechanisms leading to NH_3 production and volatilization from animal manures. Section 6.3, on the other hand, summarizes basic principles of the techniques and case-studies, either already developed or in development, for minimizing NH_3 emissions from animal manures.

*Corresponding author: ndegwa@wsu.edu; Phone: 509.335.8167; Fax: 509.335.2722.

In: Environmental and Agricultural Research Summaries ...   ISBN: 978-1-63117-090-4
Editor: Lucille T. Cacioppo   © 2014 Nova Science Publishers, Inc.

Chapter 162

ORIGINS AND IDENTITIES OF KEY MANURE ODOR COMPONENTS

Daniel N. Miller and *Vincent H. Varel*
USDA-ARS, Lincoln, Nebraska, US

RESEARCH SUMMARY

Significant increases in animal and crop production efficiency in the last century have radically changed the way that food is produced, yielding an abundance of nutritious and inexpensive food for consumers, but not without new challenges on the farm. Historically, agriculture was a highly integrated production system where crops raised on the farm were fed to the animals, and the valuable manure nutrients needed for crop production were returned to the same fields that produced the feed. Agriculture now has become much more specialized with crop production largely dependent upon chemical inputs on one farm and transport of feedstuffs to another farm specializing in concentrated animal production. Manure is viewed more frequently as a waste and not a valuable fertilizer resource. To handle the larger numbers of livestock, specialized housing and production areas (confined animal feeding operations or CAFO) have been developed and become a standard production practice. The CAFO has been utilized for many familiar animal species, including beef cattle, dairy, swine, and poultry, and for the less familiar such as buffalo, elk, and alligator. The design and size of CAFO ranges greatly and is influenced by species, climatic region, local practices, and regulations (from local to federal).

One challenge common to all CAFO is how to best manage the large volumes of concentrated manure, which is a complicated mixture of urine and feces that potentially contains bedding material, spilled feed, soil, insects, and excess water. Typically, the manure is in a highly concentrated form and accumulates in either a manure storage structure or on the soil surface, as seen with cattle feedlots. During storage, manure composition changes, either purposefully through engineered treatment systems or naturally through the activity of manure and soil microorganisms. A wide range of manure treatment systems are available.

---

* Email: dan.miller@ars.usda.gov

Most commonly in the Midwest, the treated manure or effluent is utilized for crop or forage production, based upon its nitrogen (N) or phosphorus (P) content. In other areas of the U.S., land is unavailable for manure application, and therefore animal producers rely more heavily upon manure treatment to remove excess N and P nutrients prior to land application in order to stay within prescribed land application guidelines for N and P.

A variety of environmental issues, such as gas emissions, pathogens, nutrients, and pharmaceutically active compounds, can arise at any point during the production, handling, storage, and application of manure. Gas emissions from the manure or manure/soil surface are a prominent issue due to their effects at local and global scales and include greenhouse gases (CO_2, CH_4, and N_2O), volatile nitrogen compounds (NH_3 and methylamine), volatile sulfur compounds (H_2S, and various methyl sulfides), and a multitude of volatile organic compounds (VOC). Zoonotic pathogens capable of infecting animals and humans are often detected in manures, and therefore proper precautions involving manure application to crops need to be taken to avoid human and livestock exposure. Similarly, when manure is applied to fields, nutrient losses by runoff after an extreme rainfall event occurs could affect local surface and ground waters leading to eutrophication. Recent attention to the trace levels of hormones and antibiotics in manure is also a concern given the large manure volumes generated in a typical CAFO. A common thread connecting all of these manure environmental issues is the role of microorganisms. Microbes can be directly involved through potential exposure of manure pathogens to crops, or they may be involved by virtue of their activities, as in the production of greenhouse gases during manure decomposition or nutrient transformations. The scope of this chapter is by necessity narrow and focuses exclusively on manure odor compounds, but many obvious intersections with other environmental issues will be evident, particularly with greenhouse gas production and other gaseous (potentially odorous) emissions.

In: Environmental and Agricultural Research Summaries ...   ISBN: 978-1-63117-090-4
Editor: Lucille T. Cacioppo   © 2014 Nova Science Publishers, Inc.

Chapter 163

MANURE AMINO ACID COMPOUNDS AND THEIR BIOAVAILABILITY

Zhongqi He[1,] and Daniel C. Olk[2]*

[1]USDA-ARS, New England Plant, Soil,
and Water Laboratory, Orono, Maine, US
[2]USDA-ARS, National Laboratory for Agriculture
and the Environment, Ames, Iowa, US

RESEARCH SUMMARY

Historically, microbial nitrogen (N) mineralization in soil has been viewed as the most critical aspect of the N cycle. In the traditional view, only N that is mineralized by microbes in excess of their own demand and released back into soil (i. e. net N mineralization) is available to plants. Amino acids (AA) are widely presumed to be the primary pool of organic N in soil. Thus, identification and quantification of these AA species have obvious significance in understanding N mineralization and cycling (Olk, 2008). However, our growing recognition of the importance of AA is not matched by knowledge of the amounts and types of AA in the soil.

During the last two decades, a new paradigm of terrestrial N cycling has begun to emerge that recognizes the potential for plants to acquire N from organic sources selected five grass species that were grown in a gradient from fertilized, productive pastures to extensive, low productive pastures to test their capability to take up inorganic N and a range of AA. All five grass species were able to take up directly a diversity of soil amino acids of varying complexity. Werdin-Pfisterer et al. examined water extractable AA composition of soils across a boreal forest in interior Alaska, USA. They found that the amino acid pool was dominated by six AAs: glutamine acid, glutamine, aspartic acid, asparagine, alanine, and histidine, which accounted for approximately 80% of the total water extractable soil amino acid pool. Furthermore, the AA concentrations were an order of magnitude higher in coniferous-dominated late successional stages than in early deciduous-dominated stages. The

---

* Corresponding author: Zhongqi.He@ars.usda.gov

authors concluded that AA compounds are important constituents of the biogeochemical diverse soil N pool in the boreal forest of interior Alaska.

In addition, L-tryptophan is a precursor of the growth hormone indole-3-acetic acid and is known to stimulate plant growth at extremely low concentrations found that enrichment of composted organic wastes with N and L-tryptophan can change them into a value-added organic product that could be used as a soil amendment at rates as low as 300 kg ha^{-1} to increase maize crop production on a sustainable basis. Wang et al. proposed that asparagine and glutamine may be used to partially replace nitrate-N nutrition in pak-choi (*Brassica chinensis* L.) growth to improve pak-choi shoot quality.

Amino acids have been long known to be present in animal manure and other wastes or composts. Earlier research on manure AA distribution was based on the potential re-use of the manure AA as a feed ingredient for animals. Recently, Larkin et al. investigated soil microbial community characteristics impacted by manure application, concluding that dairy manure had greater effects than swine manure on soil microbial utilization of carbohydrates and AA. Bol et al. examined the long-term dynamics of AA from a bare fallow soil experiment in unamended control plots and plots treated with ammonium sulphate, ammonium nitrate, sodium nitrate or with animal manure. Their data show that, with time, soil N, C and AA content were increased only in the plots with animal manure. Scheller and Raupp investigated AA and soil organic matter contents of topsoil in a long term trial with farmyard manure and mineral fertilizers. Higher AA contents in manure fertilized plots were observed even at the lowest rate of fertilizer application. This observation indicates that differences between the treatments not only depend on the AA supply from manure, but are also influenced by an altered AA metabolism in the soil.

Although some information on manure AA contents and their bioavailability has been accumulated over years, a review of the relevant literature has not yet been published. Therefore, the objectives of this chapter were to (1) compile and summarize the AA concentrations and proportions in various animal manure samples, and (2) review and discuss soil AA distribution impacted by manure application. We hope this review is helpful to identify gaps in knowledge and propose new research approaches in studying the dynamics of manure AA for sustainable and environment-friendly agricultural production.

In: Environmental and Agricultural Research Summaries ...   ISBN: 978-1-63117-090-4
Editor: Lucille T. Cacioppo   © 2014 Nova Science Publishers, Inc.

Chapter 164

DETERMINANTS AND PROCESSES OF MANURE NITROGEN AVAILABILITY

C. Wayne Honeycutt[1,], James F. Hunt[2], Timothy S. Griffin[3], Zhongqi He[1] and Robert P. Larkin[1]*

[1]USDA-Agricultural Research Service; New England Plant,
Soil & Water Laboratory; Orono, Maine, US
[2]Department of Plant, Soil & Environmental Sciences;
University of Maine; Orono, Maine, US
[3]Friedman School of Nutrition Science and Policy;
Tufts University; Boston, Massachusetts, US

RESEARCH SUMMARY

The value of animal production in the United States well exceeds $100 billion annually (USDA Census of Agriculture, 2007). Manure generated from these industries exceeds 834,000 Mg of dry matter per day, with nitrogen (N) concentrations ranging from approximately 15-55 kg N Mg^{-1} dry matter. Effectively managing this N to optimize its recycling to crops, while also minimizing adverse environmental consequences of manure application to cropland, requires thorough knowledge of the nutrient transformation processes and controlling factors involved when manure is added to soil. For another recent review of this area, readers are referred to Beegle et al.

---

[*] Corresponding Author – Wayne.Honeycutt@wdc.usda.gov

In: Environmental and Agricultural Research Summaries …   ISBN: 978-1-63117-090-4
Editor: Lucille T. Cacioppo   © 2014 Nova Science Publishers, Inc.

Chapter 165

SOLUBILITY OF MANURE PHOSPHORUS CHARACTERIZED BY SELECTIVE AND SEQUENTIAL EXTRACTIONS

John D. Toth[1,*], Zhengxia Dou[1] and Zhongqi He[2]
[1]University of Pennsylvania, School of Veterinary Medicine,
Pennsylvania, US
[2]USDA-ARS, New England Plant, Soil and Water Laboratory,
Orono, Maine, US

RESEARCH SUMMARY

Phosphorus (P) availability is governed by the P in soil or water that is made available by desorption and dissolution processes for uptake by plants in terrestrial and aquatic ecosystems. Solubility of manure P is a critical factor in evaluating manure's nutrient value in agriculture and its role in eutrophication of surface waters. Kuo (1996) pointed out that the quantity of labile P, the concentration of P in soil solution, as well as P buffering capacity affecting the distribution of P between the solution and solid phases, are the primary factors characterizing soil P availability. To evaluate P availability in soils, numerous soil tests have been developed which extract varying amounts of P, depending on the types of extractants used. The extractants include, but are not limited to, water or buffered salt solutions, anion exchange resins, and diluted acids or buffered alkaline solutions with or without a complexing agent. Whereas the principles of these soil P extractions could be applied to manure P research, the different physico-chemical properties of animal manure should be recognized . For example, He et al. observed that the sequentially-extracted HCl fraction of animal manure, especially poultry litter/manure, contained a large portion of organic P (P_o) which would not have been measured by a soil-based protocol.

This chapter reviews solubility of P from food animal manures (in general, swine, dairy, beef and poultry) and manure products (those undergoing further processing such as storage,

---

* Corresponding author – jdtoth@vet.upenn.edu

composting, pelletizing, etc.) determined through individual and sequential extractions with the emphasis on methodological variations. Three broad classes of extraction methods, water, other simple individual extractants, and sequential fractionation, are covered, followed by examples of research on characterization of P forms in different types of animal manures, effects of manure handling, processing, use of chemical amendments to bind P, and dietary manipulation to reduce soluble P excretion.

In: Environmental and Agricultural Research Summaries … ISBN: 978-1-63117-090-4
Editor: Lucille T. Cacioppo © 2014 Nova Science Publishers, Inc.

Chapter 166

ENZYMATIC HYDROLYSIS OF ORGANIC PHOSPHORUS

Zhongqi He[*] and C. Wayne Honeycutt
USDA-ARS, Orono, Maine, US

RESEARCH SUMMARY

Phosphorus occurs in both inorganic and organic forms. Most of organic P (P_o) is present in a certain form of phosphoric esters. In nature, phosphatases catalyze chemical reactions releasing orthophosphate from various P_o compounds. Because most, if not all P_o, must be hydrolyzed to inorganic P (P_i) prior to uptake by plants and microorganisms, enzymatic hydrolysis provides an estimate of hydrolyzable, and thus the bioavailable, P_o in environmental samples. As early as 1975, Herbe et al. enzymatically characterized soluble P_o in lake water samples. Fox and Comerford investigated the bioavailability of P_o in forested spodosols with wheat germ acid phosphatase and found that 20-30% of the water-extracted P_o was enzymatically hydrolyzable. Pant et al. reported that phytase released nearly twice (55% of P_o) the quantity of P as did acid and alkaline phosphatases (20-28% of P_o) in water extracts of 4 soils. In 2001, He and Honeycutt first examined the release of P_o in the sequentially-extracted fractions of swine manure and cattle manure by enzymatic hydrolysis. Subsequently, enzymatic hydrolysis has been used in characterizing numerous animal manures and manure–amended soils under various management practices by this group and others, which are reviewed in this chapter.

---

[*] Corresponding author: Zhongqi.He@ars.usda.gov

In: Environmental and Agricultural Research Summaries ...   ISBN: 978-1-63117-090-4
Editor: Lucille T. Cacioppo   © 2014 Nova Science Publishers, Inc.

Chapter 167

CHARACTERIZING PHOSPHORUS IN ANIMAL WASTE WITH SOLUTION ^{31}P NMR SPECTROSCOPY

Barbara J. Cade-Menun[*]

Agriculture and Agri-Food Canada, SPARC,
Swift Current, SK, Canada

RESEARCH SUMMARY

Animal manure is a rich source of nutrients, particularly nitrogen (N) and P. As such, it has long been applied to soil as a fertilizer. However, in recent years as animal production has intensified, manures have been applied to land for disposal purposes rather than to enhance soil fertility. This has lead to soil P accumulation, and an acceleration of P transfer from land to water, contributing to eutrophication.

The behavior of manure-applied P in soils depends on the forms of P in the manure, because P forms vary in their bioavailability and in their chemical dynamics in soil. As such, characterizing manure P forms is essential in order to maximize fertilizer potential and to minimize environmental impacts. One key tool for the speciation of P in manures is solution ^{31}P-NMR. First used to identify P forms in manure by Leinweber et al. (1997), solution ^{31}P-NMR has subsequently been applied to studies of manure from a wide range of animals, and to investigations of a number of manure properties, from P bioavailability to the impact of animal diet on feces composition and the effects of manure storage and handling. The objective of this chapter is to review the use of ^{31}P-NMR to characterize P forms in animal waste, discussing the requirements for successful ^{31}P-NMR experiments using animal manure and feces and reviewing the literature that has focused on method refinement, as well as summarizing the results of experiments investigating feces and manure properties, grouping these studies by animal type, and discussing future research needs. Please note that this chapter focuses on P speciation in feces (material collected from the animal at the point of excretion, referred to as dung in some studies), manure (feces deposited on the ground or

---

[*] Barbara.Cade-Menun@agr.gc.ca

mixed with bedding material, also known as litter for poultry), partially digested material removed from the animal in some way (e.g. ileal digesta removed from the ileum after slaughter) and feed when it has been analyzed and compared with feces or manure. This chapter does not include ^{31}P-NMR studies of P speciation in soil or manure-amended soils.

In: Environmental and Agricultural Research Summaries …   ISBN: 978-1-63117-090-4
Editor: Lucille T. Cacioppo   © 2014 Nova Science Publishers, Inc.

Chapter 168

METAL SPECIATION OF PHOSPHORUS DERIVED FROM SOLID STATE SPECTROSCOPIC ANALYSIS

Olalekan O. Akinremi[1,], Babasola Ajiboye[2] and Zhongqi He[3]*

[1]Department of Soil Science University of Manitoba,
Winnipeg, Manitoba, Canada
[2]Soil Science, School of Agriculture, Food and Wine, Waite Campus,
the University of Adelaide, Adelaide, Australia
[3]USDA-ARS, New England Plant, Soil, and Water Laboratory,
Orono, Maine, US

RESEARCH SUMMARY

Whereas solution-based characterization provides knowledge on manure P solubility and forms, solid-state techniques are more suitable to investigate metal-P interaction and/or metal species of P compounds. These techniques include, but are not limited, to Fourier-transform infrared (FT-IR) spectroscopy, scanning electron microscopy with energy dispersive X-ray (SEM-EDS) spectroscopy, powder X-ray diffraction (XRD) analysis, synchrotron radiation based X-ray absorption near edge structure (XANES) spectroscopy, and solid state ^{31}P nuclear magnetic resonance (NMR) spectroscopy. The objective of this chapter is to provide the current status of solid state XANES and ^{31}P NMR spectroscopic methods to identify metal species of organic and inorganic P in manure. Such characterization provides an increasing understanding of manure P release mechanism in soil and allows us to better predict the potential of P loss following manure addition to agricultural soils.

* Corresponding Author: akinremi@cc.umanitoba.ca

In: Environmental and Agricultural Research Summaries …   ISBN: 978-1-63117-090-4
Editor: Lucille T. Cacioppo   © 2014 Nova Science Publishers, Inc.

Chapter 169

MODELING PHOSPHORUS TRANSFORMATIONS AND RUNOFF LOSS FOR SURFACE-APPLIED MANURE

Peter A. Vadas[*]

USDA-ARS, Dairy Forage Research Center,
Madison, Wisconsin, US

RESEARCH SUMMARY

The USEPA reports that of the nation's 16.3 million acres of lakes, ponds, and reservoirs assessed during the 2004 reporting cycle, 64% were impaired, with nutrients cited as one of the leading causes of impairment and agricultural activities cited as the leading source of impairment (USEPA, 2009). One of the main water quality concerns is accelerated eutrophication of fresh waters by phosphorus (P), which limits water use for drinking, recreation, and industry. The subsequent challenge for the agricultural community, from scientists to producers, is to identify agricultural areas with a high potential for P export, accurately quantify that export, and assess the ability of alternative management practices to minimize P export. Water quality simulation models are seen as one relatively rapid and cost effective way to help achieve these goals.

While significant loss of P from agricultural fields can occur through leaching in sandy soils, organic soils, and soils with artificial drainage, the primary pathway of P loss from the majority of agricultural soils is through surface runoff. The three major sources of P to surface runoff are soil, plant material, and applied fertilizers, manures, or biosolids. Research has clearly shown that even though soil and plant material can be significant sources of P to runoff, their effect can be overwhelmed by P release from recently applied animal manures, especially if the manures are left unincorporated. Phosphorus loss in runoff from surface-applied manures is often greatest in the first runoff event after application and decreases in subsequent events. Surface manures can continue to be a source of P loss to runoff for several months after application.

---

[*] peter.vadas@ars.usda.gov

Given the significant degree to which surface-applied manures can contribute to P loss in runoff, it is important for water quality models to be able to reliably simulate surface application of manure P, physical and chemical transformations of manure and its P with time after application, and loss of P from manure to runoff during storm events. However, commonly used water-quality models, such as EPIC, GLEAMS, ANSWERS or SWAT, do not simulate these surface manure processes. Instead, the models immediately incorporate any applied manure and P into soil P pools and allow P loss to runoff from the soil. The result is a poor representation and prediction of P loss in runoff. Therefore, such models could be improved by adding routines to simulate surface manure P processes and loss in runoff. This chapter reviews and discusses research on processes controlling surface manure P transformations and loss in runoff and efforts to translate understanding of these processes into simulation models. The chapter also emphasizes gaps in knowledge and needed research.

In: Environmental and Agricultural Research Summaries ...   ISBN: 978-1-63117-090-4
Editor: Lucille T. Cacioppo   © 2014 Nova Science Publishers, Inc.

Chapter 170

IMPROVING THE SUSTAINABILITY OF ANIMAL AGRICULTURE BY TREATING MANURE WITH ALUM

Philip A. Moore, Jr.[*]

USDA-ARS, the Poultry Production and Product Safety Research Unit,
Fayetteville Arkansas, US

RESEARCH SUMMARY

Two of the biggest environmental problems associated with animal manure management are ammonia (NH_3) emissions and phosphorus (P) runoff. Research conducted during the past two decades has shown that a simple topical application of aluminum sulfate (alum) to manure can greatly reduce the magnitude of both of these problems. The objective of this chapter was to provide a literature review of the research on treating poultry litter and other types of manure with alum.

[*] philipm@uark.edu

In: Environmental and Agricultural Research Summaries ...   ISBN: 978-1-63117-090-4
Editor: Lucille T. Cacioppo   © 2014 Nova Science Publishers, Inc.

Chapter 171

SOURCES AND CONTENTS OF HEAVY METALS AND OTHER TRACE ELEMENTS IN ANIMAL MANURES

Jackie L. Schroder[1,], Hailin Zhang[1],*
Jaben R. Richards[1] and Zhongqi He[2]

[1]Oklahoma State University, Department of Plant and Soil Sciences,
Stillwater, Oklahaoma, US
[2]USDA-ARS, New England Plant, Soil, and Water Laboratory,
Orono, Maine, US

RESEARCH SUMMARY

Animal manures are available in many parts of the world and serve as abundant sources of macro and micronutrients for crop and grass production. Besides providing valuable nutrients to the soil, manure supplies organic matter to improve physical, chemical and biological properties of soils, thus improving water infiltration, enhancing retention of nutrients, reducing wind and water erosion, and promoting growth of beneficial organisms. Confined animal feeding operations (CAFO) are the major source of animal manures in most countries. Virtually all animal manures are land applied with approximately 2.2×10^9 wet tons of manure being produced annually in the United States and approximately 80×10^6 wet tons produced annually in the United Kingdom.

Until recently, the majority of concerns associated with land application of manure have focused on the contamination of groundwater or surface waters with N and P. However, animal manures also contain substantial amounts of potentially toxic trace elements such as As, Cu, and Zn. Nicholson et al. estimated that approximately 25 to 40% of the total annual inputs of Cu, Ni, and Zn to soil came from animal manures. Farm gate balance experiments in Sweden, where all inputs and outputs were examined, found the most important source of trace elements in manure came from purchased feedstuffs. Substantial amounts of As are

---

[*] Corresponding Author: jackie.schroder@okstate.edu

introduced to the environment of the Delaware-Maryland-Virginia Peninsula by the use of As containing compounds such as roxarsone in poultry feed. While several researchers have shown that the application of manures increases trace element concentrations in plants, only a few reports have indicated phytotoxicity due to land application of manure. For example, McGrath et al. found that growth of perennial ryegrass (*Lolium perenne*) seedlings was retarded with the addition of approximately 200 ppm of Cu to soil from pig manure slurries. In another study, Cresswell et al. observed the yield of mushrooms was decreased by excessive amounts of B and Cu in poultry manure compost. Several researchers have reported metal toxicity to ruminants grazing on pastures which had received manure applications. However, in most cases, the toxicity was due to a direct intake of trace element rich manure directly from the soil or through contaminated herbage. Conversely, several researchers have evaluated applying copper rich pig manure slurries to sheep pastures and have reported no adverse effects on sheep grazing the manure amended fields.

Elevated concentrations of As, Cu, and Zn have been observed in soils that have received long-term application of manures. Additionally, researchers have reported high concentrations of metals in runoff from soils that had received manure applications. Thus, a potential exists for manure-treated soils to serve as a non-point source of metal pollution through leaching, runoff or erosion. Edwards and Somershwar (2000) indicated that rather than focusing on only one component (i.e. N and/or P concentration), land application guidelines should consider the total composition of animal manures.

The Part 503 rule that limits land application of chemicals in biosolids is based on a risk assessment framework that originally evaluated 14 exposure pathways for humans, animals, plants, and soil organisms. The inorganic chemicals evaluated in the exposure pathways included As, Cd, Cr, Cu, Hg, Pb, Ni, Mo, Se, and Zn. According to the U.S. EPA Part 503 risk assessment, other trace elements in biosolids do not present potential risk to human health or the environment when applied at typical rates. While much literature exist dealing with metal inputs from biosolids and inorganic fertilizers, few comprehensive studies have been conducted on the sources and distributions of metals and other trace elements in animal manure. The purpose of this chapter is to examine the sources and distributions of metals and other trace elements in animal manures.

In: Environmental and Agricultural Research Summaries …   ISBN: 978-1-63117-090-4
Editor: Lucille T. Cacioppo   © 2014 Nova Science Publishers, Inc.

Chapter 172

FATE AND TRANSPORT OF ARSENIC FROM ORGANOARSENICALS FED TO POULTRY

Clinton D. Church[1,], Jane E. Hill[2] and Arthur L. Allen[3]*
[1]USDA-ARS, Pasture Systems and Watershed Management Research Unit,
University Park, Pennsylvania, US
[2]School of Engineering, University of Vermont,
Burlington, Vermont, US
[3]Dept. Agriculture, University Maryland Eastern Shore,
Princess Anne, Maryland, US

RESEARCH SUMMARY

Recently, there has been growing concern over the use of roxarsone (3-nitro-4-hydroxyphenylarsonic acid) by the poultry industry, since roxarsone contains arsenic (As) that may ultimately accumulate in the environment. Roxarsone is an organic acid feed additive that has historically been fed to broiler chickens to improve weight gain, feed consumption and manage coccidial parasites. Since it is not metabolized by poultry and therefore does not accumulate in broiler meat, the bulk of roxarsone added to broiler feed is excreted in feces, which, when mixed with bedding, forms poultry litter. As poultry manure is rich in nutrients, more than 90% of poultry litter is land-applied as fertilizer. Rutheford et al. showed that soils receiving long-term poultry litter application had high levels of water extractable As and that the As appeared to be sorbed to iron oxyhydroxides in the soil types they investigated. However, the ultimate fate of As derived from roxarsone as well as the controls on As movement in the environment are largely unknown.

The use of organoarsenicals, primarily Roxarsone, has increased as the poultry industry has grown. Concentrations of roxarsone normally added to feed are relatively low, between 45 and 90 g ton^{-1}. However, Garbarino et al. estimated that in 2000 alone, when 8.3×10^6 broiler chickens were grown in the U.S., approximately 2.5×10^5 kg of As were likely applied

---

* Corresponding Author: USDA-ARS, Curtin Road, Building 3702, University Park, PA, 16802. Telephone: 814-863-8760. Email: Clinton.Church@ars.usda.gov

in litter to U.S. soils, equivalent to an annual load of 60 to 250 g As ha^{-1}. In areas of intensive poultry production, such as the Delmarva (Delaware, Maryland, Virginia) Peninsula, the application of roxarsone-derived As to agricultural soils can be quite acute. In 2000, approximately 620,000,000 broilers were raised on the Peninsula resulting in an estimated annual load of As to Delmarva soils of 2.6×10^4 kg from land application of poultry litter. Some sources have estimated that as much as 5×10^4 kg of arsenic is spread on Delmarva soils every year. Given the proximity of the Delmarva Peninsula to the Chesapeake Bay, the nation's largest estuary, the fate of As from poultry litter amended soils is a potential water quality concern.

The American Cancer Society recently recognized that As causes cancer of the liver, lung, and skin. In 2001, the U.S. Environmental Protection Agency lowered the maximum contaminant level (MCL) of elemental As in drinking water to 10 µg/L (U.S. Environmental Protection Agency, 2000), which also is the current provisional guide used by the World Health Organization (World Health Organization, 1999). Arsenic also is toxic to fish and many aquatic organisms (Canadian Council of Ministers of the Environment, 2002) and, if present in soil water, it may be taken up by plants—rendering them unsuitable for human or animal consumption

In: Environmental and Agricultural Research Summaries …   ISBN: 978-1-63117-090-4
Editor: Lucille T. Cacioppo   © 2014 Nova Science Publishers, Inc.

Chapter 173

MERCURY IN MANURES AND TOXICITY TO ENVIRONMENTAL HEALTH

Irenus A. Tazisong[1], Zachary N. Senwo[1,*],
Robert W. Taylor[1] and Zhongqi He[2]
[1]School of Agricultural and Environmental Sciences,
Alabama A&M University, Normal, Alabama, US
[2]USDA-ARS, New England Plant, Soil, and Water Laboratory,
Orono, Maine, US

RESEARCH SUMMARY

Mercury (Hg) has been known to society for centuries and was heavily used during the industrial revolution. It occurs naturally and has an average crustal abundance by mass of approximately 0.08 parts per million. Its distribution in the environment is controlled by either natural processes or anthropogenic activities. The natural processes are mostly attributed to rock weathering, volcanic activities, and crustal degassing; whereas anthropogenic sources include mining and smelting, coal combustion, waste incineration, chlor-alkali facilities, and other industrial processes that require Hg usage. Mercury can also be commonly found in thermometers, lamps, dental amalgam fillings, cosmetics, vaccines, and eye drops. Because it is broadly spread in the environment, it occurs at various concentrations in air, soil, water, and biomass. Mercury forms strong covalent bonds in biological systems and extremely strong ionic bond with reduced sulfur. Its biogeochemical cycle is quite unique among toxic metals of environmental concerns. In the environment Hg is either in the organic or inorganic form. However, Hg is generally released into the environment in inorganic forms and can be microbially transformed into organic (methylmercury) forms.

Total Hg in most soils is usually low, although high levels have been reported. In soil, Hg occurs mainly as Hg (0) and Hg (II) forms depending on the redox conditions. Mercury speciation and distribution in soil define its toxicity and mobility. An assessment of its

---
* Corresponding author. Tel: (256) 372-4216. Fax: (256) 372-5906. Email address: zachary.senwo@aamu.edu

chemical forms (water soluble, exchangeable, organic matter bound, oxide bound, and residual), is of significant importance to improve and maintain environmental quality and sustainability. The water soluble form has been reported to account for less than 1% of the total Hg in soils. Although this form is negligible, more attention is given to it due to its ease of bioavailability and mobility. Mercury in exchangeable form is moderately bound or weakly associated with ligands, and can be exchanged with other metal ions at the binding sites. Mercury bound to organic matter represents the organic form reported to be the dominant fraction in most soils after the residual form. Residual Hg has been reported as the dominant form in most samples and represents Hg bound to sulfur (HgS), silicates, and oxides of iron and manganese. Organic matter content, soil pH, Cl⁻ ions, and the presence of sulfide are very significant parameters influencing Hg speciation in soils. Numerous studies have revealed that Hg sorption in Amazon top soils was mainly influenced by organic matter content, and poorly correlated with clay content. Just as pH influences heavy metal availability in soils, Hg availability has also been shown to be affected by pH. Jing et al. (2007) showed that Hg desorption in 0.01 M KCl is significantly enhanced by pH change and the presence of organic acids. Base on these authors, Hg desorption in soils decreased at pH range $3.0 - 5.0$, leveled off at pH $5.0 - 8.0$ and increased at pH $7.0 - 9.0$. The influence of sulfur on Hg distribution in soils is not surprising due to its affinity for sulfur and the formation of Hg sulfide, an important Hg ore. Studies by Tazisong and Senwo (2009) on Hg concentration and distribution in soils impacted by long-term applied broiler litter indicated a positive and highly significant correlation between Hg and sulfur.

In: Environmental and Agricultural Research Summaries ...   ISBN: 978-1-63117-090-4
Editor: Lucille T. Cacioppo   © 2014 Nova Science Publishers, Inc.

Chapter 174

INTEGRATING DYNAMIC SOCIAL SYSTEMS INTO ASSESSMENTS OF FUTURE WILDFIRE LOSSES: AN EXPERIENTIAL AGENT-BASED MODELING APPROACH

Travis B. Paveglio[1] and Tony Prato[2]

[1]College of Forestry and Conservation,
The University of Montana, Montana, US
[2]Agricultural and Applied Economics and Center for Applied
Research and Environmental Systems,
University of Missouri, Missouri, US

RESEARCH SUMMARY

Interactions between social and ecological systems can pose threats to humans and the natural environment. One example of this phenomenon is the increasing threat of losses from wildfire, which is influenced by both social processes (i.e., expanding human settlement, residential development patterns, forest management, and fire suppression) and ecological conditions (i.e., high surface and canopy fuel loadings, forest type, topography, and climate change). Methodological frameworks for evaluating multifaceted threats include various conceptualizations, assessments, and simulations of the interacting factors that determine human exposure to risk or that make humans less vulnerable to potential hazards. One such approach is agent-based modeling or agent based models (ABM), which simulate complex system behavior from the bottom up using simple decision rules for the behavior of different agents.

This chapter presents an ABM framework for simulating the dynamics of a coupled natural-human system for wildfire in Flathead County, Montana, USA. The ABM has three interacting agents (i.e., homeowners, community and regional planners, and land and wildfire management agencies) that influence or are influenced by potential losses from wildfire. The ABM approach is part of the *wildfire climate* (FIRECLIM) model that simulates future wildfire risk in Flathead County using different assumptions about climate change, economic growth, residential development, and forest management.

The proposed ABM framework incorporates methodologies for integrating monetary and non-monetary attributes that influence human behavior and decisions with respect to wildfire. The methodologies include collaborative approaches that can be used to evaluate the characteristics and behaviors of agents in a geographical location, providing an experientially driven way to capture the impact of social diversity on the dynamics of a coupled natural-human system for wildfire. The proposed ABM framework includes preliminary decision rules for agents that reflect how they interact with and modify the decisions of other agents and/or other processes that operate in a coupled natural-human system for wildfire.

In: Environmental and Agricultural Research Summaries …   ISBN: 978-1-63117-090-4
Editor: Lucille T. Cacioppo   © 2014 Nova Science Publishers, Inc.

Chapter 175

THE EUROPEAN EXPERIENCE ON ENVIRONMENTAL MANAGEMENT SYSTEMS AND THE THIRD REVISION OF THE "ECO MANAGEMENT AND AUDIT SCHEME" (EMAS)

*Fabio Iraldo[a,b], Francesco Testa[a],
Tiberio Daddi[a] and Marco Frey[a,b]*
[a]Sant'Anna School of Advanced Studies,
Piazza Martiri della Libertà, Pisa, Italy
[b]IEFE – Institute for Environmental and Energy Policy
and Economics, Milano, Italy

RESEARCH SUMMARY

In recent years, based on the voluntary commitment and the pro-active approach of organizations, the certification framework has gained a crucial role amongst the instruments of the European environmental policy.

Voluntary instruments (such as EMAS and the "twin" regulation Eco-label) were designed by introducing concepts and mechanisms that, for the time being, led to a radical change in the environmental policies of the European Commission. The application of these patterns, in fact, originated a highly innovative policy trend, based on voluntary certification as a marketing tool providing a competitive edge.

The Commission's purpose was clearly to attract the interest of companies and convince them to spontaneously mobilize their financial, technical and management resources towards a path of continuous improvement in environmental performance.

The inspiring criterion was the belief, stated in the European Commission Fifth Environmental Action Programme, that manufacturing sectors and, more generally, all private (and public) actors whose activities had an environmental impact, could not only be seen as a part of the "problem" but also as a crucial part of the "solution", and therefore it was necessary to encourage them to participate and cooperate in building sustainable development paths.

The guiding principle behind the definition and the implementation of EMAS and Ecolabel was very simple: if the most active players on environmental improvement had been granted official recognition as a marketable value or in social relationships as a guarantee of their credibility, then two ambitious goals were achieved: first, the increase of their competitive edge and, secondly, the improvement of the environmental performance in the economic and productive industry.

Participation in EMAS is entirely voluntary, determined as it is by competitive and social pressures perceived by organizations, rather than by binding regulatory requirements. For this reason, the framework does not set quantitative limits, technology standards or emission thresholds, but it outlines the characteristics that a system of environmental management of an organization must have to be granted a public recognition of its correctness and efficiency. The basic steps an organization must take to participate in EMAS are the following: adopt an environmental policy; carry out an initial review of the existing environmental aspects; set the objectives and targets and establish a program to improve its performance; adopt a management system aimed at achieving the program objectives; perform audits to verify the functioning and the effectiveness of the system, and then draft an environmental statement to prove its commitment to the community.

It may be interesting here to briefly describe the stages of development and dissemination of EMAS, to which the competitive pressures described above have given rise.

The framework, issued by EC Regulation 1836 of 1993, required several years of preparation, due to the need to establish supervising national bodies and define the appropriate set of rules as provided by the EU: the first registrations in Europe date back to August 1995. After a very rapid development, particularly in Germany and Austria, the spread of EMAS suffered a slight slowdown in the early 2000s, partly for the implementation of the new guidelines, issued according to EC Regulation 761/2001.

Once at full capacity, the new version of EMAS Regulation clearly produced a further acceleration in the participation of small and medium-sized businesses, public sector organizations and services, especially in tourism. To encourage the involvement of these organizations, the Regulation introduced some major changes intended to correct some critical issues resulting from the previous EMAS experience and enhanced the opportunities for development and dissemination of the framework.

This chapter aims to describe the European evolutionary path about EMAS and how European institutions attempted to evaluate hindrances, starting from the main evidences emerging from literature, and identify favoring factors and efficient solutions to overcome them. A particular focus will be devoted to the description of new requirement of the EMAS III Regulation and which are the main differences from another formal scheme, such as ISO 14001.

In: Environmental and Agricultural Research Summaries ...   ISBN: 978-1-63117-090-4
Editor: Lucille T. Cacioppo   © 2014 Nova Science Publishers, Inc.

Chapter 176

MINIMIZING ENVIRONMENTAL IMPACT FROM APPLYING SELECTED INPUTS IN PLANT PRODUCTION

Claus G. Sørensen[1], Dionysis D. Bochtis[1], Thomas Bartzanas[3], Nikolaos Katsoulas[2] and Constantinos Kittas[2]

[1]University of Aarhus, Faculty of Agricultural Sciences,
Department of Biosystems Engineering, Tjele, Denmark
[2]University of Thessaly, School of Agricultural Sciences,
Department of Agriculture Crop Production and Rural Environment,
Laboratory of Agricultural Constructions
and Environmental Control, Magnisia, Greece
[3]Center for Research and Technology of Thessaly,
Institute of Technology and Management of Agricultural Ecosystems,
Technology Park of Thessaly, Volos, Greece

RESEARCH SUMMARY

Primary agricultural production is often managed on a rather crude level. Plant nutrients and pesticides are applied equally not only within-fields, but also to all fields growing the same crop type. Fields and crops are treated according to standards defined by simple, easily observable parameters. Likewise, society's regulation of agricultural production is on a crude level as, for example, nitrogen quotas are regulated on a farm level, because only the farm's purchase and sales are available for the required supervision. Both farm management and environmental protection could be improved significantly by a more detailed management and regulation of various inputs.

In order to achieve an improved management in terms of increased profitability and reduced environmental impact in plant production, there is a need to develop and use decision support systems and other assessment tools to plan and control selected resource inputs. Such tools will cconsists of a wide range of techniques and technologies from information technology, sensor and application technologies aimed at farm and operations management and economics. The majority of farm managers are not trained to use the vast amount of operations data efficiently and face many challenges on how to interpret these data as the basis for decision making on crop management.

In this book chapter it is discussed how the application of different decision support systems and technologies affect the environmental impacts form inputs necessary for plant production systems. Specifically, the state-of-the-art and future perspectives concerning the following input factors are considered.

In: Environmental and Agricultural Research Summaries …   ISBN: 978-1-63117-090-4
Editor: Lucille T. Cacioppo   © 2014 Nova Science Publishers, Inc.

Chapter 177

NATURAL ADSORBENTS FROM TANNIN EXTRACTS: NOVEL AND SUSTAINABLE RESOURCES FOR WATER TREATMENT

J. Sánchez-Martín[*] and J. Beltrán-Heredia[1]

Department of Chemical Engineering and Physical Chemistry
University of Extremadura, Badajoz, Spain

RESEARCH SUMMARY

The adsorption of contaminants is one of the most popular processes in water treatment. The feasibility of a long variety of materials, such as clays or active carbons and multiple waste products such as biomass, tires or other kinds of industrial residues, makes the production of new adsorbents a very interesting researching subject.

This chapter is focused on a new type of natural adsorbent which is based on tannin extracts. Gelation of tannins is a recent chemical procedure that is often performed in order to obtain high quality adhesives. However, not many works have been carried out studying the ability of these gels for removing cationic pollutants from aqueous matrix. This is the scope of the current contribution.

Wastewater techniques should be improved in order to guarantee their applicability in a wide scenario: from developed countries, where no economical problems are detected; to less developed zones, where technology is usually a natural barrier. Global sustainability is evidently depending on the correct care of natural resources all over the world, not only where socioeconomic conditions allow to keep the environment clean.

Tannins from different trees, such as *Quebracho*, *Acacia*, *Pinus* or *Cypress*, have been gelified according to different gelation processes. Parameters such as aldehyde or NaOH concentration were varied and optimal conditions for gelification were applied in order to obtain efficient adsorbents for the removal of dyes, surfactants and heavy metals. Reliability of the results was technically confirmed by statistical methodologies.

---

[*] Corresponding author: Telephone number: +34 924289300 ext. 89033. E-mail addresses: jsanmar@unex.es (J. Sánchez-Martín) and jbelther@unex.es (J. Beltrán-Heredia)

In: Environmental and Agricultural Research Summaries …   ISBN: 978-1-63117-090-4
Editor: Lucille T. Cacioppo   © 2014 Nova Science Publishers, Inc.

Chapter 178

ISO 14001 RESEARCH:
AN ACADEMIC APPROACH

G. Lannelongue*, J. Gonzalez-Benito
and O. Gonzalez-Benito
Universidad de Salamanca, Facultad de Economia y Empresa, Spain

RESEARCH SUMMARY

An Environmental Management Systems (EMS) can be described by means of its primary measures; unfortunately, in contrast to the literature on quality management systems in which the most relevant aspects of the system are perfectly defined and compared, there is still lacking a consensus concerning the critical factors of an EMS. This has led to several different approaches in research on EMS, and has made it more difficult to compare scientific results.

In this chapter, we aim to deepen the theoretical bases that underpin the study of EMS. To this end, we first review the history of environmental management in firms and the appearance of formal EMS. Next, we examine nature of the standards and how they are employed within various organizations. Finally, we reconsider the literature on and the structure of the standard represented by ISO 14001:2004, and propose a model to study EMS that involves eighteen critical factors under four headings: Top Management Support, HR Management, Information System and Externals Factors. This model enables us to develop a tool that allows for a more systematic approach to empirical analyses of EMS, especially those based on ISO 14001.

* Corresponding Author: Gustavo Lannelongue, Organización de Empresas, Universidad de Salamanca, Facultad de Economía y Empresa, Campus Miguel de Unamuno, Edificio FES. 37007 Salamanca, Tel. +34 923294500 ext 3524. Fax +34 923294715. email: lannelongue@usal.es.

In: Environmental and Agricultural Research Summaries …   ISBN: 978-1-63117-090-4
Editor: Lucille T. Cacioppo   © 2014 Nova Science Publishers, Inc.

Chapter 179

MEASURING SUSTAINABLE CULTURE AMONG CONSTRUCTION STAKEHOLDERS IN HONG KONG

Robin C. P. Yip[1], C. S. Poon[1] and James M. W. Wong[2]
[1]Department of Civil and Structural Engineering,
The Hong Kong Polytechnic University, Hung Hom, Kowloon, Hong Kong
[2]Department of Civil Engineering, The University of Hong Kong, Hong Kong

RESEARCH SUMMARY

The construction industry is a leading contributor in improving the quality of the built environment, but concurrently it is a main producer of solid waste and greenhouse gas that damage the environment. Stakeholders of the construction industry thus have a decisive role to play in enhancement of sustainability and suppression of environmental damages. In the process of performing sustainable construction, stakeholders changed subconsciously their attitudes and behaviours towards a more sustainable culture. This paper aims to examine the extent of these attitudinal and behavioral changes by caterizing these changes in four sustainable cultural components. The attitudinal changes are classified into *awareness* and *concern*, while the behavioral changes are classified into *motivation* and *implementation*. The investigation was carried out by means of two surveys conducted in years 2004 and 2006 among different stakeholder groups of various disciplines including the Government, Developer, Consultant, Contractor and the frontline construction supervisors embracing site agents, site supervisors and foremen. The findings indicated that different stakeholder group carries different influential power to contribute sustainability. The consultant group and the frontline participants group demonstrated readiness in compliance by their willingness to adopt new practices favorable to sustainable construction. On the other hand, although embracing high influential power, the developer group had yet a relatively lower apprehension on sustainability, particularly in motivation and implementation aspects. Holding the highest influential power, the government group had a remarkable awareness and motivation on sustainable construction but inadequate in implementation when compared with other industry stakeholders. Although the contractor group exhibited an overall improvement in sustainable culture, but the improvement of various cultural components are relatively low. The results of investigation that reflect such a social phenomenon is an important reference for decision-makers in the government and in private sectors to formulate policies that couple with universal demands for sustainable development. The means of measurement so developed may also serve as a valuable reference for other industries.

In: Environmental and Agricultural Research Summaries ...   ISBN: 978-1-63117-090-4
Editor: Lucille T. Cacioppo   © 2014 Nova Science Publishers, Inc.

Chapter 180

THE PROS AND CONS OF ISO 14000 ENVIRONMENTAL MANAGEMENT SYSTEMS (EMS) FOR TURKISH CONSTRUCTION FIRMS

*Ahmet Murat Turk**

Department of Civil Engineering, Istanbul Kultur University,
Atakoy Kampus, Yanyol, Bakirkoy, Istanbul, Turkey

RESEARCH SUMMARY

Recently, the ISO 14000 environmental management system (EMS) has been widely utilized by all sectors throughout the world prepared by ISO (International Standard Organization). With the purpose of keep up and develop the environmental performance within all sectors, including the construction sector, some methods exist for the protection of sustainable development and the environment worldwide. ISO 14000 EMS originated from such necessity. Lately, an increased awareness has emerged related to the use of this system in the construction industry. Despite such interest, the research related to the implementation practice of the ISO 14000 EMS by the construction firms has not reached the desired level. In this study, the major motives for seeking ISO 14001 certification for Turkish construction firms is being examined by using the questionnaire survey method. Questionnaire survey was conducted with 68 individual construction firms, which represent the top firms in Turkey and operate in national and international markets as they are members of the Turkish Contractors Association (TCA). Descriptive and factor analyses were used with the obtained data from questionnaires of advantages and disadvantages related to ISO 14000 EMS. In the study, factor analysis was used to summarize many variables with a few factors. Each of the factors acquired from these analyses presents advantages and disadvantages of ISO 14000 EMS factors. As the advantages of ISO 14000 EMS, mainly two factor dimensions are found in the analysis. First dimension is entitled as "related to environment" and second one is called as dimension "related to company". As the disadvantage of ISO 14000 EMS, mainly three factor

---

* E-mail: murat.turk@iku.edu.tr phone: +90-212-4984257.

dimensions have found in the analysis. First one is named as "related to lack of the knowledge and personnel". Second one is called as "related to the cost and implementation" and third dimension is entitled as "related to no apparent benefits".

This study shows that there is a positive approach to the ISO 14000 EMS within the construction sector in Turkey as well as indicating that the utilization of the ISO 14000 EMS is not yet at the ideal level. In particular, the problems of lack of information and qualified personnel revealed in the results of the analysis should be overcome. Personnel should be qualified in the concept of EMS and on the technical details. In the global construction market, an increase in the number of firms having EMS will both reduce environmental impact and develop the potential of awarding contracts to the construction firms from underdeveloped and/or developing countries.

In: Environmental and Agricultural Research Summaries ...   ISBN: 978-1-63117-090-4
Editor: Lucille T. Cacioppo   © 2014 Nova Science Publishers, Inc.

Chapter 181

USERS' PREFERENCES AND CHOICES IN ARGENTINEAN BEACHES

*A. Faggi[1], N. Madanes[2], M. Rodriguez[3], J. Solanas[3], A. Saenz[3] and I. Espejel[4,**

[1]CONICET-MACN. A. Gallardo, Buenos Aires, Argentina
[2]FCEyN, Buenos Aires, Argentina
[3]Universidad de Flores, Buenos Aires, Argentina
[4]Facultad de Ciencias, Universidad de Baja California, Ensenada, Mexico

RESEARCH SUMMARY

This study analysed the profile and perception – composed of opinions and attitudes – of beach users in Argentina, using data from nine sandy beaches, each with unique environmental and socioeconomic features, located in two coastal municipalities. We distributed 329 surveys composed of 42 questions to Argentinean residents and tourists visiting the beach. Data on the profile were analysed by cluster analysis, and data on perception were explored by Principal Components Analysis. These results allowed grouping all beaches according to variables such as cleanliness, accommodation, infrastructure and services. Users' age and marital status were found to be associated only with certain beaches; married people visited urban and rural beaches, preferring those without infrastructure, while single and young people chose urban beaches with facilities. Contrasting answers regarding environmental beach features were recognised between both municipalities, indicating the success of awareness programs that enhance the beaches' natural values.

---

[*] Corresponding Author: Tel.: +52 646 174 5925; fax: +52 646 174 4560. E-mail: ileana.espejel@uabc.edu.mx (I. Espejel) noram@ege.fcen.uba.ar (N Madanes).

In: Environmental and Agricultural Research Summaries …   ISBN: 978-1-63117-090-4
Editor: Lucille T. Cacioppo   © 2014 Nova Science Publishers, Inc.

Chapter 182

SOIL CARBON SEQUESTRATION THROUGH THE USE OF BIOSOLIDS IN SOILS OF THE PAMPAS REGION, ARGENTINA

Silvana Irene Torri[*,1] *and Raúl Silvio Lavado*[1,2]

[1]School of Agriculture, University of Buenos Aires, Argentina
[2]INBA CONICET/FAUBA, Argentina
Av San Martín, Ciudad Autónoma de Buenos Aires, Argentina

RESEARCH SUMMARY

Carbon sequestration in agricultural soils through the increase of the soil organic carbon (SOC) pool has generated broad interest to mitigate the effects of climate change. Increases in soil carbon storage in agricultural soils may be accomplished by the production of more biomass, originating a net transfer of atmospheric CO_2 into the soil C pool through the humification of crop residues, resulting in carbon sequestration. This Chapter addresses the potential of carbon storage of representative soils of the Pampas region amended with different doses of biosolids, and their soil carbon sequestration potential. Increase in biomass or yields of crops cultivated in sludge amended soils compared to unamended control soils are also discussed. The crops considered in present chapter are a forage, rye.grass (*Lolium perenne*), an annual crop, maize (*Zea mays*) and two trees, pine (*Pinus elliottii*) and eucalyptus (*Eucalyptus dunnii*).

---

[*] E-mail: torri@agro.uba.ar.

In: Environmental and Agricultural Research Summaries ...   ISBN: 978-1-63117-090-4
Editor: Lucille T. Cacioppo   © 2014 Nova Science Publishers, Inc.

Chapter 183

DEVELOPING AN ECOSYSTEM-BASED HABITAT CONSERVATION PLANNING PROTOCOL IN SALINE WETLAND

Jennifer Hitchcock and Zhenghong Tang[*]

College of Architecture, University of Nebraska-Lincoln,
Lincoln, Nebraska, US

RESEARCH SUMMARY

The ecosystem approach to management is in its integrative form a management method that considers the system as a whole instead of as individual components. This holistic approach focuses on habitats and system integrity, and on an objective aimed at the health and integrity of the ecosystem. Ecosystem-Based Management is a unique management style that is intended to overcome the shortfalls of single-sector management and contains the following characteristics:

- Integrates ecological, social, and economic goals,
- Recognizes humans as key components of the ecosystem,
- Considers ecological instead of political boundaries,
- Addresses the complexity of natural processes and social systems,
- Uses adaptive management approach in the face of resulting uncertainties,
- Engages multiple stakeholders in a collaborative processes to define problems and find solutions,
- Incorporates understating of ecosystem processes, and
- Is concerned with the ecological integrity and the sustainability of both human and ecological systems.

---

[*] Corresponding Author: Phone: E-mail: ztang2@unl.edu , (402) 472-9281; Fax: (402) 472-3806.

Originally, ecosystem-based management was designed to manage people's impacts on the oceans. But, it can and should be extended and adapted to any ecosystem where existing policies and management practices have proved insufficient to sustain nature's services.

Nebraska's eastern saline wetlands are one of the most critically endangered ecosystems within the state. In addition to being endangered themselves, the saline wetlands are home to several at-risk species including the federally endangered Salt Creek tiger beetle (*Cicindela nevadica lincolniana*), the federally endangered Interior Least Tern (*Sterna antillarum athalassos*), the federally threatened Piping Plover (*Charadris melodus*), and the state endangered Saltwort (*Salicornia rubra A. Nels.*). Of the more than 20,000 acres that once extended Lancaster and Saunders' Counties, less than 4,000 acres remain (LaGrange *et al.* 2003). Without active conservation and planning efforts, this landscape and the species that rely upon it will continue to diminish.

Conservation of these landscapes is eminent. In 2003, the Saline Wetlands Conservation Partnership was created for their protection. Since that time, the US Fish and Wildlife Service has released the Draft Recovery Plan for the Salt Creek tiger beetle, and designated much of saline wetlands its critical habitat. The next step in the conservation process for these wetlands is the creation of a Habitat Conservation Plan. To launch this conservation plan's development, this project creates a Habitat Conservation Planning Guide.

Three phases were used to develop the Habitat Conservation Planning Guide for Nebraska's Eastern Saline Wetlands. Phase I created individual Habitat Conservation Planning Guides from the scientific literature, the US Fish and Wildlife Service's Endangered Species Habitat Conservation Planning Handbook, and Benton County, Oregon's Benton County Prairie Species Habitat Conservation Plan Revised Draft. Phase II combined these individual guides into a single Habitat Conservation Planning Guide. Finally, Phase III localized the single guide for Nebraska's Eastern Saline Wetlands using four local plans: the Lincoln/Lancaster County Comprehensive Plan, Environmental Resources Section, the Salt Creek Tiger Beetle (*Cicindela nevadica Lincolniana*) Draft Recovery Plan, the Implementation Plan for the Conservation of Nebraska's Eastern Saline Wetlands, and the Little Salt Creek Watershed Master Plan.

The outcome of the analysis was a Habitat Conservation Planning Guide Checklist for Nebraska's Eastern Saline Wetlands for use in the development or review of a Habitat Conservation Plan for Nebraska's Eastern Saline Wetlands. This guide ensures all components required by the US Fish and Wildlife Service, as well as those necessary for the plan's quality are included. Additionally, a Components Glossary has been created to further define each of the guide's components.

In: Environmental and Agricultural Research Summaries …   ISBN: 978-1-63117-090-4
Editor: Lucille T. Cacioppo   © 2014 Nova Science Publishers, Inc.

Chapter 184

ARE ECOSYSTEM MODELS AN IMPROVEMENT ON SINGLE-SPECIES MODELS FOR FISHERIES MANAGEMENT? THE CASE OF UPPER GULF OF CALIFORNIA, MEXICO

Alejandro Espinoza-Tenorio[1], Matthias Wolff[1]
and Ileana Espejel[2]*

[1]Leibniz-Zentrum für Marine Tropenökologie GmbH,
Fahrenheitstr, Bremen, Germany
[2]Facultad de Ciencias, Universidad Autónoma de Baja California,
Ensenada, Mexico

RESEARCH SUMMARY

We review the recent applications of ecosystem models (EMs) as tools for fisheries management in the Upper Gulf of California (UGC), Mexico. EMs are compared with single-species model applications in the UGC, as a basis for assessing the benefits of each ecosystem model as a tool for evaluating management alternatives capable of diminishing impacts on marine ecosystems. The strengths and weaknesses of different types of EMs and their ability to evaluate the systemic mechanisms underlying observed shifts in resource production are also examined with respect to Ecosystem-Based Fisheries Management (EBFM) general goals. Findings showed that ecosystem modeling has increasingly resulted in support for EBFM in the UGC. However, outputs also proved evidence on that EMs are facing a most complicated situation than single-species models regarding the lack of data. Thus, the step from single-species models to EMs is a stage of the management of the area that does not require the elimination of the first approach, but rather the use of both approaches in a complimentary manner. The challenge is the integration of current ecosystem information to detect the gaps in the collective knowledge on the UGC. Insights from this study are valuable

* Corresponding Author: Tel.: +52 646 174 5925; fax: +52 646 174 4560. E-mail: ileana.espejel@uabc.edu.mx (I. Espejel).

in defining a planning model scheme that supports ecosystem-based management policies in local fisheries.

In: Environmental and Agricultural Research Summaries …   ISBN: 978-1-63117-090-4
Editor: Lucille T. Cacioppo   © 2014 Nova Science Publishers, Inc.

Chapter 185

A STUDY ABOUT THE ADOPTION OF THE PRACTICE OF CLEANER PRODUCTION IN INDUSTRIAL ENTERPRISES CERTIFIED ISO 14001 IN BRAZIL

José Augusto de Oliveira, Otávio José de Oliveira
and Sílvia Renata de Oliveira Santos
UNESP – São Paulo State University, Brazil
CEUCLAR – Centro Universitário Claretiano de Batatais, Brazil

RESEARCH SUMMARY

The growth of developing countries has significantly driven the industrial activity, which has generated employment and development. However, this scenario also has its downside, in other words, due to lax laws and consumers still little conscious of the importance of effective environmental protection. The industry has been the main degrading environment in these nations. However, some technical programs and management tools have been used to minimize this serious problem, especially if the environmental management system ISO 14001:2004 and Cleaner Production (CP). For these reasons, this book chapter has as main objective to present good practices of cleaner production adopted by four industrial companies operating in Brazil with high profile and certified according to ISO 14001:2004. The companies act in the area of cellulose and paper and chemical. Their management systems ISO 14001:2004 will be characterized and the major practices of Cleaner Production will be reported. In general terms, it was observed that the EMS has greater coverage of these companies that ISO 14001:2004 due to demands from the processes related to cleaner production. They use specific methodologies and specific classifications to the elements of CP and do not follow exactly the elements proposed by UNIDO (United Nations Industrial Development Organization).

It was observed that the companies have achieved significant results by adopting the cleaner production achieved environmental and financial gains from the reuse of production inputs, internal recycling in the production process, cost reduction with treatment and disposal of waste, reducing spending with environmental liabilities promoted by prevention of the pollution, among others, which are the main benefits expected by the practice of CP.

In: Environmental and Agricultural Research Summaries ...   ISBN: 978-1-63117-090-4
Editor: Lucille T. Cacioppo   © 2014 Nova Science Publishers, Inc.

Chapter 186

TOWARDS A WATERSHED APPROACH IN NON-POINT SOURCE POLLUTION CONTROL IN THE LAKE TAI BASIN, CHINA

Xiaoying Yang, Zheng Zheng and Xingzhang Luo
Department of Environmental Science and Engineering,
Fudan University, Shanghai, China

RESEARCH SUMMARY

While accounting for 0.4% of its land area and 2.9% of its population, the Lake Tai basin generates more than 14% of China's Gross Domestic Production. Accompanied with its fast economic development is serious water environment deterioration in the Lake Tai basin. The lake is becoming increasingly eutrophied and has frequently suffered from cyanobacterial blooms in recent years. Although tremendous investment has been made to control pollutant discharge to improve its water quality, the Lake Tai's eutrophication trend has not been reversed due to the past emphasis on point pollution sources and the lack of effective measures for non-point source pollution control in the region.

A watershed approach is proposed to deal with the serious non-point source pollution issues in the region with four guiding principles: (1) Control from the source; (2) Reduction along transport; (3) Emphasis on waste reuse and nutrient recycling; and (4) Intensive treatment at key locations. Research as well as field applications that have been conducted to implement this watershed approach are introduced. Existing problems and their implications for future research needs as well as policy making are also discussed.

In: Environmental and Agricultural Research Summaries …   ISBN: 978-1-63117-090-4
Editor: Lucille T. Cacioppo   © 2014 Nova Science Publishers, Inc.

Chapter 187

SOCIO-ENVIRONMENTAL MARKETING AS AN ENVIRONMENTAL MANAGEMENT SYSTEM TO PROTECT ENDANGERED SPECIES

Juan José Mier-Terán[*,a], *María José Montero-Simó*[≠,b]
and Rafael A. Araque-Padilla[‡,b]
[a]University of Cádiz, Spain
[b]University of Córdoba, Spain

RESEARCH SUMMARY

The environmental management systems are normally used to obtain certain environmental objectives. That is why they are established as either business or institutional obligations aimed at identifying objectives that improve the environment and incorporate procedures in management to attain these objectives. Moreover, given that prevention is always better than cure, they ensure that the aforementioned is complied with.

A common objective in these systems is to change behaviour that is thought to be negative with regard to the environment, whether it is that of those working for the aforesaid organisations or that of the final users of the services. Social marketing has proven to be a very suitable technology to change behaviour, and with regard to environmental issues, the specialisation of Environmental Marketing is a good example of how it is applied to a specific subject matter. In this case its basic principles and the techniques that are applied are aimed at modifying negative behaviour towards environmental problems. In this context, the basis and foundations of the Socio-environmental Marketing are shown as a management tool used to change behaviour in the sustainable management of protected areas. Furthermore a specific case is presented whereby this management system is used to protect an endangered species, the Iberian Lynx.

[*] E-mail: juanjose.mier-teran@uca.es.
[≠] E-mail: jmontero@etea.com.
[‡] E-mail: raraque@etea.com.

In: Environmental and Agricultural Research Summaries ...   ISBN: 978-1-63117-090-4
Editor: Lucille T. Cacioppo   © 2014 Nova Science Publishers, Inc.

Chapter 188

SPATIO-TEMPORAL MODELING
OF RADIONUCLIDE DEPOSITION

Lubos Matejicek

Institute for Environmental Studies, Charles University in Prague,
Faculty of Natural Science, Prague, Czech Republic

RESEARCH SUMMARY

An integrated research on spatio-temporal modeling of radionuclide deposition is solved by a standard way, and by advanced GIS tools. In order to explore radionuclide transport in the Irish Sea, a dynamic compartment model is developed for accumulation and redistribution of plutonium ($^{239/240}$Pu) over a few decades. The compartments are situated in regions that are divided into a few vertical parts: the water column, the interface and the sediment parts. Basic transport processes are represented by advection and diffusion. Advection denotes transport by shifting particles from one place to another by the flow field. Diffusion originates from concentration differences that result in a tendency to equalize concentration levels. In dependence on the environment, there are different diffusion speeds in surface water bodies and in sediments, which is controlled by parameters in the compartment model. In order to provide model simulations, two approaches are used to demonstrate various possibilities of the non-GIS solution and the spatio-temporal modeling in the GIS environment. As an example, the scenario based on ACSL (Advanced Continuous Simulation Language) represents the standard way of dynamic modeling that is extended by sharing data between the simulation tools and the spatial database. For a more complex spatio-temporal analysis, the solution of a compartment model is implemented in the GIS programming environment. According to the measured data, the simulation results support the idea of desorption from relatively contaminated sediments in the eastern Irish Sea mud patches by pore-water exchange and tide and storm activity that is followed by transport in the dissolved phase, which can subsequently leads to accumulation of plutonium ($^{239/240}$Pu) in other regions.

In: Environmental and Agricultural Research Summaries ...   ISBN: 978-1-63117-090-4
Editor: Lucille T. Cacioppo   © 2014 Nova Science Publishers, Inc.

Chapter 189

DYNAMIC MODELING OF SURFACE WATER POLLUTION CAUSED BY THE INDUSTRIAL POLLUTANT RELEASE

Lubos Matejicek and Lenka Tlapakova
Institute for Environmental Studies, Charles University in Prague,
Faculty of Natural Science, Prague, Czech Republic

RESEARCH SUMMARY

Dynamic modeling focused on surface water pollution by accidental release is considered in the context of the GIS tools. Integration of dynamic modeling in the GIS environment is carried out by the AVSim, the software tool originally developed in the ArcView with the AVENUE programming language, and actually implemented in the ArcGIS. The presented compartment model demonstrates the AVSim capabilities to solve a simplified one-dimensional model that uses a one-dimensional representation of the river. It assumes a prevailing one-directional flow that causes varying properties of the water body along its direction. The varying properties of the water body along its flow direction are approximated by a chain of stocks of the pollutant that represent connected sections of the river. Before creation and validation of the compartment model, the linear interpolation is used to explore time changes of pollutant concentrations in a few river sections neighboring downstream the accidental release. Finally, two simulation studies are presented. The first study is based on no downstream contamination removal after the accidental release. The second study includes the pollutant removal by the remediation procedure, but only the main processes are included into the simplified compartment model. Finally, the results and methods of modeling are discussed.

In: Environmental and Agricultural Research Summaries …   ISBN: 978-1-63117-090-4
Editor: Lucille T. Cacioppo   © 2014 Nova Science Publishers, Inc.

Chapter 190

MODELING OF WATER POLLUTION IN RIVER BASINS WITH GIS

Lubos Matejicek

Institute for Environmental Studies, Charles University in Prague,
Faculty of Natural Science, Prague, Czech Republic

RESEARCH SUMMARY

The increasing importance and awareness of water quality in river basins resulted in the establishment of wide-ranging monitoring networks. Long-term measurements of physical-chemical parameters, hydrological and meteorological observations, mapping of basins with GIS, GPS and remote sensing requires development of advanced tools for data analysis and modeling in the frame of an information system. A few strategies to integrate spatially distributed environmental data and models are presented with use of the recent development in satellite technology, which can support classification of basin surface to identify potential sources of pollution. Data analysis and compartment models deal with basin characteristics extended by land cover attributes, which are in addition to standard terrain measurements estimated by processing of satellite images from Landsat 7 TM and ASTER. A number of indexes, for example NDVI is used to set model parameters. A case study focused on water pollution from nitrates demonstrates accumulation and transport of pollutants from point and non-point sources. The dynamic models are integrated into GIS from data linkage through shared data files to building models as extensions into fully functional GIS. Other way is represented by development of a standalone software application that covers GIS and modeling functionality. As an example of modeling of water pollution in the GIS environment, a computer program developed with the MapObjects programming library documents abilities to manage spatial data, calculate dynamic models and display results together with the storage of data in spatial formats or database.

In: Environmental and Agricultural Research Summaries ...   ISBN: 978-1-63117-090-4
Editor: Lucille T. Cacioppo   © 2014 Nova Science Publishers, Inc.

Chapter 191

SPATIO-TEMPORAL MODELING OF THE DUST EMISSIONS FROM AN OPENCAST COAL MINING AREA

Lubos Matejicek[1] and Zbynek Janour[2]

[1]Institute for Environmental Studies, Charles University in Prague,
Faculty of Natural Science, Prague, Czech Republic
[2]Institute of Thermomechanics, Academy of Sciences,
Prague, Czech Republic

RESEARCH SUMMARY

The described research is carried out to map the dust emission sources of opencast coal mining activities and their influence on surrounding areas. The results can be utilized by mine authorities and environmental scientists in the field of soil pollution and air quality monitoring for advance prediction.

The attached case study is focused on the opencast coal mine area in northwest Czech Republic. To achieve the objectives, spatial data from remote sensing represented by images from Landsat 7 are used for identification of large opencast coal mine areas. Data from GPS and laser scanning complemented by geodetic measurements serve as an input for building of the digital elevation model. Data inputs based on aerial images and thematic maps include spatial locations of the local dust emission sources represented by transport routes, temporary repositories and mining excavators. Spatial estimates of the dust emission rates are validated by conducting a field study. All the spatio-temporal data are integrated in the framework of the GIS project that contains complex data structures supporting advanced spatial analysis and visualization.

The influence of dust emissions on surrounding areas is estimated by dispersion modeling based on U.S. EPA models. The standalone simulation tools managed by ISC-AEROMOD View are utilized to assess deposition fluxes from selected emission sources. After the post-processing stage, simulation outputs are incorporated into the GIS project.

All the spatial data together with the dispersion modeling outputs are displayed in GIS as the map layers. Due to the obtained results of the impacts on residential areas in the neighborhood of the opencast coal mine, remediation procedures focused on relocation and reduction of the main emission sources are needed to minimize the influence of the coal dust on living environment. In this case, GIS can assist to optimize the opencast coal mine infrastructure considering to the decreasing major mining activities that cause the significant dust emissions and soil pollution.

In: Environmental and Agricultural Research Summaries ...   ISBN: 978-1-63117-090-4
Editor: Lucille T. Cacioppo   © 2014 Nova Science Publishers, Inc.

Chapter 192

SPATIAL MODELING AND OPTIMIZATION OF MUNICIPAL SOLID WASTE COLLECTION IN URBAN REGIONS

Lubos Matejicek

Institute for Environmental Studies Charles University in Prague,
Faculty of Natural Science, Prague, Czech Republic

RESEARCH SUMMARY

Growing production of municipal solid waste in the recent years caused by increasing global levels of economic activity needs more sophisticated management tools for its collection. Despite some local efforts to reduce the waste, disposal in landfills is still the most predominate way. Considering to restrictive environmental regulations, more efficient and sustainable systems of municipal solid waste management are carried out to protect our living environment. They deal with the waste sorting, which is mainly focused on categories represented by paper, mixed plastics, mixed glass, mixed waste, hazardous waste and metals. Thus, specific transport vehicles and optimized routes are needed to manage the collection of all the waste categories from local sites to landfills, incineration plants, collecting yards and recovery sites. This contribution presents the waste collection methods based on spatial analysis and operations research. The spatial analysis is focused on development of the road network datasets for waste collection, finding the best routes, defining the service area and creating the origin-destination cost matrix in geographic information systems (GISs). The identified routes and local service areas together with the cost per unit and the total amount of the transported waste form data inputs into operations research. The transportation problem in linear programming is used to optimize the total cost for transportation of each waste category in the framework of municipal solid waste collection. As an example, the urban areas of Prague are included into a case study to illustrate spatial modeling in the GIS environment and optimization focused on collection networks. The individual collection sites are grouped into the urban areas. Waste production in each urban area is estimated in dependence on available data from reports about the living environment in Prague. The locations of target collection points represented by recycling places, incineration plants and landfills are based on larger urban districts. The developed GIS project can manage various scenarios, which indicate different total costs. In spite of its actual lower total cost, the landfill will become more difficult to implement due to the increasing cost caused by limited land availability and environmental community opposition. On the other hand, the recovery/recycling will become more important because of its minimal negative interaction with the living environment. In order to minimize the costs and degradation of our living environment, spatial modeling extended by methods focused on linear programming can assist to find suitable waste management scenarios for collection of municipal solid waste in urban areas.

In: Environmental and Agricultural Research Summaries ...   ISBN: 978-1-63117-090-4
Editor: Lucille T. Cacioppo   © 2014 Nova Science Publishers, Inc.

Chapter 193

SPATIAL MODELING OF AIR POLLUTION BASED ON TRAFFIC EMISSIONS IN URBAN AREAS

Lubos Matejicek[1], Zbynek Janour[2] and Michal Strizik[3]

[1]Institute for Environmental Studies, Charles University in Prague
Prague, Czech Republic
[2]Institute of Thermomechanics, Academy of Sciences,
Prague, Czech Republic
[3]Laboratory of Risk Research and Management,
Technical University of Ostrava, Ostrava, Czech Republic

RESEARCH SUMMARY

Road traffic becomes a dominant source of air pollution in urban areas. The emissions of inorganic compounds and volatile organic compounds caused by motor vehicles have increased trends, particularly in urban areas, which together with other emitted compounds can cause human health problems in a long-time period. Procedures for estimating of road traffic emissions in the USA and in the European region are based on guidelines and recommendations. In order to implement the guidelines, decision-making tools are necessary to provide information in an easy understandable form. Thus, the spatial information system is needed to manage spatio-temporal data, provide analysis, solve numerical models and visualize the results. Generally, spatial data include street networks and monitoring networks. Temporal data are represented by changes of traffic intensity and by time series of measured pollutants. Geographic information systems (GISs) extended by environmental modeling tools offer advance estimates of traffic emissions improved by the digital terrain data and by the wind flow effects. The estimates of air pollution in the surrounded areas can be based on spatial interpolation. In a wide range of spatial interpolations, the deterministic techniques or the geostatistical methods are used in dependence on the input data and the results provided by the exploratory spatial data analysis (ESDA). Each spatial interpolation attached to the map layer defines concentration levels at a specified time period. The time series of map layers can demonstrate the variability of the air pollution distribution, which brings a new insight into this research.

In addition to mapping of the urban air pollution in dependence on the traffic intensity and the measured concentrations, numerical modeling and simulation in wind tunnels are presented as important tools for exploration of the dispersion and the transport of pollutants caused by wind flows and other effects. A number of software tools based on Gaussian dispersion principles are mentioned in the framework of US EPA guidelines.

As a case study, spatial modeling of air pollution is focused on the urban area of the city of Prague, because a number of motor vehicles registered on the Prague territory is growing. In addition to the registered vehicles, the specific phenomenon in the central Europe is represented by the abrupt increase in traffic of trucks. In spite of new methods for reduction of emissions from motor vehicles, urban development and successive reconstructions of existing roads cause other emissions. Thus, the street network also becomes a set of line sources of stirred up suspended particulates generated by the passing vehicles. These dust emissions, so-called secondary dust, are estimated and partially validated by measurements of the fraction PM_{10}. As an example, estimates of nitrogen oxides are carried out by spatial interpolation based on data from the surface monitoring network and the DIAL-LIDAR measurements.

Integration of spatio-temporal data together with environmental modeling tools brings new possibilities to compare spatial interpolations created for individual compounds at the high temporal and spatial resolution. In the framework of the GIS, mapping of air pollution and human exposures in streets, at workplace locations and residence addresses can help to reduce traffic emissions by optimization of transport scenarios.

In: Environmental and Agricultural Research Summaries …   ISBN: 978-1-63117-090-4
Editor: Lucille T. Cacioppo   © 2014 Nova Science Publishers, Inc.

Chapter 194

MODELING OF TRAFFIC-RELATED ENVIRONMENTAL POLLUTION IN THE GIS

Lubos Matejicek[1] and Zbynek Janour[2]
[1]Institute for Environmental Studies, Charles University in Prague,
Prague, Czech Republic
[2]Institute of Thermomechanics, Academy of Sciences,
Prague, Czech Republic

RESEARCH SUMMARY

The numerical models are based on dispersion modeling and statistical analysis. In case of dispersion modeling, the ISC-AEROMOD View is used for modeling multiple pollutants with the U.S. EPA modeling tool ISCST3. The Mobile View assists as an interface for the U.S. EPA MOBILE6 model that predict arterial street emissions focused on hydrocarbons, carbon monoxide, nitrogen oxides, carbon dioxide, particulate matter, and toxics from cars, motorcycles, light- and heavy-duty trucks under various conditions. The potential impacts of accidental releases are solved by SLAB View that complements the modeling tools by analysis of emissions from accidental releases of toxic gases. Analysis of urban traffic-induced noise pollution is assessed by U.S. FHWA-TNM tools. The GIS is finally used to serve as a common analysis framework for individual modeling tools. In order to display the numerical simulation outputs together with urban area map layers, numerical modeling based on U.S. EPA software tools is integrated into the GIS for spatial interpolations and spatial analysis. It assists to evaluate high levels of air pollution and noise pollution together with the thematic map layers of residential zones, business centers, schools, and hospitals. Finally, finding alternative routes can decreases air pollution and noise pollution in selected zones. As a case study, the city of Prague sample data set helps to demonstrate data processing and modeling of traffic-related environmental pollution. The ESRI's geodatabase is used for implementation a comprehensive information model and a transaction model in the GIS environment. It is also the common application logic used in ArcGIS for accessing and working with all spatial thematic data and simulation inputs/outputs. Spatial interpolation for prediction maps and probability maps complement the existing thematic map layers, which enable cell based modeling for spatial multi criteria decision analysis. The synthesis of environmental models and GISs creates a more complex base for environmental simulation that can support decision-making processes in a more straightforward way.

In: Environmental and Agricultural Research Summaries ...   ISBN: 978-1-63117-090-4
Editor: Lucille T. Cacioppo   © 2014 Nova Science Publishers, Inc.

Chapter 195

ESTIMATING THE ENVIRONMENTAL EFFECTS ON RESIDENTIAL PROPERTY VALUE WITH GIS

Lubos Matejicek

Institute for Environmental Studies, Charles University in Prague,
Faculty of Natural Science, Prague, Czech Republic

RESEARCH SUMMARY

Ongoing research to develop a new generation of decision-making tools for estimating the environmental effects on residential property value has significantly increased the demand for land surface data, information on the state of living environment, and the corresponding need for the advanced use of geographic information systems (GIS). In order to provide the foundation for price estimates, all the existing data focused on building and environment are integrated in the framework of a GIS spatial database. Traditional methods mostly emphasize the relationship between the effects of accessibility to central locations, and ignore location-specific attributes of housing. However, little has been done on high-rise, densely populated residential areas. Thus, the paper aims to investigate the neighboring and environmental characteristics of the selected site. A more advanced approach based on spatial analysis and modeling in the GIS environment is used to manage spatio-temporal data, to process aerial images and satellite images, to import measurements from GPS, to create digital terrain models, to analyze topography together with environmental data, and to visualize the results. The partial results based on the traveling time to the closest services and the origin-destination cost matrixes are derived from the network analysis. The landscape characteristics can be demonstrated on animated sequences showing the flight over a landscape model that is based on the digital terrain model with draped images over it to show the area. The living environment contains a few compartments: air pollution, water pollution, waste management, noise assessment, and monitoring of environmental impacts on population health. Air pollution is estimated by continuous map surfaces, predicting the values of pollutants concentration for the selected site in dependence on the sample points at the air quality monitoring stations. Water pollution covers surface water pollution, drinking water supply and quality, waste water, accidental contaminant spills, and optionally, flood control measures. The waste compartment is focused on the system of municipal waste management with sorting of reusable components of municipal waste, and hazardous chemicals information. Noise assessment covers road traffic noise and air traffic noise. The environmental impacts on population health come out from reports of the national institute of public health. In addition to the main compartments, other data can complement the partial inputs to the system (energy prices, public transport schema, locations of neighbor natural reservation sites and historical sites). In the framework of spatio-temporal analysis, the spatial weighting matrixes are used for prediction of the final rating. The final results are represented by the thematic map layers in the GIS project based on ArcGIS and its extensions. The attached case study shows a scenario in dependence on setting the weight parameters. Unexpected findings are caused by rapid changes in the dense living environment and slow conversion of the reality market in the selected site in Prague, the Czech Republic. For all that, the case study brings better understanding of how the residential site rating depends on various environmental attributes.

In: Environmental and Agricultural Research Summaries ...   ISBN: 978-1-63117-090-4
Editor: Lucille T. Cacioppo   © 2014 Nova Science Publishers, Inc.

Chapter 196

SPATIO-TEMPORAL DATA MANAGEMENT FOR ENVIRONMENTAL MODELING OF DUST DISPERSION OVER OPENCAST COAL MINING AREAS

Lubos Matejicek

Institute for Environmental Studies, Charles University in Prague,
Faculty of Natural Science, Prague, Czech Republic

RESEARCH SUMMARY

There is a significant need for an integrated environmental information system containing both a knowledge base and decision-support tools to manage environmental protection of living environment near the opencast mining areas. Effective environmental management and research require spatio-temporal data to anticipate and predict the impact of the mining development. However, current data, while often extensive, are fragmented and inconsistent. Given that there already exists data repositories and collections of tools and modeling systems like continuous monitoring and dispersion modeling, the major contribution of the proposed GIS framework is to facilitate access to these items. An attached case study demonstrates GIS mapping of the opencast mining sites, and geodatabase management that supports spatial analysis and environmental modeling. A few spatial data inputs exist for building digital terrain models. The 3D laser scanner is used to acquire surface scans of the local sites. While the laser scans are used for mapping of the continuous parts, the differential GPS assists in the capturing of slope lines, surface points, and surface objects, such as mining facilities and residential buildings. In order to create the digital terrain model of the whole area of interest, all the input data are complemented by contour lines from existing digital map sources. For surface analysis and visualization of the opencast sites in a more realistic way, satellite images and aerial images are draped over the surface. This digital terrain model extended by data linked to emission sources, meteorological measurements and continuous air pollution monitoring represents the main input for spatial analysis and environmental modeling. Their outputs can form spatial interpolations, probability maps, wind flow layers, and isolines of pollutant concentrations based on dispersion modeling. All the data are managed by the ESRI's geodatabase. Each geodatabase data model represents both the ordered collections of simple features and rasters, as well as the rules and schema properties that add rich GIS behavior. It offers to use simultaneously several approaches to integrate spatio-temporally distributed environmental analyses and numerical simulations in the framework of GIS. They can range from simple linkage through shared data files to building environmental models as analytical functions into fully functional GIS. The geodatabase data models can also effectively be configured in a user-friendly environmental decision support system that is problem-specific and customized for environmental protection of residential zones.

In: Environmental and Agricultural Research Summaries …   ISBN: 978-1-63117-090-4
Editor: Lucille T. Cacioppo   © 2014 Nova Science Publishers, Inc.

Chapter 197

SPATIO-TEMPORAL MODELING OF ENVIRONMENTAL STRESS IMPACTS ON VEGETATION CHANGES IN MOUNTAIN FORESTS

Lubos Matejicek and Eva Vavrova

Institute for Environmental Studies, Charles University in Prague,
Faculty of Natural Science, Prague, Czech Republic

RESEARCH SUMMARY

Innovative techniques, properly used, can offer exciting opportunities for the advancement of ecology. In case of geographic information systems (GISs), ecologists have a powerful and rapidly growing set of methods and tools with which to solve fundamental problems of a theoretical and applied nature. Previous analytical methods used in these subdisciplines have become implemented into GIS software. Current research in the field of ecology is increasingly integrated with the evolution of GPS, geostatistics, remote sensing and other techniques for data collection and spatial analysis, which promotes the use GIS. As an example, the data model for forest management is introduced and other extensions for spatio-temporal modeling are discussed. It is supported by the ESRI's geodatabase that can manage geographic data for GIS. The described forestry data model originates from research results created by forestry users attending the 1999 ESRI Users Conference in the framework of presentations of GIS and the geodatabase technology. The areas of interest for implementation of the data model include the White Mountain National Forest and the mountain Norway spruce forests that belong to the most endangered Central-European forest ecosystems.

In: Environmental and Agricultural Research Summaries …   ISBN: 978-1-63117-090-4
Editor: Lucille T. Cacioppo   © 2014 Nova Science Publishers, Inc.

Chapter 198

SPATIO-TEMPORAL MODELING BY FIELD COMPUTERS WITH GPS

Lubos Matejicek and Jana Konradova

Institute for Environmental Studies, Charles University in Prague,
Faculty of Natural Science, Prague, Czech Republic

RESEARCH SUMMARY

Using field computers with GPS advanced tools can benefit from availability of a computing system, GPS data collection, and sharing data with other external sensors. It offers a complete range of properties that provide flexibility, and ease of use required by environmental mapping professionals and modelers. Using GPS and external sensors for GIS data collection and data maintenance is essential for timely decision-making and the wise use of many resources. Thus, all over the world, scientific organizations, environmental agencies, and utility companies can use GIS data collection and predictions based on model simulations to stay up-to-date and competitive. In order to demonstrate environmental mapping and spatio-temporal modeling by the field computing tools, two attached case studies have been developed to show monitoring and modeling of water quality in the small basins, and estimates in ecological terrain research. The first study focused on water quality assessment is based on the GPS high-accuracy data collection for development of the local digital terrain model, the location of hydrometric profiles, and the measurement of selected water quality indicators. The indicators are selected from the sets of general physical and chemical indicators, specific organic substances, metals and metalloids, microbiological and biological indicators, and radiological indicators. The built-in compartment models deal with basin characteristics extended by land cover attributes. Some model parameters are also estimated by experimental data and land cover types that serve as detention media or transformers. Land cover classification is provided by terrain observations, and by the spatial data derived from satellite images, and aerial photographs. Model simulations are solved by programming modules implemented in the GIS mobile software tools. Spatial analyses are based on case oriented tasks that expand the benefits of a geographic information system to field mapping efforts. All the data can be shared with the datasets managed by GIS or other information systems. The results show that the spatio-temporal modeling approach extended by the GIS and remote sensing data can support decision-making processes for better management practices in a more efficient way. The second study focused on terrain ecological exploratory analysis deals with quantitative estimates of ecological systems, such as abundance, exponential and logistic growth, migration, diversity, and similarity. Dynamic modeling formed by built-in standard ecological models is extended by spatial interactions. In addition to dynamics and spatial interactions of each population, the interaction on the level of communities or ecosystems can be subjoined. The implemented dynamic models are mostly based on the models for competition and predation. In case of spatio-temporal modeling, the diffusion and advection phenomena are implemented to simulate the migration of individuals, biomass or energy. As an example, mapping of the trees attacked by the insect species is carried out to demonstrate the mobile computing abilities. Considering to the climate conditions, the vegetation and the forest land-cover, the spreading of insect species causes large damage in the selected sites. Thus, if the attacked trees are regularly observed, the migration of the insect species can be predicted by spatial dynamic models, and consequently, compared together with the observations for the model calibration. The progress in GISs, mobile computing systems, satellite images, aerial photographs, and network interconnections represents just a part of a wide range of new approaches and technology. The presented mobile computing tools try to implement all the new phenomena in the framework of the standard surface water quality assessment, and the ecological modeling methodology.

In: Environmental and Agricultural Research Summaries ...   ISBN: 978-1-63117-090-4
Editor: Lucille T. Cacioppo   © 2014 Nova Science Publishers, Inc.

Chapter 199

ENVIRONMENTAL POLLUTANTS-INDUCED OXIDATIVE STRESS: A ROLE FOR ANTIOXIDANTS IN HEALTH PROMOTION AND AGING PREVENTION

Borut Poljsak and Uros Glavan

Faculty of Health Sciences, Department of Environmental Health,
University of Ljubljana, Ljubljana, Slovenia, EU

RESEARCH SUMMARY

The book offers a comprehensive review of current research regarding the influences of environmental factors involved in human health and aging. Many environmental compounds promote excessive oxidative stress, which is the primary cause of accelerated aging and which also contributes to the development of human diseases. The basic concepts of aging theories are discussed, as is the promotion of oxidative stress which has been identified as one of the most important mechanisms responsible for the toxic effects of the majority of environmental pollutants. Antioxidants play an important role in the defense against pollutant-induced toxicity.

In: Environmental and Agricultural Research Summaries ...   ISBN: 978-1-63117-090-4
Editor: Lucille T. Cacioppo   © 2014 Nova Science Publishers, Inc.

Chapter 200

LINKS BETWEEN AIR POLLUTION AND CLIMATE CHANGE AND THEIR INTERACTIVE EFFECTS

Ahmed El Nemr[1]

Department of Pollution, Environmental Division,
National Institute of Oceanography and Fisheries,
Kayet Bey, El Anfoushy, Alexandria, Egypt

RESEARCH SUMMARY

Many air pollutants and greenhouse gases have common sources, contribute to radiative balance, interact in the atmosphere, and affect ecosystems. The impacts on ecosystems have been traditionally treated separately for air pollution and climate change. However, the combined effects may significantly differ from a sum of separate effects. This chapter reviews the changes in greenhouse gases and the links between air pollution and climate change and their interactive effects. A simultaneous addressing of the air pollution and climate change effects on earth may result in more effective research, management and monitoring as well as a better integration of local, national and global environmental policies.

---

[1]E-mail: ahmedmoustafaelnemr@yahoo.com.

In: Environmental and Agricultural Research Summaries …   ISBN: 978-1-63117-090-4
Editor: Lucille T. Cacioppo   © 2014 Nova Science Publishers, Inc.

Chapter 201

REVIEWING EXPERIENCES FROM MANAGING ATMOSPHERIC POLLUTION TO HELP FACILITATE RESPONSES TO CLIMATE CHANGE

*Livia Bizikova[*1], Ian Burton[2], Erica Crawford-Boettcher[3], and Thea Dickinson[4†]*

[1] International Institute for Sustainable Development (IISD), Winnipeg, MB, Canada
[2] Adaptation and Impact Research Division (AIRD, Environment Canada
Downsview, Toronto, Ontario, Canada
[3] School of Community and Regional Planning,
University of British Columbia, Vancouver Canada
[4] Burton Dickinson Consulting, Toronto, Ontario, Canada

RESEARCH SUMMARY

Anthropogenic climate change was brought to the public's attention in the 1980s. It was seen as the next in a succession of atmospheric pollution issues—following from experiences with acid precipitation and stratospheric ozone depletion—and almost instantly became a part of the global policy agenda. Much attention has been paid to the forces behind the development of international agreements and domestic regulations, as well as to the role played by evolution of scientific understanding in designing policy responses to all three atmospheric issues. Seeing the favorable outcomes of the Montreal protocol, some analyses have compared the Montreal and Kyoto Protocols and the political, technological, and economic circumstances surrounding their development and implementation. Undoubtedly, there are many lessons from how acid precipitation and ozone depletion were tackled in international negotiations and policy processes that can be applied to climate change adaptation and mitigation actions. But basing approaches to climate change on previous experiences with acid precipitation and ozone depletion management has also caused some

[*] Canada, R3B 0Y4, Tel: +204-958-7753, Fax: +204-958-7710.
[†] thea.dickinson@rogers.com.

problems, due to significant differences in the nature of these atmospheric issues. Notably, this orientation has led to a dichotomisation of responses into "mitigation" and "adaptation," which in turn penetrated the research and policy processes. This paper aims to clarify how the dichotomy between adaptation and mitigation occurred in light of experiences with other atmospheric pollution issues, and to explore the major similarities and differences in managing the succession of the three atmospheric pollution issues. Specifically, in this paper we aim to address the following questions:

a. What are the key features of each atmospheric pollution issue and what types of actual mitigation and adaptation actions were applied to address the issues?
b. How does the interplay between local, national and international actors and institutions influence responses to atmospheric pollution challenges?
c. What are the major differences and similarities between measures to address climate change mitigation and adaptation, as compared to responses to preceding atmospheric issues?

First, this paper provides an overview of major features of the three atmospheric issues of acid rain, stratospheric ozone depletion and climate change. This discussion centres on the characteristics of mitigation and adaptation actions and the role of local, national and global stakeholders in shaping the policy agenda. The second part of the paper is focused on comparing key features of the three issues so as to shed light on the form of current actions on climate change. Finally, we suggest policy implications for current mitigation and adaptation actions based on the evolution of policy and research within the three domains.

In: Environmental and Agricultural Research Summaries …   ISBN: 978-1-63117-090-4
Editor: Lucille T. Cacioppo   © 2014 Nova Science Publishers, Inc.

Chapter 202

CATALYTIC REGULATION AND UTILIZATION OF GREENHOUSE GASES

Benjaram M. Reddy[1], Gode Thrimurthulu and Pankaj Bharali

Inorganic and Physical Chemistry Division, Indian Institute
of Chemical Technology, Hyderabad, India

RESEARCH SUMMARY

As known, the most abundant greenhouse gases in the order of their relative abundance are water vapor, carbon dioxide, methane, nitrous oxide, ozone, and halogenated gases. It is rather complicated to affirm that a certain gas causes a certain percentage of the greenhouse effect, because the influence of various gases is not simple additive. Research on the application of catalytic materials for regulation and utilization of greenhouse gases has been receiving continued attention in view of the gravity of the problem. There have long been major areas of research on the design of most efficient catalytic materials to reduce greenhouse gas emissions and hence global warming. The greenhouse gases could be transformed to different value-added products or decomposed into nontoxic gases through various catalytic approaches. Currently, a number of reactions and processes are under active investigation which hold promise for the utilization of carbon dioxide and other greenhouse gases in chemicals synthesis. This chapter is focused on the application of catalytic materials in the regulation of greenhouse gas emissions. Also special emphasis has been given to different catalytic processes in which greenhouse gases could be converted into value-added products thereby reducing their large quantities.

---

[1] E-mail: bmreddy@iict.res.in, mreddyb@yahoo.com.

In: Environmental and Agricultural Research Summaries …   ISBN: 978-1-63117-090-4
Editor: Lucille T. Cacioppo   © 2014 Nova Science Publishers, Inc.

Chapter 203

REDUCING TRANSPORT'S IMPACT ON CLIMATE CHANGE

Patrick Moriarty[1] and Damon Honnery[2]
[1]Department of Design, Monash University, Australia
[2]Department of Mechanical and Aerospace Engineering,
Monash University, Australia

RESEARCH SUMMARY

In 2004, transport was responsible for 23% of global energy-related CO_2 emissions, or some 6.3 gigatonnes (Gt) CO_2. The 2007 Intergovernmental Panel on Climate Change (IPCC) Report on Mitigation projected a rise of 80% in CO_2 emissions by 2030 in the absence of specific reduction policies. The report estimated that emission reduction policies would only lower the total in 2030 from 11.34 Gt to at best 8.8 Gt. Yet elsewhere the IPCC report showed that to limit global temperature rise since the industrial revolution to 2°C, thought to represent a prudent limit for avoiding dangerous climatic change, CO_2 emissions may have to be cut by the year 2050 to as little as 15% of the year 2000 values. In this chapter we look at the emission reduction potentials for the various transport modes, both passenger and freight, that could be achieved by the year 2030. The major options for each transport mode include increases in vehicle fuel efficiency and loading, and shifts to non-carbon fuels. We show that these options, even combined, cannot deliver anywhere near the reductions needed. Instead we will need not only massive shifts to more energy-and greenhouse-efficient transport modes, especially for passenger transport, but particularly in the high-income countries, travel reductions as well.

In: Environmental and Agricultural Research Summaries …   ISBN: 978-1-63117-090-4
Editor: Lucille T. Cacioppo   © 2014 Nova Science Publishers, Inc.

Chapter 204

AEROSOL-CLIMATE INTERACTIONS: EXAMPLES FROM HONG KONG AND THE PEARL RIVER DELTA REGION

*Long S. Chiu**

Institute of Space and Earth Information Science, Chinese University
of Hong Kong, Shatin NT, Hong Kong

RESEARCH SUMMARY

While the effect of increases in atmospheric carbon dioxide on climate has been relatively well-documented, there is still large uncertainty associated with aerosol effects on climate. Aerosols affect both the hydrological and energy cycles. Their presence is crucial for the formation of clouds and hence they will affect the radiative budget and precipitation type, amount and processes. Aerosols associated with burning of biomass have been shown to inhibit rain formation. Aerosols also reflect and absorb shortwave radiations, causing surface cooling and upper level heating, thus contributing to stabilize the atmosphere. Because of their shortwave absorption, they act as elevated atmospheric heat sources and induce low level convergence, and hence possibly early onset of monsoon systems.

We analyzed the aerosol and cloud parameters derived from the Moderate Resolution Imaging Spectroradiometer (MODIS) on board NASA's EOS satellite and TRMM rainfall over the Pearl River Delta (PRD) region. While the seasonal variations of AOD over southern China show a peak in the summer, there are two AOD peaks, respectively in the spring and fall, in the PRD. This bimodal behavior is due to the influence of the modulating effect of wind changes and wet deposition by monsoon rain. Increases in the aerosol optical depth (AOD) is associated with increases in the Fine Mode Fraction (FMF) and the Angstrom Exponent, suggesting that the increases in AOD are associated with small size ($<2.5\mu m$) aerosols. Significant correlations exist between AOD and columnar water vapor (WV), and marginally significant correlation with cloud fraction (CF), cloud top pressure (CTP) and rain rates (RR). The rain rate tends to be associated with large (large cloud coverage) and high

---

* On leave from College of Science, AOES, MSN 6A2, George Mason Univeristy, Fairfax, VA 22030. Email: lchiu@gmu.edu. Phone: (1) 703-993-1984.

(low cloud top temperature and pressure) clouds. Linear trend analyses show significant increases in stratiform rain in June and decrease in January. This is associated with significant increases in AOD for both months. Correlation analyses also show significant negative correlation between AOD and rain rate in December and January. It is suggested that in the presence of moisture abundance, aerosols act as cloud condensation nuclei and increases the cloud fraction. The compensating effect of aerosol removal by wet deposition reduces the positive correlation between AOD and rain rate, and hence no significant rainfall trends are observed. This contrasts with the conditions observed in central southeast China which show a general drying trend due to increases in aerosol concentration.

In: Environmental and Agricultural Research Summaries ...   ISBN: 978-1-63117-090-4
Editor: Lucille T. Cacioppo   © 2014 Nova Science Publishers, Inc.

Chapter 205

RECENT CLIMATIC CHANGES IN SOME SELECTED CITIES IN BANGLADESH – A CASE STUDY ON SYLHET

Jahir Bin Alam[1], Sirajul Islam[2] and Rezaul Kabir Chowdhuary[1]

[1]Department of Civil and Environmental Engineering,
Shahjalal University of Science and Technology,
Sylhet, Bangladesh
[2]Department of Environmental Science and Management,
North South University, Dhaka

RESEARCH SUMMARY

Urbanization trend in the present world is increasing at an unprecedented rate, especially in the developing countries. In Bangladesh, along with global climate change, local effect like high population growth, unplanned industrialization, destruction of natural ecosystem and topography, etc leading to change in urban climate at an even faster rate. This study investigated the changes in climatic parameters viz. annual mean temperature, annual total rainfall and annual mean humidity of four divisional cities in Bangladesh Dhaka, Chittagong, Rajshahi and Sylhet. Primary data of several climatic parameters have been collected from Bangladesh Meteorological Department for the period as Dhaka (1960-1999), Chittagong (1950-1999), Rajshahi (1964-1999) and Sylhet (1957-1999). Average value of the entire period, average of ten year's value and five-year running average value of each parameter have been plotted against corresponding year. It has been found that annual mean temperature has an increasing trend for all the cities. Annual total rainfall has decreasing trend for all the cities except Dhaka. Annual mean humidity of Dhaka city has decreasing trend during 1960-1980 and increasing trend during 1980-1990. For Rajshahi and Sylhet city, it has increasing trend, whereas for Chittagong city it has decreasing trend. A number of factors affected the changes are global climate change, high growth rate and destruction of local topography.

In: Environmental and Agricultural Research Summaries ...   ISBN: 978-1-63117-090-4
Editor: Lucille T. Cacioppo   © 2014 Nova Science Publishers, Inc.

Chapter 206

TRANSITION TO A CARBON-FRUGAL FUTURE

Fereidoon P. Sioshansi[1]

Menlo Energy Economics, Walnut Creek, California, US

RESEARCH SUMMARY

Since the dawn of industrial revolution, humankind has been extracting enormous amounts of fossil fuels and burning it indiscriminately in pursuit of economic growth and higher standards of living. Global climate change, however, appears to be on a collision course with this paradigm. While policymakers are debating the options, many experts believe that incremental fixes will not suffice given the enormous scale of the problem. This article examines the historical context, the options and ramifications of transition to a more carbon-frugal future.

[1] Tel 650-207-4902; Fax 925-946-0870. E-mail: fpsioshansi@aol.com.

In: Environmental and Agricultural Research Summaries …   ISBN: 978-1-63117-090-4
Editor: Lucille T. Cacioppo   © 2014 Nova Science Publishers, Inc.

Chapter 207

ENERGY RESEARCH, ENVIRONMENT, APPLICATIONS AND SUSTAINABLE DEVELOPMENT

*Abdeen Mustafa Omer**

Energy Research Institute (ERI), Nottingham, UK

RESEARCH SUMMARY

People rely upon oil for primary energy and this for a few more decades. Other orthodox sources may be more enduring, but are not without serious disadvantages. Power from natural resources has always had great appeal. Coal is plentiful, though there is concern about despoliation in winning it and pollution in burning it. Nuclear power has been developed with remarkable timeliness, but is not universally welcomed since construction of the plant is energy-intensive and there is concern about the disposal of its long-lived active wastes. Barrels of oil, lumps of coal, even uranium come from nature but the possibilities of almost limitless power from the atmosphere and the oceans seem to have special attraction. The wind machine provided an early way of developing motive power. The massive increases in fuel prices over the last years have however, made any scheme not requiring fuel appear to be more attractive and to be worth reinvestigation. In considering the atmosphere and the oceans as energy sources the four main contenders are solar energy, wind power, wave power, tidal and power from ocean thermal gradients. The renewable energy resources are particularly suited for the provision of rural power supplies and a major advantage is that equipment such as flat plate solar driers, wind machines, etc., can be constructed using local resources and without the advantage results from the feasibility of local maintenance and the general encouragement such local manufacture gives to the buildup of small-scale rural based industry. The present situation is best characterised as one of very rapid growth for wind and solar technologies and of significant promise for biomass and geothermal technologies. This chapter gives some examples of small-scale energy converters, nevertheless it should be noted that small conventional, i.e., engines are currently the major source of power in rural

---

* 17 Juniper Court, Forest Road West, Nottingham NG7 4EU, UK. Fax: +44-1159513159. E-mail address: abdeenomer2@yahoo.co.uk.

areas and will continue to be so for a long time to come. There is a need for some further development to suit local conditions, to minimise spares holdings, to maximise interchangeability both of engine parts and of the engine application. Emphasis should be placed on full local manufacture.

In: Environmental and Agricultural Research Summaries …   ISBN: 978-1-63117-090-4
Editor: Lucille T. Cacioppo   © 2014 Nova Science Publishers, Inc.

Chapter 208

THE NEW EU CLIMATE AND ENERGY POLICY – SUSTAINABILITY PERFORMANCE OF THE DIFFERENT POWER GENERATION TECHNOLOGIES

Christian Kirchsteiger[1]

European Commission, Directorate-General
for Energy, Luxembourg

RESEARCH SUMMARY

The objective of this article is to analyse factors influencing the sustainability performance of different energy sources in order to come to an effective decarbonisation of the fuel mix in a competitive manner. This is of course in the light of the new climate and energy policy of the EU and shall consider the most important energy sources currently used in Europe.

Neither a single current nor future energy source – be it nuclear, fossil, renewable or hydrogen – nor a single support technology, such as carbon capture and storage, can alone represent the remedy to cope with the challenges of increasing energy demand, increasing levels of greenhouse gas emissions and increasing dependence on fuel supply from outside Europe.

However, the different sources and related technologies can effectively complement each other. Nuclear power should thus be seen in combination with its alternatives. How the mixture is done in order to achieve an appropriate, "sustainable" energy mix depends on the resources and local conditions of each country or region. There are, nevertheless, some basic commonalities and inevitable limiting conditions related to the specificities of the use of the various sources which should form the basis of any such decision-making and which will be introduced in this article.

Getting eventually to a decarbonised, non-fossil world will demand great determination, huge financial burden and true patience. But there is hope on the short- and mid-term horizons by means of effectively complementing and synchronising existing technologies,

---

[1] E-mail: Christian.kirchsteiger@ec.europa.eu.

such as nuclear baseload electricity generation with other low CO_2-intensive sources, e.g. some of the renewables.

On the long-term horizon, only large-scale technological innovation will help, including advanced nuclear technologies in combination with significantly improved renewables and technologies to store energy, to largely replace fossil fuels also as power source for non-electrical applications.

In: Environmental and Agricultural Research Summaries ...   ISBN: 978-1-63117-090-4
Editor: Lucille T. Cacioppo   © 2014 Nova Science Publishers, Inc.

Chapter 209

VULNERABILITY OF RENEWABLE ENERGY TO GLOBAL CLIMATE CHANGE: THE CASES OF HYDRO AND WIND POWER GENERATION IN BRAZIL[*]

*André Frossard Pereira de Lucena[†], Alexandre Szklo[†],
Roberto Schaeffer[†], Isabella Vaz Leal Costa[†]
and Ricardo Marques Dutra*
Energy Planning Program, Graduate School of Engineering,
Federal University of Rio de Janeiro,
Cidade Universitária Fundão, Rio de Janeiro, RJ, Brazil

RESEARCH SUMMARY

The availability and reliability of renewable energy sources depend very much on current and future climate conditions, which may vary in light of possible global climate change (GCC). Long-term energy planning, however, does not normally take into account possible future GCC, which may turn out to be a risky exercise, mainly for those countries that rely heavily on renewable energy sources. In fact, although renewable energy sources are being greatly promoted worldwide to curb greenhouse gases emissions, these energy sources are likely to be the most vulnerable ones to climate change itself.

The case of Brazil is elucidative. The Brazilian energy sector relies heavily on renewable energy sources. Some 45% of all energy produced in the country comes from renewable energy sources (MME, 2009). In the power sector alone, this reliance is even higher[1]. Hydroelectric power plants accounted for 80% of Brazil's power generation in 2008 (MME,

---

[*] This document derives from a full report published in April 2008 (Schaeffer et al., 2008).
[†] andrelucena@ppe.ufrj.br, szklo@ppe.ufrj.br, roberto@ppe.ufrj.br, isabella-costa@ppe.ufrj.br.
[1] Bioenergy has also become increasingly important in the Brazilian energy sector, both for electricity generation and liquid biofuels production. For further references on the impacts of GCC on the production of biofuels, see (Pinto and Assad, 2008).

2009). Although not fully exploited, wind power potential is also quite impressive in certain regions of the country, such as in the Northeast coastal region and in parts of the South and the Southeast (CEPEL, 2001).

With this as the background, the focus of this chapter is to analyze some possible impacts of GCC on wind and hydro power generation, using the example of Brazil as a case study. The impacts of GCC on these primary renewable energy sources are assessed by simulating scenarios taking into account climate projections based on IPCC A2 and B2 scenarios (IPCC, 2000). These climate projections for Brazil were carried out by a team of Brazilian climate specialists of the CPTEC/INPE using the PRECIS (Providing REgional Climates for Impacts Studies) model[2], which provided projections for precipitation, temperature, wind velocity and humidity at a 50 km x 50 km square resolution for the 2071 – 2100 time period.

---

[2] PRECIS is a regional climate model system developed by the Hadley Centre which downscales the results of the HadCM3 global climate model. The lateral boundary conditions for the PRECIS model is given by the global atmosphere general circulation model HadAM3P, which constitutes the atmospheric component of the ocean-atmosphere global climate model HadCM3, forced with sea surface temperature anomalies. It uses the present and future concentrations of greenhouse gases and sulphur projected by the A2 and B2 IPCC emission scenarios to make regional climate projections which are consistent with the global model.

In: Environmental and Agricultural Research Summaries ...   ISBN: 978-1-63117-090-4
Editor: Lucille T. Cacioppo   © 2014 Nova Science Publishers, Inc.

Chapter 210

USE OF REMOTE SENSING IN ENVIRONMENTAL POLLUTION AND CLIMATE CHANGE

Yuanzhi Zhang[*] and Su Yan

The Chinese University of Hong Kong, Institute of Space and Earth
Information Science, Shatin, NT, Hong Kong

RESEARCH SUMMARY

This chapter mainly describes the use of remote sensing in environmental pollution and climate change at local, regional, and global scales. The information derived from satellite-based observations has a number of distinct advantages over ground-based measurements. The remote information is comparable between different areas over different periods of time, and also provides the different parts of electromagnetic measurements. Up to date, remote sensing technology has proven to be a powerful tool to monitor and assess environmental pollution and climate change on a regular basis. Remotely sensed data acquired from various satellites, with increasing capabilities in terms of spatial, temporal and spectral resolution, allow more efficient and reliable monitoring of environment and climate change over time at different scales.

---

[*] Email: yuanzhizhang@cuhk.edu.hk.

In: Environmental and Agricultural Research Summaries ...   ISBN: 978-1-63117-090-4
Editor: Lucille T. Cacioppo   © 2014 Nova Science Publishers, Inc.

Chapter 211

THE USE OF SPECTRAL REMOTE SENSING FOR DETECTING AND MONITORING GASEOUS EMISSION FROM ACTIVE COAL FIRES

Prasun K. Gangopadhyay*, Freek van der Meer[†]
and Paul van Dijk[#]
ESA Department, International Institute
for Geo-Information Science and Earth Observation
(ITC) Hengelostraat, AA Enschede, The Netherlands

RESEARCH SUMMARY

Over the time-scale, earth's atmospheric CO_2 concentration has varied and that is mostly determined by balance among the geochemical processes including burial of organic carbon in sediments, silicate rock weathering and volcanic activity. However, the present CO_2 concentration of earth's atmosphere has exceeded far that it was predicted from the Vostok ice core data. Other than rapid industrialization and urbanization since last century, geo-natural hazards such as volcanic activity, leakage from hydrocarbon reservoirs and spontaneous combustion of coal contribute a considerable amount of CO_2 to the atmosphere. Spontaneous combustion of coal is common occurrence in most coal producing countries and CO_2 emission from these coalfires are one of the most alarming factor because of high quantity. Remote sensing of coalfires has achieved a standard; however, quantification of CO_2 emission from coalfires using remote sensing has not endeavoured due to few limitations. The present study has first identified the most susceptible CO_2 bands (in compare to present hyperspectral sensors) using radiative transfer models and later used those bands to quantify CO_2 emission from coalfires. Two methods (band ratioing and radiative transport) were used

---

* Corresponding author. Currently located at The Energy and Resources Institute (TERI). IHC Complex, Lodhi Road, New Delhi 110 003, India. Email: prasun.gangopadhyay@teri.res.in. Ph: +31 (0)53 4874248, Fax: +31 (0)53 4874336. prasun@itc.nl

[†] vdmeer@itc.nl.

[#] vandijk@itc.nl.

in the present study and it was observed that the first method is fast and second method is source specific for atmospheric CO_2 retrieval.

In: Environmental and Agricultural Research Summaries …   ISBN: 978-1-63117-090-4
Editor: Lucille T. Cacioppo   © 2014 Nova Science Publishers, Inc.

Chapter 212

AN INTEGRATED ANALYSIS OF AEROSOLS, TRACE GASES AND PARTICULATE MATTER OVER TROPICAL URBAN REGION, HYDERABAD, INDIA USING GROUND BASED MEASUREMENTS AND SATELLITE DATA

K. V. S. Badarinath[1], Shailesh Kumar Kharol[1],
Anu Rani Sharma[1] and Krishna Prasad Vadrevu[2]
[1]Atmospheric Science Section, Oceanography Division,
National Remote Sensing Centre, Dept. of Space, Govt. of India,
Balanagar, Hyderabad, India
[2]Agroecosystem Management Program, The Ohio State University, US

RESEARCH SUMMARY

Aerosols and trace gas emissions in urban areas constitute one of the major sources of pollution that is of prime concern in the climate change studies. In this study, we report integrated and comprehensive results from aerosols and trace gases over a typical urban environment of Hyderabad, south India. Intensive ground based measurements were undertaken to quantify variations in aerosol optical depth (AOD), particle size distribution, particulate matter, aerosol backscattering, in addition to black carbon, carbon monoxide and ozone. Several remote sensing products, i.e., MODIS, TOMS-OMI, KALPANA and DMSP-OLS have been invoked to characterize large scale variations in aerosol optical depth, ozone and to assess influence of dust and fire events over the study area. We also used robust Mesoscale Meteorological model (MM5) to understand variations in local as well as regional scale meteorology. Also, aerosol radiative forcing has been assessed using SBDART model. Results from ground based measurements for aerosols and trace gases showed clear diurnal and temporal variations. The aerosol optical depth values at 380, 440, 500, 675, 870 and 1020 nm showed a significant spectral dependence and presence of aerosols of different size distributions and chemical composition. A sharp peak in black carbon concentrations occurred during morning and evening hours and has been attributed to traffic patterns in the study area. The high standard deviations of AOD found on certain Julian days during January to first fortnight of April were attributed to frequent forest fire events towards north of the study area. In contrast, high AOD loadings during second fortnight of April to May were attributed to dust aerosols transported from Thar Desert. These results were supported from MODIS, IRS-P4 OCM, DMSP-OLS and KALPANA satellite remote sensing products as well as back trajectory air transport model. Results on UV irradiance suggested relatively higher attenuation of UV radiation from smoke than dust particles. Further, Radiative forcing due to enhanced loading of aerosols associated with crop residue burning was found to be -107.81 Wm^{-2} compared to -53 Wm^{-2} under normal conditions. We also present results relating to aerosol vertical distribution from LIDAR measurements as well implications of long-range transport of aerosols and dust particles influencing urban environment in the study area.

In: Environmental and Agricultural Research Summaries ...   ISBN: 978-1-63117-090-4
Editor: Lucille T. Cacioppo   © 2014 Nova Science Publishers, Inc.

Chapter 213

DEVELOPMENT OF REGIONAL CLIMATE CHANGE SCENARIOS AND THEIR APPLICATION INTO AGRICULTURAL RISK ASSESSMENT: A REVIEW

Qunying Luo[1, 2,*]

[1]The University of Adelaide, Department of Geographical and Environmental Studies, University of Adelaide, South Australia, Australia
[2]NSW Department of Primary Industries, Beecroft, Australia

RESEARCH SUMMARY

This paper comprehensively reviewed the advances made in the field of development of regional climate change scenarios and their application in agricultural impact, adaptation and vulnerability assessment. Construction of regional climate change scenarios evolved from the application of arbitrary scenarios to the application of GCMs based climate change scenarios. GCMs based climate change scenarios progressed from equilibrium climate change scenarios to transient climate change scenarios, from the use of direct GCMs outputs to the use of downscaled GCMs outputs, from the use of single scenarios to the use of probabilistic climate change scenarios and from the application of mean climate change scenarios to the application of integrated climate change scenarios with changes in both mean climate and climate variability considered.

Greater attention from government, industry, business and scientific research bodies are being paid to climate change and its impact, adaptation and vulnerability. Climate change and its associated impacts have become the foci of nowadays policy, business and research. This paper provided invaluable information for those interested in climate change and its impacts.

---

* luo.qunying122@gmail.com

In: Environmental and Agricultural Research Summaries …   ISBN: 978-1-63117-090-4
Editor: Lucille T. Cacioppo   © 2014 Nova Science Publishers, Inc.

Chapter 214

PLANT RESPONSES DUE TO CLIMATE CHANGE

*Ahmed El Nemr**

Department of Pollution, Environmental Division, National Institute
of Oceanography and Fisheries, Kayet Bey, El Anfoushy, Alexandria, Egypt

RESEARCH SUMMARY

The climate change issue is increasingly receiving attention from scientists, public, and policy makers. The United Nations Convention on Climate Change defines climate change as "a change of climate which is attributed directly or indirectly to human activity that alters the composition of the global atmosphere and which is, in addition to natural climate variability, observed over comparable time periods". Greenhouse gases and many air pollutants have known common sources, contribute to radiative balance, interact in the atmosphere, and affect the ecosystems. The study of the impacts of both air pollution and climate change on plant ecosystems may significantly differ from a sum of separate effects. This chapter reviews the links between air pollution and climate change and their interactive effects on plants. A simultaneous addressing of the air pollution and climate change effects on plants may result in more effective research, management and monitoring, as well as a better integration of local, national and global environmental policies.

---

* E-mail: ahmedmoustafaelnemr@yahoo.com.

In: Environmental and Agricultural Research Summaries ...   ISBN: 978-1-63117-090-4
Editor: Lucille T. Cacioppo   © 2014 Nova Science Publishers, Inc.

Chapter 215

CLIMATE CHANGE, ADAPTATION STRATEGIES AND ANNUAL CROP PRODUCTION ON THE CANADIAN PRAIRIES

Herb W. Cutforth[1]

Semiarid Prairie Agricultural Research Centre, Agriculture
and Agri-Food Canada, Swift Current, SK, Canada

RESEARCH SUMMARY

Climate on the Canadian Prairies has been steadily warming since about 1950. The rate of warming has varied temporally and spatially, with the western and northwestern regions warming faster than other regions on the Prairies. The late winter-early spring season has warmed faster than summer or fall, the frost-free duration has lengthened, especially in the northwest, and incident solar radiation amounts have been decreasing. Precipitation patterns on the prairies have changed - some regions receiving less, some regions receiving more precipitation. On average, precipitation amounts have increased slightly on the Prairies. Current trends in temperature and precipitation generally coincide with the predicted direction of climate change, reinforcing the need for initiating/ developing adaptation strategies for agriculture in response to future climates. Adaptation strategies discussed include: breeding crops, or obtaining crops from other environments, that are adapted to warmer climates with longer growing seasons, higher atmospheric CO_2 concentrations, higher temperatures, and increased aridity; growing winter crops; altering crop sequences within crop rotations; adopting tillage practices that increase water use efficiency of cropping systems, and/or reduce soil degradation. One relatively simple practice that may have large positive impacts on agricultural production in the future is earlier seeding.

---

[1] Email: herb.cutforth@agr.gc.ca.

In: Environmental and Agricultural Research Summaries ...   ISBN: 978-1-63117-090-4
Editor: Lucille T. Cacioppo   © 2014 Nova Science Publishers, Inc.

Chapter 216

A SIMPLE GEOSPATIAL MODEL CLIMATE-BASED FOR DESIGNING EROSIVE RAINFALL PATTERNS

Nazzareno Diodato[1] and Massimo Fagnano[2]†*
[1]Euro-Mediterranean Centre for Climate Change –
TEDASS (University of Sannio), Benevento, Italy
[2]Agricolure Engineering and Agronomy Department,
University of Naples Federico II, Portici, Naples, Italy

RESEARCH SUMMARY

In the Earth Climatic System (ECS), water can be viewed as both a resource and a land disturbing force. In particular, the rainstorms influence of weather increases with its amount and intensity, whilst the protective effect of the landscape equipment network counteract this influence. Accurate estimation of the climate aggressiveness by erosive rainfall events plays a major role for agricultural and urban areas management and, in turn, for indirectly affecting ECS protection's (e.g., deluges, flash-floods, soil erosion and sediment transport). Although several studies have focused on the climate aggressiveness spatial pattern in Geographic Information System (GIS) within different methodologies, only a few have recently studied how the RUSLE–erosivity factor is affected by both climate and its extremes annuality. This was mainly due to the scarcity of erosivity–data in individual months or years, especially in mountainous and developing countries, where hourly and sub-hourly pluviometrical data are not available for the erosivity calculus.

With the purpose to skip over these drawbacks, a parsimonious framework is firstly developed in this paper for designing spatial variability of long-term average rain-erosivity and its extremes annuality within assigned return period (T). This methodology was successively applied for a test-site placed in a mountainous agricultural basin of the Campania Region (Southern Italy). In the third step, the approach was set to extend the information from point to landscapes with stochastic geospatial tools in GIS, using mainly

---

* Email: scodalabdiodato@gmail.com.
† Email: massimo.fagnano@unina.it.

daily records of 62 rain-stations of the Department of Civil Protection established by Campania and Basilicata Regional Monitoring Networks. To such goal, Regression Ordinary Kriging (ROK) based–maps have been generated for depicting the erosive rainfall spatial variability on annual-basis across the Sele River Basin (SRB), and to delineate its current trend in the regional climate change context.

In: Environmental and Agricultural Research Summaries ...   ISBN: 978-1-63117-090-4
Editor: Lucille T. Cacioppo   © 2014 Nova Science Publishers, Inc.

Chapter 217

CLIMATE CHANGE AND MICROBIAL INTERACTION

Nermeen A. El-Sersy[*] and Gehan M. Abou-Elela
Marine Microbiology, Environmental Division, National Institute
of Oceanography and Fisheries, Alexandria, Egypt

RESEARCH SUMMARY

Microbes run the world. It's that simple. Although we can't usually see them, microbes are essential for every part of human life. Indeed all life on earth. Every process in the biosphere is touched by the seemingly endless capacity of microbes to transform the world around them. The chemical cycles that convert the key elements of life carbon, nitrogen, and sulfur into biological accessible forms are largely directed by and dependent on microbes. Microbial role in global change include: Producing and consuming atmospheric gasses that affect climate, mobilizing toxic elements such as mercury, arsenic and selenium and producing toxic algal blooms and creating oxygen depletion zone in lakes, rivers and coastal environment (eutrophication). Furthermore, the incidence of microbial diseases such as plague, cholera, west Nile viruses and fish pathogenesis in addition to coral reef diseases and fouling phenomena, linked to global change.

Soil microbes produce and consume methane. The thawing of permafrost in the Arctic creates low-oxygen (anaerobic) and water-logged soil conditions in which microorganisms that produce methane dominate. Moreover, methane released into the atmosphere from under-sea volcanoes contributes to abrupt climate change. This is because methane is a more effective Green House Gas (GHG) than Carbon Dioxide. So the higher incidence of methane release into the atmosphere, the closer we are too big global trouble.

Metagenomics is a powerful genomic analysis applied to entire communities of microbes, by passing the need to isolate and culture individual's bacterial community members. It can be used for monitoring environmental damage at all levels (from climate change to leaking gas storage tanks) and microbe-based methods for restoring healthy ecosystems. This chapter represents how microbial interactions and activities can affects and altered climate. Ways of damage monitoring will be displayed as well.

---

[*] Email: nermeen_ok@yahoo.co.uk.

In: Environmental and Agricultural Research Summaries ...   ISBN: 978-1-63117-090-4
Editor: Lucille T. Cacioppo   © 2014 Nova Science Publishers, Inc.

Chapter 218

HARMFUL ALGAL BLOOMS: FUTURE THREATS IN A WARMER WORLD

Lorraine C. Backer[*1] *and Stephanie K. Moore*[2†]

[1] National Center for Environmental Health, Centers for Disease Control
and Prevention, Chamblee, Georgia, US
[2] NOAA Northwest Fisheries Science Center, West Coast Center
for Oceans and Human Health, Washington, US

RESEARCH SUMMARY

There is mounting evidence that the frequency of occurrence and geographic extent of potentially harmful algal blooms (HABs) are increasing. Some of this increase can be attributed to shifts in ocean conditions and local weather patterns, large-scale climate oscillations, and more recently, climate change. More frequent and widespread HABs increase the risk for human encounters with the algae and the toxins they produce. Specific interfaces across which people are exposed to HABs include contaminated seafood and drinking water. Also, as more of our global population migrates to coasts and shorelines, there is increased risk for exposures to any contaminants in the nearby water environment, including HAB toxins. Finally, global tourism puts naïve populations at risk for exposure to HABs during recreational activities such as swimming, using personal water craft, sport fishing, and recreational shellfish harvesting. The public health costs of increases in HAB exposures will likely include more cases of human diseases such as ciguatera fish poisoning and respiratory effects from inhaling aerosols containing HAB toxins, such as brevetoxins from Florida red tides. Another public health-related cost will be expending resources to monitor HABs and develop and implement early detection systems to prevent exposures and subsequent diseases. In this chapter, we review impending changes in public health risk associated with potential climate-driven changes in the occurrence and distribution of marine

* lbacker@cdc.gov.
† stephanie.moore@noaa.gov.

HABs, and assess the potential for adaptation and mitigation of the impacts of future HABs through technological development, education, and policy changes.

In: Environmental and Agricultural Research Summaries ...   ISBN: 978-1-63117-090-4
Editor: Lucille T. Cacioppo   © 2014 Nova Science Publishers, Inc.

Chapter 219

CONTINUOUS GLOBAL WARMING OR PROGRESSIVE PART OF LONG TERM TEMPERATURE CYCLE "PERSONAL HISTORY WITH THE PROBLEM"

Ibrahim A. A. Maiyza[*]
National Institute of Oceanography and Fisheries,
Kayet Bey, Alexandria, Egypt

RESEARCH SUMMARY

The variation and formation of temperature anomalies, positive or negative, of the upper surface layer of the ocean are key elements in understanding a wide range of physical oceanographic and meteorological problems. The study of which is of particular scientific interest. The temperature anomalies are so intensive that they may noticeably affect the atmospheric processes for example the 1955, 1962, 1966, 1968, 1977, 1988 and 1999 were recorded as warm years while the 1959, 1961, 1972, 1976, 1985 and1997 were recorded as cold years. The effect of surface warming (or cooling) can affect not only the surface layer but also the subsurface, intermediate and deep layers. The effect may affect the water bodies in both its presenting layer and core level but also its hydrographic characteristics. The thermal, haline and total steric departures coincide with the phase of the observed sea level fluctuation.

Time distribution of surface temperature anomaly (SSTA) values display both positive and negative cycles. The periods of these cycles fluctuated between 8 and 15 years. These cycles are nearly associated with the 11 year cycle of sunspots activities. Normal SSTA band occupies only 21.41%, while the positive and negative bands occupy 32.90% and 45.69%, respectively. The active period of the year is from June to August. The coastal areas are more active especially in the positive and rang bands due to the interannual variations in coastal heating and cooling. The anti-cyclonic gyre areas are more active especially in the negative band due to interannual variations in gyre strength. The linear regression and model results

---

[*] E-mail: ia_maiyza@hotmail.com and i_maiyza@yahoo.com.

reveal a trend of general decrease of SST, with time in the order of about –0.3oC / 61 years. The quadratic regression trend of the mean monthly and annual SST has a parabola form. The parabolas show a decrease in SST in the period from 1948 to 1985 then increasing forward. The present Chapter may strengthen the suggestion of oscillating sea surface temperature (SST) with time rather than continuous increasing due to the so called global warming. The cycle of that oscillation must have a period much more than 61 years and may reach to centuries.

In: Environmental and Agricultural Research Summaries ...   ISBN: 978-1-63117-090-4
Editor: Lucille T. Cacioppo   © 2014 Nova Science Publishers, Inc.

Chapter 220

THE IMPACT OF ENVIRONMENTAL POLLUTION ON IMMOVABLE CULTURAL HERITAGE: DECAY MECHANISMS, PRODUCTS AND ANALYTICAL TECHNIQUES TO EVALUATE THE IMPACT

M. Maguregui[*], I. Martínez-Arkarazo,
K. Castro and J. M. Madariaga
Department of Analytical Chemistry, University of the Basque Country,
Bilbao, Spain

RESEARCH SUMMARY

In recent decades, environmental pollution has become one of the main causes in the deterioration of the "Immovable Cultural Heritage" (ICH) also known as "Physical Cultural Heritage" (PCH) or "Built Heritage" (BH). There is a wide variety of materials in which the ICH can be built or made, for example, stone, brick, mortar, clay, cement, tiles, marble, glaze, wood, alloys, etc. All these materials can suffer decay processes, most of them due to the impact of anthropogenic sources, such as, synthesized products (pesticides, fertilizers, etc.), heavy metals, irrigation saline waters... But the source which most damages the ICH is the environmental pollution; that is, acid pollutants emission (CO_2, SO_x, NO_x), solid particles, hydrocarbons etc. coming from industrial sources and/or from road traffic. The systematic study of the degradation products of the ICH can provide useful information about the environmental pollution impact on building materials. In fact, the decay processes in buildings provide useful information about the particular environment around the ICH. This article describes the most common atmospheric pollutants types, their degradation process and monitoring of them on the ICH. Furthermore, the study of the reactivity mechanisms between atmospheric pollutants and building materials and the most employed methodologies to characterise the impacts on the artefacts from the ICH are described. Finally, the contribution of biodeterioration to enhance weathering in the ICH is also discussed.

[*] e-mail: maite.maguregui@ehu.es.

In: Environmental and Agricultural Research Summaries ...   ISBN: 978-1-63117-090-4
Editor: Lucille T. Cacioppo   © 2014 Nova Science Publishers, Inc.

Chapter 221

MITIGATING CLIMATE CHANGE

Patrick Moriarty[1] and Damon Honnery[2]
[1]Department of Design, Monash University, Australia
[2]Department of Mechanical and Aerospace Engineering,
Monash University, Australia

RESEARCH SUMMARY

The 2007 Intergovernmental Panel on Climate Change (IPCC) report showed that to limit global temperature rise since the industrial revolution to 2 °C (thought by the European Union to represent a prudent limit to avoid dangerous climatic change) CO_2 emissions may have to be cut by the year 2050 to as little as 15% of the year 2000 value, with the peak emission year in 2000-2015. Since about 77% of the climatic radiative forcing of anthropogenic greenhouse gas emissions from all sources comes from carbon dioxide, (with most of this in turn coming from fossil fuel use) this chapter mainly considers these emissions. Geoengineering is the only mitigation approach that does not require emission reductions, but carries serious risks—in attempting to solve one problem it creates others. Mitigating climate change will thus require that large emission reductions be made rapidly. The three most commonly discussed measures, carbon sequestration, use of non-carbon fuels and energy efficiency, can do little to reduce emissions in the time frame required, a point tacitly acknowledged by the IPCC and other authorities. Heavy emphasis will therefore need to be placed on a very different approach. Particularly in countries with high-energy per capita use, we argue emission cuts will also require reductions in the use of energy-using devices—including cars, airplanes and domestic appliances. Although this approach can be implemented quickly, it evidently requires profound changes in the global economy.

In: Environmental and Agricultural Research Summaries …   ISBN: 978-1-63117-090-4
Editor: Lucille T. Cacioppo   © 2014 Nova Science Publishers, Inc.

Chapter 222

CLIMATE CHANGE MITIGATION POLICIES AND POST-KYOTO CLIMATE CHANGE MITIGATION REGIMES: LITHUANIAN CASE

Dalia Streimikiene[1]
Lithuanian Energy Institute,
Breslaujos 3, Kaunas, Lithuania

RESEARCH SUMMARY

The paper deals with climate change mitigation policies and measures on local level and their role in implementing post-Kyoto climate change mitigation regimes. The aim of the paper is based on the case study of Annex I country – Lithuania to analyse the impact of future international climate change regimes on future energy options for specific Annex-I country based on requirements set by these regimes for GHG emission reduction in 2020 and 2050. The main tasks to achieve the target is to analyse possible international post-Kyoto climate change regime an define their requirement for GHG emission reduction for Annex I countries; to develop GHG emission projection scenarios for Lithuania taking into account impact of climate change mitigation measures; to compare various possible GHG emission projection scenarios including impact of climate change mitigation measures with requirements set by international regimes and to identify energy supply options for Lithuania driven by these future regimes. The case study of Lithuania is presented for analysis of requirements of various post-Kyoto climate change mitigation regimes on GHG emissions reduction and for the evaluation of impact of various GHG emission reduction measures.

---

[1] dalia@mail.lei.lt.

In: Environmental and Agricultural Research Summaries …   ISBN: 978-1-63117-090-4
Editor: Lucille T. Cacioppo   © 2014 Nova Science Publishers, Inc.

Chapter 223

GOVERNMENTAL POLICIES ON PERFLUOROCOMPOUNDS (PFCS) EMISSIONS MITIGATION AND ITS CLEANER PRODUCTION MEASURES – CASE STUDY IN TAIWAN

Wen-Tien Tsai[*]

Graduate Institute of Bioresources, National Pingtung
University of Science and Technology, Pingtung, Taiwan

RESEARCH SUMMARY

Taiwan, a country in southeastern Asia, is playing a vital role in mitigating saturated perfluorocompounds (PFCs), including gaseous PFCs (i.e., SF_6, NF_3, CF_4, C_2F_6, C_3F_8, c-C_4F_8, and C_4F_{10}) and liquid PFCs (i.e., C_5F_{12}, C_6F_{14}, C_7F_{16}, C_8F_{18}, and C_9F_{20}), because these commercially industrial substances are potent greenhouse gases mostly blanketed into the Kyoto Protocol. Furthermore, the Government has established the National Council for Sustainable Development (NCSD), a ministry-level organization, for pursuing sustainability in this country and fulfilling its responsibility as a member of the international community. This review paper was thus centered on reviewing the commercial/industrial uses, the environmental hazards of PFCs, their current consumption status, and the cleaner production measures adopted by the local industries in Taiwan. This review paper was also centered on summarizing the governmental policies on promoting PFCs mitigation through the encouragement of regulatory, economic and financial approaches. It was concluded that Taiwan was in a positive trend to mitigate PFCs emissions in the past decade under the promotion of its policy framework. Further, the successful case could be developed into providing a demonstrated example for other islands and developed countries in progress toward global sustainability.

---

[*] Corresponding author. Tel: +886-8-7703202 ext 7399; Fax: +886-8-7740134. E-mail address: wttsai@mail.npust.edu.tw.

In: Environmental and Agricultural Research Summaries …   ISBN: 978-1-63117-090-4
Editor: Lucille T. Cacioppo   © 2014 Nova Science Publishers, Inc.

Chapter 224

GLOBAL AND REGIONAL IMPACTS OF THE CLEAN DEVELOPMENT MECHANISM

Shunli Wang, Henri L.F. de Groot, Peter Nijkamp[1] and Erik T. Verhoef[2]

Department of Spatial Economics, VU University Amsterdam,
Amsterdam, The Netherlands

RESEARCH SUMMARY

Climate change is a serious concern worldwide. Policy research on climate change in the past decades has largely focused on applied modelling exercises. However, the implications of specific policy strategies such as the clean development mechanism (CDM) for global and regional economic and environmental developments have received relatively little attention. This is partly caused by the complexities of modelling an instrument like CDM. By using and modifying the GTAP-E modelling system, this paper sets out to trace the combined economic and environmental impacts of CDM policies. Particular emphasis is placed on technology transfer induced by alternative CDM policies. Specific attention is devoted to the possible negative consequences of non-participation of the USA in the global coalition, and the associated distributional impacts world-wide.

---

[1] E-mail for correspondence: pnijkamp@feweb.vu.nl.
[2] The authors gratefully acknowledge the support and comments of Truong P. Truong.

In: Environmental and Agricultural Research Summaries …   ISBN: 978-1-63117-090-4
Editor: Lucille T. Cacioppo   © 2014 Nova Science Publishers, Inc.

Chapter 225

TWO MAPS SERVING THE INTERCELULAR EXCHANGE OF BIOCHEMICAL SUBSTANCES AND THEIR BEHAVIOUR IN THE PRESENCE OF FLUCTUATIONS

D. T. Mihailović[1,], M. Budinčević[2], I. Balaž[3] and D. Perišić[2]*

[1]Department of Field and Vegetable Crops, Faculty of Agriculture,
University of Novi Sad, Novi Sad, Serbia
[2]Department of Mathematics and Informatics, Faculty of Sciences,
University of Novi Sad, Novi Sad, Serbia
[3]Department of Physics, Faculty of Sciences,
University of Novi Sad, Novi Sad, Serbia

RESEARCH SUMMARY

The exchange of biochemical substances is an essential way to establish the communication between cells. Despite great diversity among organisms in specific mechanisms where proteins and small molecules are involved, the general scheme of the communication process remains fairly universal. It is notable that all phases of the process are heavily influenced by perturbations of either internal or external parameters of such systems. We propose a form of coupled difference logistic equations as a suitable approach for modeling the exchange of biochemical substances between two cells. We then investigate the synchronization of exchanges between cells and their sensitivity to fluctuations of intra- and intercellular environmental parameters using methods of nonlinear dynamics, i.e., using the largest Lyapunov exponent and cross sample entropy as measures. Instead of developing an accurate quantitative model of substance exchanges between cells, we are instead interested in the formalization of the basic shape of the process and creating an appropriate strategy that

---
* Corresponding author: E-mail address: guto@uns.ac.rs; Phone: +381 21 485 3203. Fax: +381 21 635 0552.

allows further investigation of synchronization induced by fluctuations of intra- and intercellular environmental parameters.

In: Environmental and Agricultural Research Summaries …　　　ISBN: 978-1-63117-090-4
Editor: Lucille T. Cacioppo　　　　　　　　　　　© 2014 Nova Science Publishers, Inc.

Chapter 226

FORMAL CONCEPT ANALYSIS AND CATEGORY THEORY IN MODELING INTERACTIONS OF LIVING SYSTEMS AND THEIR ENVIRONMENTS

S. Crvenković[1,*], D. T. Mihailović[2] and I. Balaz[3]

[1]Department of Mathematics and Informatics, Faculty of Sciences,
University of Novi Sad, Novi Sad, Serbia
[2]Department for Field and Vegetable Crops, Faculty of Agriculture,
University of Novi Sad, Novi Sad, Serbia
[3]Department of Physics, Faculty of Sciences, University of Novi Sad,
Novi Sad, Serbia

RESEARCH SUMMARY

All functional systems are able to receive inputs, perform some transformations on them, and produce proper outputs. When dealing with mechanical systems, identifying the input/output relation is usually unambiguous because it is purposely designed. However, in biological systems, the situation is more complicated. First, because of their complexity, many specific purposes can be identified, such as feeding, moving, or reproducing. Therefore, decisions regarding what signals or changes should be identified as inputs or outputs are governed by the purpose of investigation. In this case, the difference between mechanical and biological systems is only a matter of scale. Second, and fundamentally different, is the ability of biological systems to treat the same signal in different manners, depending on their current state or context. As a consequence, it is very difficult to straightforwardly identify functional inputs or outputs for any process within a biological system. Usually, this problem is avoided by assuming that the common form of processing within the defined context is the only one. In this way, a modeling approach is reduced to the standard form of sequential machines and can be performed efficiently and satisfy the power of prediction. However, we believe that this is accompanied by the cost of losing deeper insight into some of the specific and important features of biological system functions, such as flexibility and evolvability. In

* Corresponding author: E-mail address: sima@dmi.uns.ac.rs; Phone: +381 21 485 2859. Fax: +381 21 635 0458.

this chapter, after some theoretical considerations, we develop a formal representation of the manner in which organisms "observe" the environment using formal concept analysis (FCA) and category theory. FCA is a branch of applied lattice theory that defines a concept as a unit of two parts: extension and intension. The extension covers all objects belonging to the particular concept, and the intension comprises all attributes that are valid for all of those objects. Both attributes and objects are united by a triple (G, M, I), which is called a formal context, while the ordered set of all formal concepts of (G, M, I) forms a concept lattice that is always complete. By using FCA alone, we can clearly represent how the available set of attributes governs the process of concept formation. However, it is not powerful enough to examine the variation of "observations" because it deals only with isolated lattices. To analyze the algebraic properties of such changeable systems, we further consider concept lattices as objects in the category of lattices and morphisms that preserve lattice completeness. Based on this analysis, we elaborate on some of the functional consequences of the ability of biological systems to perform at different scales with the variable identification of environmental signals.